Of Patient Bearing –

A History of General Practice in Eight Generations

Stephen Gillam

Preface

I recall the timbre of my father's voice on the mobile. His health was failing then. He was physically and vocally frail. I was driving north from Cambridge under grey November skies. 'And why are you going to Wisbech?' he asked. I explained I was talking to a group of doctors about the latest twists and turns of NHS policy. He listened with sceptical amusement before saying finally: 'Well, get out at lunchtime and see if you can find Scrimshires Passage. It was named after your great-great-great grandfather who practised from a house round the corner.' The passage turned out to be a short step from the Freedom Bridge over the river Nene in the centre of town. I listened in astonishment as he proceeded to tell me more.

I was 47 years old. I was dimly aware that I had many medical forebears but had never stopped to contemplate what this meant. Who were they? Where had they come from? And how had they altered the course of my life? Most of us nurture a sense of our own discretion and free will. We have to believe that our life choices are own. In my case, I was conscious of little or no pressure applied when I came to make my own career choices.

Actually, my father was two 'greats' short. Medicine often runs in the family. Many doctors have relatives in the profession, and obituaries in the British Medical Journal (BMJ) show how common it is for doctors to have siblings and children who are also doctors. Even today, around a fifth of doctors have parents who were both doctors.[1] Debate continues about whether having doctors in the family influences career decisions and makes life easier for those who follow relatives into the profession (footnote).[2] I may have been unconscious of medicine as the family business but perhaps this was so quietly ingrained in the family culture that I did not recognise it.

A quirky work, this book is part family memoir. It stands as a gentle tribute to the ordinary men and women who shaped my life - and the lives of others - in ways I had not begun to appreciate until that damp November morning nearly twenty years ago. This is also a book about place: a specific house and town in which my forebears practised for over a century, my home today.

While historians differ as to timing and emphases, all agree that the period from around 1790 to 1860 yielded major medical reforms in Britain. These years saw remarkable changes to the education and working conditions of rank-and-file medical men (for then they were). Irvine Loudon dates the first use of the term 'general practitioner' (GP) in its modern sense to a letter written in 1809.[3] The term was not initially popular with the profession and little used in legal documents,

Footnote: The propensity for medical offspring to follow their parents is not universal. The profession in China is neither prestigious, safe nor well-paid. Hence, the sardonic saying *yi buguo erdai*: 'no doctor's child becomes a doctor.'

having no statutory definition. For the GP was not a sudden creation but evolved from the surgeon-apothecary and man-midwife in the first half of the eighteenth century. This evolution was as much a product of political struggle as of planned progress in medical education and practice. By the middle of the nineteenth century, the term was in common use among a confident new medical cadre with a growing sense of corporate identity.

Occasional earlier usage denoted the practitioner's broad base rather than describing a specific type of doctor. The term was slow to catch on with the general public. Even in mid-Victorian times, the local family doctor was often referred to as an apothecary or surgeon, the term preferred by many doctors themselves.

This book aspires also to offer a brief history of general medical practice - my (pre)occupation for 40 years. Told through the eyes of participants, it provides a partial 'view from below'. I am not a professional historian or sociologist but, as a medical academic, I have sought to ensure that my sources are rigorous and based in evidence.

Structure
The book begins with an introduction. It is aimed at a general readership and assumes no knowledge of medical history. Some readers may choose to skip or scan this chapter. Where should one begin to tell the story of general practice?

Working in the Himalayan foothills over 30 years ago, I was struck by the power of the traditional healers, dhamis and jhankris.[4] My team preached the virtues of vaccination while these village health workers warded off the same afflictions with amulets and sacrifices. We could thus start with the shamans and faith healers that are first found in many primitive societies. The linkages between medicine and religion are, after all, central to our history. At the other extreme, many accounts begin in 1858 with the Medical Act that reified the tripartite distinction between physicians, surgeons and general practitioners.

Rather conventionally, I choose to begin with Hippocrates on the island of Kos. He - or 'they' as the corpus associated with his name is likely to have had multiple authors - is salient for his emphasis on public health and his influence on Galen (see Introduction) whose own shadow extended into the middle of the eighteenth century where my story properly begins.

Interwoven over the following chapters is a family fable drawing out themes that marked the rise of general practice. These themes include the changing burden of disease and conditions of work, education and training, how livings were earned and professional status evolved. After all, 'the practice' can nowadays refer to a surgery building, a team of professionals, a model of organisation or a set of business accounts.

Later chapters lengthen for two main reasons. Firstly, though the mid-Victorians were valiant letter writers, I know rather less of the relatives that preceded them. Secondly, over time GPs' working lives were increasingly influenced by government health policy. With the making of the modern state in the latter part of the nineteenth century, medical bureaucracy and the volume of accompanying documentation increased exponentially. The final chapters contain much of the more or less informed prejudice that nowadays passes for policy analysis.

The conclusion draws these themes together and examines the current decline of the generalist. All generations are prone to indulge in 'golden-ageism'. The inclination to see your own early life as optimal both condescends to the past and devalues the present. However, the loss of a certain style of personal care has undoubtedly been the price of technological progress. As one in a long line of stolid optimists, I look in hope rather than expectation to a brighter future.

Bibliography

Footnotes are found at the bottom of each page. Read them for some lighter relief. Each chapter is referenced in some detail at the end of the book. This section is followed by a list of the works that have most influenced me. On the history of general practice, a particular mention must go to the ground-breaking work of Irvine Loudon and Anne Digby.

A book of this length cannot be entirely comprehensive. For example, others have covered the history of institutions such as the Royal College of General Practitioners or the British Medical Association in depth. I have focussed on those developments that seemed to have most impact on day-to-day working lives.

Obituaries are a necessary source of information but suffer predictable biases. They sometimes lend the pen portraits a Boy's Own, comic quality. They are frequently dreary. GPs are inclined to take their most revealing thoughts to the grave.

My particular, sentimental delight was the discovery of many letters written between members of my family in the 1800s. Most of them deal with day-to-day family matters and social encounters - the tea parties and soirées of the nascent middle class. Letters from medical students to their fathers are amusingly formulaic: the genial greeting, the newsy update with careful reference to their studies, followed by an obsequious request for cash. Only a few, therefore, are quoted at length.

These sources also reflect and amplify the extent to which my profession and family were, until recently, disconcertingly patriarchal. It is not possible in a few short pages to do justice to all those who have contributed to this discipline. Other histories of general practice remain to be written.

**This book is dedicated to the doctors described here
(mostly male) and many wonderful colleagues
(mostly female).**

Contents

Introduction - This provides a short, simple summary of the history of medicine until the 18th century for someone new to the field. Each subsequent chapter covers a generation including brief biographies, major legislative and other developments. Date ranges relate to biographical material; for the medical history they are less rigidly indicative.

Chapter One - Humble origins (1770-1800). Tells of surgeon-apothecary William Skrimshire (the Older), his beginnings near Wisbech, describes the 18th century medical marketplace, the practice of physic and pharmacy at that time, the Poor Laws, apothecaries' training and incomes.

Chapter Two - Upward mobility (1800-1830). William the Younger was the first to qualify as a doctor but more attention is devoted to his brother. Fenwick Skrimshire set up the Peterborough dispensary, wrote extensively and included among his patients, the 'People's Poet' John Clare. The 1815 Apothecaries Act is the first major legislative milestone to be considered in detail along with its main architect, George Man Burrows. The Act supposedly defined training requirements for a new breed of generalist.

Chapter Three - Years of transition (1830-1860). In which George Skrimshire moves to Holt, Norfolk, and works hard to establish his practice. GPs' status and income were beginning to rise, if not their self-esteem. The impact of the much-feted 1858 Medical Act is disputed. The rise of laboratory medicine and its impact on practice is considered.

Chapter Four - Ebbs and flows (1860-1890). Treats of how John Truscott's otherwise long and successful life was blighted by tragedy. The main medical focus is on mental health care. This period saw advances in public health and the emergence of the 'family doctor'.

Chapter Five - State intent (1890-1925). My great grandfather, Joseph Gillam, married his boss's daughter and joined the partnership. He died young; medicine was always a perilous calling. Most attention is devoted to the last two medical brothers Skrimshire. The nature of practice and training are considered. Professional survival required the adoption of extended roles. The impact of the 1911 National Health Insurance Act was substantial.

Chapter Six - The birth of the NHS (1925-1955). My grandfather's generation worked either side of the establishment of the NHS. The medical politics surrounding its advent and difficult early years are detailed. Two brothers began their careers in general practice before specializing as consultants in the new service. General practice reached a nadir as reflected in the Collings report.

Chapter Seven - High water (1955-1985). Renewal is generally attributed to the Family Doctor Charter of 1966 which spurred the development of staffing and clinical practice. Ironically, the decline of a style of family doctoring can be dated back to this period also. Improvements to training and working conditions greatly enhanced the popularity of general practice. However, these years yielded major critiques of high-tech biomedicine, which tends to be funded at the expense of primary care.

Chapter Eight - Markets and recessi[on] [...] 2020). Just as an individual clinician's feelings may reflect thos[e] [...] too does the NHS hold a mirror to wider society. The author[...] [...] steady decline in the status of generalists, despite impr[...] [...]s. The advent of the 'internal market' has fragmented[...] [...]ance has reduced continuity. General practice fac[...]

Conclusion - After the Fall. [...] [...]overed and draws out the main messages, including c[...] [...]e future.

Contents

List of Figures and Tables

Figures:

Tables

Abbreviations

BMA	British Medical Association
BMJ	British Medical Journal
CCG	Clinical Commissioning Group
CQC	Care Quality Commission
DoH	Department of Health
DHSS	Department of Health and Social Services
EDP	Eastern Daily Press
FPC	Family Practitioner Committee
FRCGP	Fellow of Royal College of General Practitioners
FRCP	Fellow of Royal College of Physicians
FRCS	Fellow of Royal College of Surgeons
GMC	General Medical Council
GMSC	General Medical Services Committee
LSA	Licentiate of Society of Apothecaries
MB, BChir	Batchelor of Medicine and Surgery
MD	Doctor of Medicine (higher research degree)
MOH	Medical Officer of Health
MoH	Ministry of Health
MPU	Medical Practitioners Union
MRCGP	Member of Royal College of General Practitioners
MRCP	Member of Royal College of Physicians
MRCS	Member of Royal College of Surgeons
NAGP	National Association of General Practitioners
NHI	National Health Insurance
NICE	National Centre for Health & Care Excellence
PCT	Primary Care Trust
PHC	Primary Health Care
PMS	Personal Medical Services
PMSA	Provincial Medical and Surgical Association
PRO	Public Records Office
QOF	Quality & Outcomes Framework
RCGP	Royal College of General Practitioners
RCP	Royal College of Physicians
RCS	Royal College of Surgeons
SMA	Socialist Medical Association
WHO	World Health Organisation

The medical lineage of Skrimshires and Gillams

William Skrimshire m Elizabeth
1739-1814   1740-1813

Dr William	Elizabeth	Rev Thomas	**Dr Fenwick**	George	Burgess	Stephen	Anne
1766-1829	1772-1844	1774-1835	1775-1855	1777-1856	1768-?	1777-79	1782-86

Elizabeth	William	**Dr George**	Ann	Jane	William Wright
1798-1857	1800-01	1802-77	1804-83	1805-74	1809-48

Fenwick Skrimshire m Charlotte Cobb 1785-1866

Susan	Charles	Rev Henry	**Dr Arthur James**	Charlotte	Frederick	Edward
1808-68	1809-32	1810-61	1814-1906	1815-43	1816-91	1820-96

George Skrimshire m Lavinia Truscott 1807-77

Dr George	**Dr John Truscott**	**Dr Charles Parnham**	**Dr Frederic William**
1827-82	1835-1912	1844-1912	1848-99

Other sons

Thomas	Edmund B	Henry T	Ernest	Arthur
1831-63	1839-1913	1842-1910	1850-1931	1855-1932

Daughters

Anne	Lavinia	Elizabeth	Emily m Dr Alfred Whitlock
1829-1906	1833-54	1837-84	1852-1904

John Truscott Skrimshire m Elizabeth Finch 1848-1923

Dorothy Jane m	**Joseph Gillam**	**Dr John (Jack)**	**Dr Henry (Harry)**	Elizabeth	Amy
1870-1950	1870-1911	1872-1918	1874-1953	1876-76	1879-1952

Dr John m	Sally Pooler	**Dr Geoffrey** m	Mary Davies	Margery	Josephine
1903-81	1909-96	1905-1970	1903-89	1907-71	1910-58

Dr Pat	Sue	Jane	John	**Dr Peter** m	Anne O'Brien Bell	Anthony
1935-2019	1938-	1944-2012	1930-	1930-2008	1931-	1939-

Dr Stephen /	**Dr Anne Yardumian**	David	Emma	James
1955-	1957-	1957-	1965-	1967-

Introduction

'Is not a science
But the intuitive art
Of wooing nature.'
W.H. Auden

What is history?

Historia has been defined as 'inquiry, knowledge acquired by investigation.'[1] The earliest historians are associated with Ancient Greece; writers such as Herodotus who focussed on social and cultural history and Thucydides who detailed military events.

History can be seen as an end in itself or as a way of providing perspectives on the present. Insofar as interpretation is refracted through the experiences of the writer, 'all history is contemporary history'. The central challenge for historians is to produce a true discourse of the past through narrative and analysis. History can be organized in many ways, for example chronologically, culturally, territorially, and thematically.[2]

The term 'historiography' refers to how history has been produced: the development of methodology, for example the move from short-term biographical narrative (the stories of 'great men') towards long-term thematic analysis. It is also used to refer to what has been produced: a specific body of historical writing; or why history is produced, the philosophy of history. An example of the latter would be the 'whiggish' interpretation of history which implies an underlying forward momentum or purpose to historical events.[3] This is a pit into which many science writers fall.

The history of medicine was previously the preserve of doctors who tended to emphasize the advance of technical knowledge and celebrated discoveries such as Harvey's description of the circulation. Low status specialisms, such as general practice, were marginalised as stress was placed on hospital medicine. This 'great man' approach came to be criticized for being euro-centric and magnifying the importance of the present day.

Since the 1970s, medical knowledge and practice has been recognised as the product of a much wider array of social and cultural forces. The left-wing historian E.P. Thompson drew attention to how little notice had been taken of the experiences of common people and famously sought to rescue them from the 'condescension of posterity'.[4] Today's 'history from below' emphasizes the patient's voice, for example. We now have feminist and minority ethnic versions of history.

These later interpretations are linked with academic critiques of medicine dating from the same period. Writers such as Ivan Illich, Thomas Szasz and Michel Foucault saw medical knowledge as a form of power and potential exploitation. They precipitated for my generation a lasting re-evaluation of the role of medicine and the power of the medical profession.

What is medicine?
The word 'medicine' is used both to refer to the science or practice of the diagnosis, treatment, and prevention of disease and to drugs, *materia medica*, pharmacy. Medicine can be traditional, alternative or complementary raising the question of whether it can properly be provided by the untrained. Society's responses to this question have been a source of recurrent conflict to the present day.

Modern medicine is also about a plethora of institutions that support its delivery - from training schools for different health professionals, through pharmaceutical and device manufacturers to the providers themselves. Any consideration of general practice must also unravel the complex roles of political bodies such as medical trade unions and the Royal Colleges.

Today's distinction between hospital-based specialist and community-based generalist is of recent origin. For most of the period leading up to the formation of the NHS in 1948, Anne Digby's work suggests we need to think not of GPs and specialists but of medical careers falling along a continuum between general and consulting practice.[5] She identified five career trajectories:
- The 'classic' GP who practised medicine among a mix of social classes.
- The GP surgeon who practised general medicine and had a part-time appointment as a surgeon in a small hospital.
- The GP/Specialist who worked as a GP but also did some consulting work in one area of medicine, such as obstetrics.
- GPs who became consultants - doctors who started their careers in general practice but switched to full-time consulting.
- 'Pure' consultants who belonged to prestigious medical institutions, held posts in hospitals and had a private, general practice.

Examples of all such trajectories feature among my family but, before considering the evolution of British general practice, a brief and simplified summary of early medical history helps place later developments in context.

Hippocrates (c460-377 BC)
Most comprehensive histories of medicine begin with Hippocrates. Born on the island of Kos, almost nothing else is known of the man himself. Over 60 texts on a range of subjects comprise his corpus but they were penned by many hands and only brought together around 250 BC in Alexandria.

Hippocratic medicine was grounded upon material philosophy rather than the supernatural. Man was seen to be governed by the same physical laws as the cosmos. Medicine should henceforth be based on an understanding of the workings of the body in its natural environment. Borrowing from pre-Socratic philosophers (e.g. Pythagoras and Alcmaeon), the body was viewed as in perpetual flux and ill health the result of internal or environmental imbalance. If Hippocrates is our story's most celebrated physician, he is regarded also as the father of public health. In *Airs, Waters, Places*, he noted the influence of climate and other environmental factors on health.[6]

Humoral theory (see below) was physiological rather than based on any anatomical understanding. Health was maintained or restored by establishing equilibrium. Hippocratic physicians were therapeutically conservative (especially in relation to surgery) preferring to emphasize behavioural, dietary and environmental approaches.

Hippocratic healing was patient-centred, encouraging bedside visits and trust-based clinical relationships. The art of diagnosis involved creating a detailed profile of the patient's way of life, diet work and habitation. Clinical observation and acuity were central but prognostication was the most prized skill.

The significance of Hippocratic medicine was twofold. Firstly, it carved out a role for the selfless physician, an enduring model for professional identity and conduct. My forebears would have taken the oath of Hippocrates until the early 1900s (footnote 1). Secondly, it taught that an understanding of sickness required an understanding of nature.

Galen (c129-210 AD)

Born and trained in Pergamon, and much the most prolific ancient writer with 350 authentic titles, he had vast erudition and a matching ego. Galen moved to Rome in AD169 and eventually became physician to Emperor Marcus Aurelius, before travelling to Alexandria.

Galen taught that the physician must master philosophy - logic (the discipline of thinking), physics (the science of nature) and ethics (the science of action). He presented his work as perfecting Hippocrates' legacy: systematizing humoral theory and elaborating the arts of diagnosis and prognosis. He too stressed the importance of the patient's trust to the healing process. This required a punctilious bedside manner and well-honed clinical skills. He wrote sixteen books on the pulse, for example.[7]

Footnote 1. Hippocrates is renowned for various aphorisms. 'Walking is a man's best medicine.' 'The greatest medicine of all is teaching people how not to need it.' 'To do nothing can also be a good remedy.' As it happens, none of these appear in the Oath's original translation of 245 AD.

He was also a medical scientist undertaking animal dissections and detailed anatomical observations (of bodies on gibbets and in gladiator schools). He believed that veins originated in the liver where blood was made, carrying nutrition to where it was needed, while arteries originated in the heart where blood crossed inter-septal pores to be mixed with 'pneuma' (vital spirit) in the lungs. Such was his authority that these circulatory errors persisted for over a thousand years. His impact on teaching in the Middle Ages throughout the Christian and Arab world is hard to exaggerate.

Galen took clinical Hippocratic medicine and set it in a broader anatomical and physiological framework central to which was Humoral Theory. All organs and vessels could be reduced to four qualities: hot, wet, cold and dry. An individual's particular mix of qualities was called his/her complexion or temperament. The balance of these qualities was maintained through the four essential body fluids or humours: yellow bile, black bile, phlegm and blood (figure I.1). The balance of humours was thought to influence character, e.g. the sanguine person in whom blood was predominant was warm and easy-going. On the other hand, disease was the result of internal imbalance due to an excess or deficiency of humours.[8]

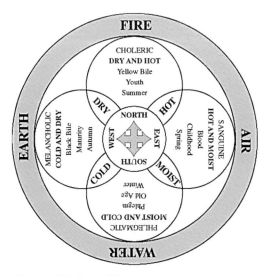

Galen listed six major influences that might change the humoral balance and induce disease: air, exercise, sleep, substances taken, excretion and what happens to the soul. By managing these 'non-naturals' through a detailed daily regimen, the physician could restore and maintain health.

For the removal of superfluous humours he advocated energetic blood-letting. He described some 473 drugs of vegetable, animal and mineral origin as well as many compounds - notably theriac (footnote 2) and other herbal preparations. According to his Theory of the Opposites, an imbalance towards one humour required its opposite. For example, an excess of phlegm (cold and moist) required something hot and dry (e.g. hot peppers to cure coryzal illness).

Figure I.1 Four Humours

In broad terms, Galen built on the Platonic doctrine that distinguished vital functions governed by animal, vegetative and rational 'souls'. Animal and human life was possible only because of pneuma (air), the life force that was modified in

Footnote 2. Theriac was a medical concoction formulated by the Ancient Greeks as an antidote to poisons. Constituents varied but often included opium, myrrh, saffron, ginger, cinnamon and castor. True to form, the English recommended sugar-based treacle.

different ways by the liver, heart and brain. For Galen, anatomy, logic and experience were tightly integrated. The complete physician had to master philosophy.

Hippocrates is a misty figure but Galen less so. He comes across as humane, compassionate, wise, arrogant, self-regarding and opinionated - a typical doctor, in other words. He brings to mind AN Whitehead's aphorism on Plato's contribution to western philosophy[9]: Galen felt he had written medicine (though he hadn't); the rest was footnotes.

Arab Medicine (7th to 12th centuries)
This is significant as much for preserving and systematising the medicine of classical antiquity as for developments of its own. Adherents of Muhammed adopted Hellenistic medicine on contact with physicians in conquered lands. During the ninth century, Hippocrates and Galen were translated into Arabic in Baghdad, the intellectual centre and capital of the Islamic empire. Islamic medicine integrated Persian and Ayurvedic concepts with an original medical literature of its own.[8] This and the classical texts were then rediscovered when Islamic authors were translated during the Renaissance. The names of the best known would have been familiar to my forebears.

The physician and philosopher Rhazes (865-925) asserted that reason rather than slavish repetition of Galenic precepts should be the governing authority. A prolific author of over 200 treatises, he enjoyed ascendancy in the Latin West for books such as *On Surgery* and *Continens*, a comprehensive medical notebook. He wrote on childhood ailments distinguishing various contagious diseases such as smallpox and measles. He was an early proponent of experimental medicine and a committed teacher.

Avicenna (980-1037) is sometimes described as the 'Father of Early Modern Medicine'. This Persian polymath's discoveries included the airborne transmission of disease, the use of forceps and central/peripheral nerves. His best-known work, the *Canon of Medicine*, arranged in a million words the whole of medical science. It comprises five volumes, including a pharmacopoeia, and was another standard text in the West into the seventeenth century.

Vesalius (1514-64)
Andreas Vesalius began his studies in Paris before moving in 1537 to Padua where he was to become Professor of Surgery. He is generally regarded as the founder of modern anatomy. His masterpiece, *De Humani Corporis Fabrica*, published in 1543, was based on painstaking human dissection. The book contains full-size drawings of the dissected human body in lifelike poses set against landscape backgrounds (figure I.2). He disproved Galen's theory of the circulation and the existence of the *rete mirabile* (thought to be the seat of the soul). With regards to

bloodletting, he favoured 'derivation' - drawing blood from the affected side - based on his elucidation of the azygos venous circulation.

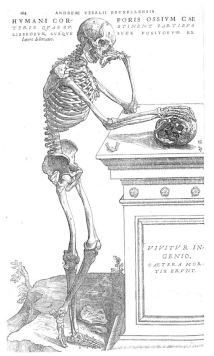

Figure I.2 Vesalian plate

He was controversial with many detractors on account of his supposedly heretical claim that Galen erred for never having dissected human bodies. Jacobus Sylvus (1478-1555) went so far as to attribute any differences to change in the nature of the human body over time (footnote 3). In reality, Vesalius' mission was to revive and complete the work of his revered master, Galen, begun in Rome 1400 years earlier. Vesalius' own legacy was to ensure that anatomy became central to the study of medicine. Thereafter, anatomy provided educational spectacle (in dissecting room or theatre), as well as the means to describe and localize disease.

Paracelsus (1493-1541)
Paralleling dramatic social, political and religious changes of the period, Philippus Aureolus Theophrastus Bombastus von Hohenheim issued a major challenge to orthodox, western medicine (footnote 4). Swiss German, a philosopher, physician, botanist, astrologer and occultist, Paracelsus placed revolutionary emphasis on natural observation rather than ancient texts. He was a radical critic of scholastic methods in theology and medical science whose ideas sprang directly from his religious beliefs (figure I.3).

Paracelsianism came to be regarded as beginning a new type of medicine based on chemical properties. Paracelsus rejected Galenism and Aristotelian natural philosophy and replaced the four elements (earth, air, fire and water) with his own primary substances of salt, sulphur and mercury. He saw them not as material substances but as spiritual principles representing solidity, metallicity and liquidity respectively. Alchemical forces (*alchei*) controlled bodily processes such as digestion. Paracelsus believed that disease was the result not of internal imbalance of humours, but of external forces. The essence of disease was spiritual, building on the belief in a close correspondence between the macrocosm (universe) and microcosm (human body). Humans did not merely resemble heaven and earth but were composed from them as a result of God's great alchemical act - the creation

Footnotes 3. A French anatomist whose original name was Jacques Dubois, he was the first to describe venous valves.
    4. The name is usually interpreted as either a latinization of *Hohenheim* (based on *celsus* 'high, tall') or as the claim of 'surpassing Celsus'. Immodest but not necessarily the invention of Paracelsus himself.

of the world. They therefore consisted of both chemical and astral 'seeds' (*semina*) which had both mortal and immortal elements, each with an identifiable signature.

In opposition to Galen, Paracelsus stated that like cured like. A disease could be fought by knowing what was appropriate to the affected part, rather than by giving something contrary. This led him to formulate chemical remedies for specific ailments in place of traditional herbal medicine. He therefore pre-empted the development of pharmacology and modern therapeutics.

Paracelsus' ideas are rooted in Neoplatonic mysticism and often difficult to follow. He lacked connections and formal academic credentials. His iconoclastic and volatile personality made for a behaviourally eccentric, sometimes isolated individual. He clashed with lay and ecclesiastical authorities wherever he went. He adopted his nickname around 1527 and emulated Celsus by writing in vernacular German rather than in the Latin of the university-educated medical establishment he so despised. He aimed, like Luther, to communicate with a broader, lay audience. Paracelsus' fierce attacks on the Catholic church and its practices demonstrates how close his thinking was to the Protestant reformers but, paradoxical in so many ways, he never left the Catholic faith.[10]

Figure I.3 Paracelsus

Thomas Sydenham (1624-89)
Known as 'The English Hippocrates', he based his practice on empirical grounds following Francis Bacon and challenged the standard approach based on pre-conceived theory. Traditionally, physicians took their patients' predisposition to fever or other illness as their starting point and sought to remedy their manner of life or other physical characteristics. By contrast, Sydenham directed attention to the disease which he presented as having a distinct ontological status. He differentiated *'accidental & adventitious'* symptoms (e.g. fever, rash) from *'peculiar & perpetual'* phenomena (e.g. age-related symptoms) and regarded types of ill-health as comparable to types of animal and vegetable species.[11]

Sydenham was among the first to advocate the use of laudanum for pain and peruvian bark (cinchona) for malaria. He is credited, among others, with the aphorism: *Primum non nocere* (First, do no harm). In *Observationes Medicae*, published in 1676, he drew up complete accounts of different diseases. This was still a standard medical text a century later when my story properly begins. The conformity of symptoms and course of a malady was due to the uniformity of cause. His method was therefore essentially modern except for a want of knowledge of morbid anatomy (footnote 5). The reification of disease entities endures today in the medical preoccupation with diagnosis.

New models of the body

New ways of understanding and representing the body came into vogue between 1600 and 1800. In different ways they helped over time to loosen the grip of Galenic theory. These different models reflected advances in the natural sciences.[12]

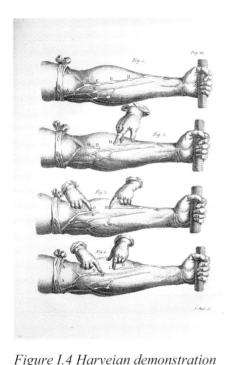

Figure I.4 Harveian demonstration

The best known is the discovery of the circulation of the blood by William Harvey (1578-1657). His sequential demonstrations (in *Exercitatio Anatomica de Motu Cordis et Sanguinis*, 1628) plainly undermined the notion that blood was 'used up' by the body and constantly replenished (figure I.4). His focus on the structure and function of the heart foreshadowed physiological enquiries into the purpose of other organs such as the kidney. Meanwhile, Marcello Malphigi (1628-1694) used new microscopic techniques to prompt the first histological discoveries. He identified glandular structures in most organs and regarded the body as a compound of glands.

René Descartes (1596-1650) argued that body and soul were separate entities (Dualism) and viewed the body as a machine. He felt that physiological processes could be explained by the laws regulating the movement of inanimate matter. His image of the body was of a mechanical automaton. By extension, Isaac Newton's mathematical approach to nature underpinned new approaches to bodily measurement, for example Sanctorius' *De Statica Medicina* (1614) exploring ingestion and excretion.

Nerves had been understood as hollow ducts distributing animal spirits to sustain sensation and motion. Albrecht von Haller (1708-1777) argued that nerve fibres possessed an intrinsic quality of 'sensibility' while muscles exhibited 'irritability'.

Footnote 5. Giovanni Battista Morgagni (1682-1771) is generally regarded as the father of modern anatomical pathology. He taught for over 50 years at the University of Padua. His most significant contribution, the monumental five-volume *On the Seats and Causes of Disease*, established the fundamental principle that most diseases are not vaguely dispersed, but originate in specific organs and tissues.

William Cullen (1710-1790) viewed these as the most important qualities of individuals.

These models were once celebrated as exemplary manifestations of scientific progress but their impact on actual practice was minimal and they had little effect on lay perceptions of the body, health and disease. They were less a product of scientific innovation than of changing social and political assumptions about nature and the social order.

Religion and medicine

Supernatural ideas are more prominent in non-literate societies. They divide into three categories: mystical (illness as consequence of an act or experience), animistic (illness-causing agent a supernatural being), and magical (caused by malicious humans using secret means).

With agriculture, population growth and the emergence of new epidemics, new medical beliefs and practices arose. These reflected growing economic, political and social complexity. Communities became hierarchical with divisions of labour and prestige. Medical expertise became the metier of particular individuals: shamans, diviners and spiritual healers.

Religion and the classical past inform all aspects of early modern medicine. The training of physicians inculcated an ethical imperative and codes of behaviour. For early Christians (and other Abrahamic religions), God was the Source of all healing. In the Dark Ages, monasteries became the repositories of medical knowledge. There was little conflict between Christianity and medicine.

The Reformation and the religious upheavals of the sixteenth century challenged the Classical text-based traditions that dominated medieval medicine. They did not, however, diminish the ongoing importance of Christian charity to welfare. Religious orders reinforced the role of early hospitals in physical and spiritual care.[13]

The distinction between physical and spiritual care is reflected in the earliest medical texts where the art and science of medicine are juxtaposed. It was once a commonplace to draw parallels between medicine and the priesthood but such linkages recur in the pen portraits below; most notably in the person of a cousin (six generations removed), one Arthur James Skrimshire who qualified in 1838 before his subsequent ordination in 1854. His father, Fenwick, wrote a popular medical guide for resident village pastors. In so doing, he overcame the doubts *'of many professional brethren, whether medical works, written for unprofessional readers, were not calculated to do as much mischief as good.'*[14]

Scientific revolution

The inter-relationship between science and medicine has always reflected political and socio-economic influences. While science in its modern sense is popularly supposed to be a nineteenth century phenomenon, its origins lie much earlier. Natural philosophers in the seventeenth century were seeking to understand the world in new ways. Francis Bacon (1561-1626), for example, sought to base knowledge on empirical evidence and inductive reasoning. Physicians such as Sydenham and Boerhaave emphasised the importance of observation in medicine.

The eighteenth century Enlightenment centred on reason as the primary source of authority and legitimacy, and came to advance ideals such as liberty, progress, tolerance, fraternity, constitutional government, and the separation of church and state. In France, the central doctrines of *les Lumières* were individual liberty and religious tolerance in opposition to an absolute monarchy and the fixed dogmas of the Roman Catholic Church. The Enlightenment was marked by an emphasis on scientific method and reductionism, along with increased questioning of religious orthodoxy.

The empiricist philosophy of David Hume (1711-1776) was enduringly influential. Beginning with *A Treatise of Human Nature* (1739), Hume strove to create a naturalistic science of man. He argued against the existence of innate ideas, positing that all human knowledge is ultimately founded solely in experience. Hume argued that inductive reasoning, and belief in causality, cannot be justified rationally. Our trust in causality and induction is attributable only to the experience of 'constant conjunction' rather than logic. For we can never, in experience, perceive that one event causes another, but only that the two are always conjoined.

Hume was notorious for his anti-teleological opposition to the argument for God's existence from design, but his ideas were of lasting influence on the philosophy of science. The advent of experimental method and systematic enquiry challenged established doctrine and was to alter the nature of medical knowledge.

Another key figure of the Enlightenment - and notable critic of the Church - was the eighteenth century French philosopher, Francois-Marie Arouet (1694-1778), better known by his nom-de-plume. Voltaire was generally sceptical of doctors too whom he knew had little to offer their patients. *'Doctors are men who prescribe medicine of which they know little to cure diseases of which they know less in human beings of whom they know nothing.'* Or my favourite quote and one that goes close to the heart of general practice: *'The efficient physician is the man who successfully amuses his patients while nature effects a cure.'* It was not, after all, until the middle of the twentieth century with the trials of sulphonamides and early antibiotics that we started to compile evidence in support of medical practice.

As conventionally understood, the new faith in reason generated inevitable conflict between religion and science resulting in the triumphant emergence of secular medicine. Recent scholarship suggests this undervalues the ongoing, complex connections between theology, politics and medical science.[15] Certainly, religion and medicine were entirely compatible in the views and working lives of my nineteenth century forebears. They may have accepted natural causes in their explanations of disease but, if the body was a machine, who moved it?

The idea that medicine has been steadily secularised over the last 250 years is a simplification. Even now, the boundaries between medicine and religion are permeable, as evidenced in debates over abortion, stem cell research and euthanasia. The religious beliefs of campaigners and communities continue to structure debate and shape regulation.

Early medical training
From around 1200, masters in several cathedrals formed corporations (universities) and began conferring qualifications - for example, in Montpellier, Bologna and Padua. At this time in Salerno, there arose a tradition of medical instruction grounded in the canonical texts (*Articella*) we have previously considered. Medicine was still largely based on Greek and Roman ideas.[16]

Early curricula covered liberal arts, natural and Aristotelian moral philosophy, and astrology. Rules of comportment were elaborated to increase patients' trust and confidence. From the fourteenth century, students would attend public dissections, often on hanged criminals. Otherwise, students learnt mostly from attending and taking notes from the expositions of learned professors. In Padua, Giambattista da Monte (1498-1552) was an early but unusual exponent of taking students into hospital and talking about the conditions of actual patients. Generally, there was little hands-on or practical training till the eighteenth century.

The content of medical training traditionally centred on Galenic theory and iatrochemistry (after Paracelsus) with a leavening of anatomy and surgery from the mid-fifteenth century. Ancillary subjects such as physiology, chemistry, pharmacy, obstetrics and gynaecology began to be included in the eighteenth century. In Leiden, Hermann Boerhaave (1668-1738) led the way in encouraging more practical training in out-patients and hospitals. Even then, qualifying exams were notoriously lax and usually limited to *vivas*.

Surgical faculties in centres such as Edinburgh and Paris began to offer more extensive training and doctors were increasingly encouraged to take up apprenticeships and assistantships. As demand outstripped supply, private courses were established. From the 1770s, Edinburgh was our foremost medical training centre but London's entrepreneurial physicians and surgeons seized the opportunity to compete with their own hands-on courses in what were to evolve into new teaching hospitals.

The eighteenth century saw sustained economic growth with the development of a wealthier, intellectually emancipated middle class with a keener interest in ensuring that the medical profession was properly regulated. Licensing procedures remained corporately structured but widely diverse arrangements obtained across Europe. The increasing power of the state allowed for more central control in France. By contrast, separate medical corporations controlled entry in London and other cities such as York, Glasgow and Norwich. For example, only Anglican licentiates of the Royal College of Physicians were permitted to practice in London.

Early medical practice
Most students in medical training thus spent their first two years studying logic and natural philosophy which was regarded as the ideal foundation for understanding health and sickness. Learning about medical theory and practice (diseases and their remedies) occupied the next three years, focussing almost entirely on the standard ancient and medieval texts. This respect for established authorities may have induced a certain dogmatism and inflexibility. Such qualities have always afflicted some medical minds.

Diagnosis involved taking a careful history seeking the cause of illness. The body was believed to rid itself of accumulating pollutants through excretions (faeces, blood, sweat and especially urine) which merited close examination. As a sign of vitality, measurement of the pulse was central. Different types indicated different conditions.

The patient's trust was essential to the healing process and a good bedside manner all important. Accuracy in prognosis - the result of experience and observational skills - was (and is) the hallmark of a good doctor. This was often based on the doctrine of 'crisis' or 'critical days'. The ability to predict deterioration served usefully to limit patients' expectations.

Physicians prescribed both to prevent (prophylaxis) and to cure disease. Maintaining health required attention to the six non-naturals. Medication was based on herbs and minerals from the *materia medica* classified in terms of the four qualities. These could be prescribed individually as 'simples' or mixed to form compounds such as theriac. Prescribing was based on the principle of opposition with the aim of restoring balance. Thus an illness that caused excessive dryness was treated with medicines that had wet qualities, taking account of both the illness itself and the temperament of the patient. Surgical interventions (performed for the most part by surgeons and barber surgeons) included the treatment of wounds, bone-setting and cautery.

The most widespread practice was bloodletting to rid the body of excess humours. Blood was believed to be a product of food but, according to Galen and his followers, the body sometimes produced more blood than it could use (*plethora*). This in turn was thought to cause a variety of ailments including tumours. This was addressed by reducing food intake, emetic or purgative drugs, and/or phlebotomy. Various rules, prohibitions and astrological principles guided the timing of venesection. For example, young children, pregnant women and old people were generally not phlebotomized. Its enduring popularity owed much to it being less dangerous than many other interventions.

Then as now, the final challenge was to bring science and art together in a management plan (*concilium*), reflecting the particular physical, psychological and social circumstances of the patient. In some respects, today's management plans with their over-emphasis on pharmaceutical remedies seem limited by comparison. On the other hand, there was then little appreciation of the nuances of what would nowadays be called mental illness.

The consultation might also have required a referral for basic surgery. Bloodletting too was performed for the most part by surgeons and barber surgeons. The prescription of herbal remedies would likely have required further consultation with an apothecary. The wealthy frequently consulted more than one physician. Doctors might therefore be presenting their findings to peer as well as patient.

The changing clinical gaze
During the sixteenth and seventeenth centuries, hospitals were increasingly 'medicalised' in the sense of whom they served (the sick rather than the indigent) and who ran them (doctors or rich patrons rather than church authorities). The move from bedside to hospital medicine began in Paris. Following the Revolution of 1789, citizens' rights were affirmed in many areas including health care. The medical education and licensing arrangements of the *Ancien Régime* were dismantled and many existing hospitals were replaced.

The French sociologist, Michel Foucault, described in his most famous work what he called 'the Birth of the Clinic.'[17] This was accompanied by a new discourse (language, concepts, ideas) which shaped the way doctors viewed patients and their diseases. Henceforth, there was less concern with environment and lifestyle, and more interest in organic changes within the body. Following Sydenham, a disease was no longer unique to the patient and his/her conditions but existed as an entity in its own right. For Foucault, however, the process of defining boundaries between the normal and the pathological was a social construction that drew heavily on medical expertise and ideas. He stressed the links between knowledge and power: patients in hospital were increasingly subservient. From this period dates the development of new techniques (which only doctors could employ) for visualizing internal as well as external pathological changes.

Exemplars included Jean-Nicolas Corvisart (1755-1821) who perfected the use of chest percussion as a diagnostic tool. From 1777 he studied at the Ecole de Médecine in Paris, later qualifying as *docteur régent* of the Faculté de Paris. In 1797, Corvisart began to teach at the Collège de France, where he gained a reputation as a cardiologist. Among his students were René Laennec, Guillaume Dupuytren and Xavier Bichat. In 1804, Corvisart became the primary physician of Napoléon Bonaparte.

Rene Laennec (1781-1826) described the first stethoscope in *De l'Auscultation Médiate,* published in 1819. What he called his 'cylinder' allowed him to follow chest patients from bedside to the autopsy table and correlate sounds with specific pathological changes. In effect, Laennec pioneered a new non-invasive diagnostic tool. He was the first to classify and discuss the terms rales, rhonchi and crepitations. He furthered understanding of peritonitis, cirrhosis, melanoma - and tuberculosis.

Medicine and change
In many ways, constant change is the defining feature of modern medicine.[18] Yet this introduction serves to remind us that for most of the last two millenia medical practice changed little. 1500 years separate the birth of Galen from Harvey's discovery of the circulation. Another 300 years elapsed before the first major therapeutic breakthroughs - the isolation of insulin, Fleming's penicillium moulds - that were to transform therapeutics. As we shall see, in essential respects, the business of general practice also has changed very little.

Forty years ago, in the second of two seminal papers, Nicholas Jewson helped to recast medical historiography.[19] Earlier historians of medicine focussed on scientific developments, the origins of theories and treatments. Hitherto, intellectual progress had been regarded as the inexorable driver of therapeutic and institutional advance. Jewson was one of a new wave of sociologists for whom medicine was a social phenomenon, shaped by wider political, economic and cultural influences.

Jewson was concerned with what he called 'the disappearance of the sick man' from medical cosmology in the period from 1770 to 1870. He used the term 'medical cosmology' as shorthand for the prevailing theories and practices that defined the nature of medical discourse at that time. He sought to demonstrate how the social relations underpinning eighteenth century medicine had been supplanted - with major consequences for knowledge and practice that endure to the present day.

Jewson's thesis
Until the late eighteenth century, a system of 'bedside medicine' had prevailed in the western world. In the Galenic tradition, as we have seen, diseases were thought

to result from an imbalance of humours. Health was restored through various therapeutic actions and interventions devised to restore the disrupted equilibrium. Thus the sick person was not viewed in isolation. Rather, an individual's psychological and social circumstances, behaviours and life history were central to diagnosis and treatment.

In a paper published two years earlier, Jewson had sought to show how this system was influenced by the economic power exercised by patients.[20] The fee-payer could choose the doctor who met his or her needs. The clinical encounter was also influenced by what Jewson called 'epistemological parity' - the extent of shared medical knowledge between practitioner and patient. The sick person's narrative was central to their encounter. The well-informed lay person at that time could converse on an almost equal footing with their physician.

Around 1800, a new cosmology or conceptual structure emerged in the form of 'hospital medicine' - first evident in post-revolutionary France and then across the rest of Europe. This reflected a change in the space in which medical knowledge was elaborated and applied. The setting for bedside medicine was domestic; at home, the patient exercised more autonomy. The hospital, on the other hand, was the doctor's 'bailiwick'. Jewson was borrowing here from the work of Erwin Ackerknecht who first noted these distinctions.[21]

Existing power relations were unbalanced by an associated economic shift. Hospital patients came from all classes and were treated freely. Doctors looked for recognition and remuneration to professional peers rather than most patients. Increasingly, the discourse of hospital medicine employed concepts and technical language that were alien to lay understandings.

The new regime depended on three principal techniques. The first of these was detailed physical examination, supplemented by instrumental aids such as the stethoscope. The second was autopsy that aimed to link symptoms to pathological bodily changes in the event of death. Finally, these correlations were analysed statistically to identify recurrent patterns of disease.[22]

The hospital patient's more dependent position allowed doctors to practice in ways that would have been impossible under the earlier dispensation. Physical examination of previously 'private' parts of the body and autopsy frequently violated conventional codes of decorum in the name of medical necessity. This shift in power relations was reinforced in other ways. At the bedside, doctors had offered prognosis and prediction which with treatment were the patient's main concerns. In hospital, the emphasis was on diagnosis and nosology. The patient ceased to be a person (or 'sick man' with his own agenda) and became a 'case' (or diseased body) contributing to the wider pool of medical knowledge.

This cosmological shift coincided in Britain with the emergence - after protracted battles with the Royal College of Physicians over licensing - of the forerunners of today's general practitioners: trained in medicine and surgery, plying their trade in the community.

According to Jewson, another new cosmology emerged, particularly from German-speaking states, in the mid-nineteenth century: 'laboratory medicine'. This sought disease at the cellular level and intensified the reductionist tendencies of the preceding stage. Clinicians could not detect pathogenic changes without a new set of skills. The locus for advancement and application of medical knowledge now became the laboratory, under the control of a new breed of scientific researchers. Lab scientists would over time become detached from the patient as they depended for their advancement on academic patrons. The gulf between the personal phenomenology of disease and the technical terrain of the medical profession continued to widen.

Jewson's writings are not always easily accessible and they have been subject to subsequent criticism.[23] They are schematic rather than evidence-based. In fairness, Jewson was not suggesting that bedside practice was entirely eclipsed under the hegemony of hospital and laboratory medicine. Rather, he was exposing a change in the 'dominant mode of production of medical knowledge' or a shift in the 'locus of epistemological authority'.[19] His work has prompted further research much of which substantiates his central thesis. For example, Mary Fissell's study of Bristol Infirmary details how wards came to be viewed as repositories of clinical material and surgical training grounds as their control passed to surgeons from administrators.[24]

However, the essentials of Jewson's thesis ring true. There is a strong connection between medical knowledge and the power relations between patient and practitioner. We continue to grapple today with the consequences of a move from person-centred to object-oriented health systems. Arguably today a new cosmology is emerging which might be termed 'virtual medicine'.

Conclusion
This swift glide over two and a half millenia can only hint at the complex relationship between medical theory and practice. Medical science is ever shaped by its political and socioeconomic context. Disease may have a biological reality but health, sickness and healing are culturally defined. 'Progress' in health care delivery was not linear. Interested readers are referred to the bibliography.

Down the centuries to the present day, doctors have continued to wrestle with the dilemmas that preoccupied Galen. These included the balance of preventive versus curative activities and how to reconcile the art and science of medicine. Early writers were well aware of the importance of what we would now term the 'doctor-patient relationship'. The tensions implicit in that relationship and the diversity of sometimes conflicting roles preoccupy today's general practitioners but the roots of these preoccupations lie deeper than they know.

Chapter One – Humble origins
(1770-1800)

'I'd rather die happy than not die at all,
The man is a fool who will not heed the call.'
W.S. Walcott Medicine Show (R. Robertson)

The first generation

My story begins some six miles north of Wisbech in Cambridgeshire. By the eighteenth century, Tydd St Giles was a large village with a sizeable church; two non-conformist chapels were to follow. There was no sinecure for the incumbent, the Reverend Burgess Fenwick, who baptised William Skrimshire there on August 21st, 1739. The Reverend might have come to look back on that day's work with especial satisfaction for twenty-six years later William was destined to marry his only child, Elizabeth. However, Burgess and his wife died together from marsh fever when Elizabeth was just eight years old. It is not known who brought her up.

A wide river leads eight miles from Wisbech to the sea. In those days, high-masted ships lined the banks, bringing coal and timber to the town, and exporting beer and grain. The dark silt soil of the Fens has ever been fertile. Its fields are enclosed by dykes whose water levels were formerly controlled by windmills. Winter mists swirl over the flat land, now famous for bulbs and apple orchards, then studded with straggling settlements. The isolated cottagers were notorious for the consumption of opium and ardent spirits. The bad airs promoted malarial 'ague' and cholera epidemics were frequent. These were the people and places amongst whom William Skrimshire was to live and work.

His father, John, was from Holbeach where he was apprenticed to John Callean, a grocer. His mother, Ann, was the daughter of William Brown, tenant of the Crown Inn which operates to this day (figure 1.1). John established himself as a successful mercer, grocer and linen draper at nearby Tyddgate. William was their second son.

Figure 1.1 Crown Inn, Holbeach

He chose apprenticeship to a local apothecary and flourished. Though initially resisted by its inhabitants (the infamous 'Fen Tigers'), drainage of the Fens had transformed Wisbech into a prosperous port handling agricultural produce. Wealthy mercantile patrons abounded. On June 11th 1765, he married Elizabeth Fenwick, sole heiress of the priest who baptised him. The Reverend had bestowed upon her property on either side of a small street in Wisbech which is known to this day as Scrimshires Passage (figure 1.2). In 1770 he put up his plate in neighbouring Ship Lane.

At some stage, it appears that William may have 'walked the wards' at a local hospital though of this there is no record. Certainly, he acquired enough experience to undertake surgery. He gained no medical qualifications, nor is he registered as a licentiate of the Society of Apothecaries. The market was, as yet, entirely unregulated. That did not preclude his being master to four apprentices between 1777 and 1796 (and paying duties accordingly) to all of whom he was described as a 'surgeon'. He was a trainer as well as a practitioner.

Figure 1.2 The Passage

William quickly became well known in Wisbech. As early as 1773, and again in 1781 and 1800, he was elected Town Bailiff (equivalent to Mayor). In 1803 and in 1813, he is known to have been Commissioner of the Sewers for the Hundred of Wisbech, a function important for public health. Yet against this backdrop of prosperity, there was sadness. Elizabeth gave birth to eight children, three of whom (including one Stephen born in 1779) died in infancy.

His eldest son, William the Younger, was born in 1766 and eventually joined him in his practice in 1798. His daughter, Elizabeth, born 1773, married Charles Metcalfe, a Wisbech solicitor whose firm still survives. His next son, Thomas, followed his grandfather and entered the church. He moved eventually to Norfolk. Thomas's son, George, was to become the first of a line of doctors based in Holt who dominate this saga. William's third son, Fenwick, became a distinguished doctor in Peterborough, and the fortunes of his line will also be followed. His fourth son, George, was to farm at Kettlestone in Norfolk.

All the boys were educated at the ancient Grammar School in the town, founded originally in 1379 by the Guild of the Holy Trinity, and chartered by Edward VI in 1549. It had a strong link with Magdalene College, Cambridge, where Thomas spent a final year after starting at Clare. Fenwick chose Edinburgh University, foremost in those days for its medical school.

William the Older made a will before he died in 1814. In it, he described himself as *'late surgeon and apothecary.'* He was laid to rest with some pomp in St Peter's church in the centre of Wisbech.

#   #   #

The 18ᵗʰ century medical marketplace

Four main categories of orthodox medicine can be distinguished before 1800: physic, surgery, pharmacy, midwifery. Within the hierarchical system of medical practice three 'estates' were demarcated with their own legal rights, duties, functions and legitimacy. This tripartite model was less rigidly applied in the provinces where moving between the different branches was common and easy. Some indeed practised in all three branches. With no formal division between the qualified and unqualified, there was altogether a plurality of practitioners offering their services.[1]

Apothecaries

The profession of apothecary can be dated back to 2500 BC. Babylonian clay tablets record symptoms, prescriptions and directions for compounding them. Chaucer refers to an English apothecary in the Nun's Priest's tale. By the 1500s, the apothecary had gained the status of skilled medical practitioner alongside the physician and barber-surgeon for whom they formulated *materia medica*.

In what then did the first William Skrimshire's practice consist? Before 1800, there was not one medical profession but three. The physicians, members of a learned profession, dealt with internal disorders. Surgeons were craftsmen whose sphere was still largely external. Apothecaries were but tradesmen who compounded and dispensed physicians' prescriptions until they won the right to visit, advise and prescribe (following the Rose case of 1704, see below). This well-known division conceals the extent to which their respective practices overlapped with one another - and those of many untrained 'irregulars'.

The traditional view of rank-and-file practitioners such as William characterizes them as ill-educated and near-illiterate tradesmen who kept shops selling medicines and groceries to supplement earnings from their primitive practice. This caricature is harsh. Legally, apothecaries could dispense but not advise, treat or visit patients without risk of prosecution. In practice, and in order to survive in a marketplace where they outnumbered physicians by ten to one, they defied the law.

In addition to dispensing medicines directly to patients, the apothecary offered general medical advice and a range of services that are now performed by other specialist practitioners, such as surgeons and obstetricians. Apothecaries often operated through a retail shop which, in addition to ingredients for medicines, sold tobacco and patent medicines. They were, in other words, frequently the sick person's point of first contact.

Much had changed on 15ᵗʰ March, 1704 when William Rose was prosecuted for treating William Seale, a butcher at Hungerford Market. Annoyed at his £50 bill, Seale had sought redress through the College of Physicians. Lord Chief Justice Holt reluctantly found in favour of the College on a point of law but the House of

Lords sensibly reversed the judgement in the light of customary practice. The outdated legislation would have ruined apothecaries and oppressed the poor. *'Sick persons in case of sudden accidents or new symptoms appearing in the night time, generally send for an apothecary knowing that a physician would not attend if at dinner or abed'.*[2]

Much has been attributed to this infamous case including the generalists' present-day tendency to over-prescribe. Its impact on the status of apothecaries was ambiguous. On the one hand, the decision perpetuated their inferior status as financially dependent on sales of goods rather than expert knowledge. On the other hand, apothecaries were free to practice physic and become the doctors of the poorer classes. It gave legal confirmation for the first time to their role as medical practitioners rather than tradesmen and facilitated the merging of all four branches of practice. However, by the late eighteenth century, they were sorely aggrieved about the rampant quackery of their main competitors.

The rise of the surgeon-apothecary in the eighteenth century was in large measure driven by economic expediency. Most surgeons practiced physic and pharmacy in order to survive while apothecaries frequently undertook simple surgical procedures. Across the country in small towns and villages, most medical men - however they styled themselves - were undertaking much the same kind of general practice, involving all branches of medicine.

GPs today may offer many of his services but the modern pharmacist is the apothecary's more obvious descendent. By the end of the nineteenth century when the medical professions had taken on their current institutional form, the role of the apothecary was more narrowly conceived as that of pharmacist or dispensing chemist. The apothecaries' investigation of herbal and chemical ingredients was nevertheless a precursor to the modern sciences of chemistry and pharmacology.

In England, the apothecaries originated as members of the Company of Grocers but their own livery company, the Worshipful Society of Apothecaries, was founded in 1617.[3] It admits members by examination to this day. Elizabeth Garrett Anderson became the first woman to gain a medical qualification in Britain when she passed the Society's examination in 1865.

Barber-Surgeons
Although there had been some innovation in techniques, surgery changed little over the early modern period. The activities of early barber surgeons were greatly restricted - to bloodletting, setting fractures, excising skin tumours, lancing boils, pulling teeth, for example. Only a few undertook amputations, cut for bladder stone or repaired hernias. In other words, surgeons were confined to the external and immediately visible. The notion that surgery might cure internal disease was incompatible with perceptions of the body prevailing in the eighteenth century.

According to Humoral Theory, the body was seen as a functional whole interacting with its environment. Opening up the body to remove or repair made little sense.[4]

The knowledge to guide resective surgery derived from the steady, stepwise advances in pathological anatomy. In post-revolutionary Paris, Xavier Bichat (1771-1802) was among the most prominent in setting medicine on a sound anatomical footing. Later in the nineteenth century, the rise of laboratory medicine and burgeoning understanding of physiology (associated initially with Claude Bernard) underpinned restorative surgery. The aim here was not simply cutting out disease but restoring the function of diseased organs. Emil Kocher (1841-1917) later exemplified this stance and its inter-dependence with anaesthesia and antisepsis (thereby reducing death rates from his thyroid surgery).[5]

Modern surgeons started to view the body as composed of organs with particular functions; removing diseased structures restored healthy function. This localised approach led surgeons to turn the way they viewed the body 'outside-in' - from external signs to internal processes. This changed medicine as a whole.[6]

In London, the Guild of Surgeons came into being in 1368 while a Company of Barbers was chartered in 1376. They later merged. Barber-Surgeons tended to be from lower social strata than physicians though traditional distinctions in wealth and status were eroded dramatically in the eighteenth century. The Company of Surgeons eventually severed links with the Barbers in 1745 but few surgeons outside London were yet members. They were considerably more numerous than physicians and played an important role in medical care, particularly in urban areas. Only with the formation of the Royal College of Surgeons (RCS) in 1800 was provincial practice affected.

Traditionally, surgeons were equipped through lengthy apprenticeships. These came to be replaced by formal hospital training and taught courses in surgery, pathology and midwifery. Across Europe new surgical schools were expanded, for example in Paris at Saint-Côme.

A surgeon's education came to resemble that of a physician, and the form as well as the content of that education needed to be based on collective consensus. A common education presupposed a common body of theoretical knowledge as the basis for competence in practice. Surgical training eventually acquired more uniform entry requirements and licensing standards though these varied from country to country.[4]

Physicians
We have already considered the early training and practice of physicians in some detail (see Introduction). They were the elite, or so - as now - they regarded themselves. They possessed a university degree though not necessarily the

concomitant education since medical doctorates could be bought. At this time, the most celebrated centres of medical learning were in mainland Europe. In 1780, 30% with medical degrees had qualified in Edinburgh. Aberdeen and Cambridge were next in popularity, followed by Oxford, Leiden, Rheims, Glasgow and Dublin. Over the following century, with the steady expansion of clinical schools in London and the provinces, the majority of English doctors listed in the Medical Directory came to hold a medical degree from an English university.

Physicians dealt with the inside of the body: diseases, fevers and inflammations. They scarcely touched their patients - maintaining their distance literally and metaphorically - but their superior education conferred the right to oversee the work of surgeons and apothecaries. With some reluctance they accepted the plurality of healers in part because they needed the lower class of practitioner to do less exalted work, e.g. dressings, childbirth. Despite their relative paucity, they faced competition in building up their patient base.

Their history over this period can be seen as a constant battle to maintain their monopoly on diagnosis and prescription. In this regard, a major political advance had been the establishment of the College of Physicians which was chartered by Henry VIII in 1518. By the late seventeenth century, the physicians were increasingly angered by the encroachment of apothecaries on their practice. The hegemony of the physicians faded with the spectacular rise of surgery during the following century. The transformation of hospital medicine, its increasing specialisation and how this affected general practice, will feature prominently in subsequent chapters.

Midwives

It is often maintained that obstetrics was revolutionised in the eighteenth century when properly trained doctors wielding forceps displaced ignorant midwives and village women. This is simplistic. Earlier rituals of childbirth amounted to a shared heritage of women, regardless of social origin.[7] Practices included the presence of gossips, swaddling and the nature of lying in. Men were excluded with physicians only rarely attending in the event of serious complications. Their presence was associated with sorrow and death rather than the happiness of a successful delivery.[8]

The roles and activities of midwives expanded in recognition of their importance. This was one of the few public positions open to women and, in contrast to the physicians who sought control over their activities, midwives were practically experienced (footnote 1).[9] Women combined the roles of healer, nurse, midwife

Footnote 1. In the eighteenth century the need for training was recognised by midwives themselves. Sarah Stone published one of the earliest guides for midwives in 1737 (*A Complete Practice of Midwifery*). She complained that many of her colleagues knew nothing of the anatomy of the female pelvis and that male practitioners were as ignorant.[9]

and layer-out of the dead.

The obstetric forceps were invented by Peter Chamberlen (1560-1631) and popularised in this country by William Smellie (1697-1763) among others. The availability of safer delivery under life-threatening conditions presaged more routine acceptance of men's role in the lying-in chamber. The true value of forceps in reducing the dangers of labour was contested but their use marked a major symbolic shift. Henceforth greater power and influence were placed in the hands of the trained medical practitioner.

The reputation of medically trained *accoucheurs* such as William Hunter helped popularize man-midwives among the prosperous classes.[10] This coincided with a new demand among educated women in the upper echelons of society for a more distinctive experience in childbirth. In this view, to call for an expensive man-midwife was a sign of social status rather than of distrust in female midwives. Indeed, many of the established birthing rituals were retained well into the nineteenth century.[11]

Irregulars

Prior to the eighteenth century, there were broadly two types of practitioner: the educated (usually) licensed and the unlicensed, unqualified. However, with no system of formal education, registration or licensing, no sharp dividing lines could be drawn between the two. Ordinary medical practice at this time cannot be defined in the absence of a clear distinction between the orthodox, regular practitioner and the unorthodox irregular or 'quack' (footnote 2).

Medicine was not yet a 'closed shop' but rather a subject for informed argument among educated men from all walks of life - to be discussed like science and the humanities. Thus, the clergy were fond of treating their flock and anyone else who consulted them. Many irregulars were capable and respected; they cannot simply be dismissed as fraudulent opportunists.

The economy of healing mirrored social divisions between the rich and poor with only the former able to afford the fees of physicians. Hence the enduring appeal of the 'charlatans'. By the end of the eighteenth century, rank-and-file practitioners, like the physicians before them, were complaining stridently about the scandal of irregulars and the financial threat they posed.

The Surgeon-Apothecary's early years

The typical entrant to medicine at this time was a grammar schoolboy and son of a professional man, especially doctor, clergyman or minor gentry. His success at

Footnote 2. The term 'quack' may be derived from the Dutch 'quacksalver' for a quicksilver doctor; mercury was widely used to treat syphilis.

school was measured in terms of his reading in the classics. He left school at fifteen with some knowledge of Latin and Greek to become an apprentice. From the mid-1700s, increasingly this was followed by a period of instruction. This could involve 'walking the wards' of a provincial hospital as a surgeon's pupil or attending private lecture courses in London. Such instruction was haphazard - there was no official syllabus or examination - but the student at least returned with impressive certificates of attendance. Finally, a university MD (*Medicinae Doctor*) might be obtained from Aberdeen, Edinburgh or St Andrews for a modest fee and the recommendations of two colleagues. There was thus already a well-trodden path, a recognised system of general medical education both for the intending elite and for surgeon-apothecaries.

This evolution is nicely exemplified in the experiences of William whose father had prospered sufficiently to send his children to grammar school. From there William had apprenticed himself to a local surgeon-apothecary before flourishing in independent practice. In a town like Wisbech and in the face of more intense competition, his own son was to require the stamp of a degree.

Views on apprenticeship as the basis for medical training changed between 1750 and 1850 with increasing criticism of the system after 1815. Apprenticeship provided practical knowledge of drugs, their preparation and how to run a business. As apothecaries began to give more time to hands-on care, their apprentices were increasingly important for 'looking after the shop'. Until the mid-eighteenth century this was the only formal method of training.

In the late eighteenth century, £300 was usually enough to cover the costs of apprenticeship and starting in practice. Parents, choosing a career for their sons, might balance initial costs against expected annual income in middle age. In William's time these were roughly equivalent but all that had changed - for the worse - within a generation (see chapter 3).

With the development of hospital training, more systematic courses of reading and clinical experience needed to be provided in the community. Even then, the advantages of country practice as compared with hospital for gaining experience of common disorders - *'he can best see the ultimate results of treatment'* - were appreciated.[12] The apprentice was also versed in appropriate humanity towards their patients and the cultivation of *'prudence, decency of manners, candour and circumspection'*.[13] For apprentices were potentially indolent or rebellious and needed moral instruction and discipline.[14]

Then as now, hospital experience with its emphasis on surgery was not necessarily the best preparation for the realities of the job: *'The young lad goes to London to attend lectures and hospitals…He never considers that if he is to practise as an apothecary he must in the course of his practice have twenty medical cases for one that is chirurgical; yet he returns to the country with an ostentatious display of hospital certificates; though in this trait he has been mispending both his time and his money.'*[15]

Apprentices could be exploited but serving under a good master was a great advantage. Influential masters of good repute could help ensure early professional progress. In the days before affiliations were defined by your London teaching hospital, apprenticeship yielded an important medical identity. For provincial practitioners receiving a couple of hundred pounds, they were also a useful source of income.

The early years in practice tended to be the most difficult. The advantages of being able to join a medical relation, perhaps first as an apprentice then partner, were self-evident. Hence a high proportion of entrants had fathers in medicine (table 1.1).[16] Confirming their supposed superiority, there tended to be a higher proportion of professional and upper-class fathers among physicians. GPs after 1815 came from the same broad ranks as apothecaries and surgeon-apothecaries in the eighteenth century.[17]

Across Europe the training requirements for physicians and surgeons gradually converged, transforming surgeons and apothecaries from literate artisans to learned professionals. A new hybrid of 'general practitioner' began to emerge. These divisions were to be formalised in the UK with the Medical Act of 1858. These developments will be considered in greater detail in the following chapters.

18th century practice - fever, physic and pharmacy
In 1780, the economy was still predominantly agrarian and the population rural. Cultural traditions often reflected seasonal change. Outside major towns and cities, transportation and communication systems were limited. Communities were to a large extent self-regulating. Society was more starkly structured before the rise of the working and middle classes.[18]

What diseases did the first William Skrimshire encounter and how did he tackle them? Mortality data began to be collected from the late sixteenth century onwards. John Graunt (1620-1674) was the first to compare causes of death in different age groups in London but the available data on rural morbidity and mortality are limited. The reliability of mortality statistics before the introduction of death registration in 1838 is contested (footnote 3). Common morbidities cannot simply be inferred from causes of death and studies of disease in the community are of relatively recent origin. Hospital statistics are available from the eighteenth century

Footnote 3. The first major statistical analyses using registered data on births and deaths were compiled by William Farr (1807-83).

Table 1.1   Occupation of fathers of medical practitioners in West of England, 1760-1830[16]

Father's occupation	Surgeons/Apoths/GPs	Physns
Surgeon/Apothecary	19	4
Clergy	11	3
Lawyer	2	
Army/Naval Officer	2	
Landed/Esq	8	4
Farmer	3	
Bank employee	2	
Clothier	2	
Schoolmaster	1	1
Merchant	4	1
Sailmaker	1	
Liquor dealer	1	
Dyer of feathers	1	
Grocer		1
Sugar baker		1
Wine cooper	1	
Other	10	
TOTAL	68	15

but these reflect selective admission criteria rather than representative disease beyond the hospital walls. Historians are anyway mindful of the dangers of retrospective diagnoses that affix our medical understanding to culturally specific, past experiences of illness. Disease diagnoses are socially constructed.[19]

That said, the spectrum of illness encountered was probably much like that of the poorest pre-industrial communities today. Population growth and the impact of war in France depressed wages in the 1790s. Poor harvests in these years aggravated food shortages. Against a background of chronic malnutrition among the poor, infectious diseases were rife. Occasional diaries kept by exceptional practitioners provide a valuable source for understanding the spectrum of disorders encountered by my ancestors. One such diarist was James Clegg (1679-1755), a physician at Chapel-le-Frith in Cumbria; his records are summarised in table 1.2.[20] Infectious disease predominated though mental afflictions were recognised. Most disease labels are recognizable though what, one wonders, was 'iliac passion'? A reminder, perhaps that what we nowadays term 'medically unexplained symptoms' have always been part of the daily round.

More comprehensive are the lists of diseases recorded at dispensaries which provided free out-patient primary care, though these outlets were generally urban (table 1.3). The registers demonstrate the hazards of simple comparison. How much did any differences in the morbidity described reflect the diagnostic predilections of the practitioner? (Was there really no venereal disease in London?) Fevers and chest infections dominated practice:

'A surgeon-apothecary is called up soon after retiring to bed, from a hard day's work to attend a patient in an acute disease five or six miles off. Weary as he is, his necessities compel him to mount his jaded horse…and to make his way through the wind and the rain in the darkest night…to a farm house where he finds his patient labouring under a severe attack of inflammation of the lungs. He takes some active measures immediately and waits, probably two or three hours, cold and shivering in his wet clothes to see the effect of the remedies employed…and these results are repeated twice a day… '[21]

Table 1.2   Illnesses recorded by James Clegg in Chapel-en-Frith, early 18th century[20]

Infections		Respiratory	
Fever	101	Consumption	19
Smallpox	81	Pleurisy	51
Ague	39	Quinsy	35
Measles	12	Chincough	12
Scarlet Fever	3	Empyema	5
		Peripneumony	3
		Cold/catarrh	2
Gastro-intestinal			
Colic	44		
Diarrhoea	16	*Surgical disorders*	
Dysentery	2	Injuries, eg fractures	13
Hypochondriac colic	6	Cancer	15
Cholera	3	Toothache	6
Iliac passion	6	Fistula-in-ano	3
Jaundice	3	Tumor	3
Worms	2	Gangrene	2
		Ulcers	2
Genito-urinary		Abscess	1
Gravel	9	Rupture	1
Nephritic pain	7	Piles	6
Stone	5		
Strangury	9	Accidents eg industrial	49
		Accidents concerning horses	26
Mental disorders			
Melancholy	16	*Other*	
Hysterick fit	9	Convulsions	26
Mental disorder	6	Rheumatism	16
Idiot	4	Paralysis/palsy	15

Both urban and rural communities were susceptible to epidemic respiratory and diarrhoeal disease. Fevers dominated the practice of physic and were classified into three main groups: continued fevers, intermittent and remittent, and the eruptive. There is perhaps only a loose correlation between these categories and modern descriptions of infection. The continued fevers are thought to have been a mixture of typhus and typhoid. Since Hippocratic times, marshy locations had been particularly linked with intermittent fevers. In those days, mosquitoes bred in the

Table 1.3   Most common disease categories reported by four dispensaries[22]

Newcastle Disp (John Clark,1777-90)		General Disp, London (J Lettsom,1773-4)	
Putrid fevers	1992	Febris putrida	192
Diarrhoeal diseases	700	Rheumatisms and sciatica	128
Consumption	690	Febris hectica	86
Stomach complaints	660	Asthma and dyspnoea	84
Rheumatism	581	Febris remittens	82
Catarrh	537	Tussis and catarrhus	80
Pleurisy	490	Diarrhoea and dysentriae	72
Intermittent fevers	362	Febris nervosa	62
Venereal diseases	347	Phthisis pulmonale	56
Skin eruptions	326	Tussis convulsiva vel pertussis	47
TOTAL	9830		1662

Liverpool Disp (Anon, 1800-01)		Finsbury Disp (J Reid, W Webb, 1800-01)	
Fevers	2603	Typhus, continued fever	431
Skin eruptions	2287	Diarrhoeal diseases	278
Diarrh, dysentery, cholera	1593	Cough and dyspnoea	229
Dyspnoea and cough	1523	Asthenia	189
Stomach complaints	658	Infantile fever	152
Syphilis	511	Amenorrhoea and chlorosis	128
Catarrh	434	Consumption	123
Debility	356	Pulmonary complaints	107
Amenorrhoea	320	Dyspepsia	105
Diseases of the eyes	283	Menorrhagia	74
TOTAL	1302		2771

undrained wetlands of East Anglia and the 'ague' (malaria) was prevalent. Specific infections in the eruptive group - smallpox, chickenpox, measles, scarlet fever - were often confused with each other. Phthisis (TB) was another much-feared killer.

'A fashionable physician attending on the rich, and another in the same district and at the same time, visiting the sick poor, would present lists of diseases widely different: gout and hysteria might stand foremost in the one; contagious fever and dysentery in the other.'[22] Such socio-economic differentials were being demonstrated in Paris by Louis-René Villermé (1782-1863). Physicians working in the community, and shocked by their experiences, were partly responsible for opening the eyes of the medical profession as a whole to the links between poverty and disease. Though striking, they were rather a matter of degree. The full spectrum treated by surgeon-apothecaries would broadly correspond to that seen at dispensaries. Serving both the prosperous of Wisbech and outlying agricultural hamlets, my forebears bore witness to the same patterns of illness.

The doctor's most important functions, as ever, were diagnosis and prognosis. Prescribed regimens concerned the 'non-naturals' detailed previously. Much of the advice offered concerned diet but also central to the maintenance of health were *'air, meat and drink, sleep and watching, motion and rest, retention, excretion and the affections of the mind.'*[23]

Only a handful of therapies were clinically effective from a modern perspective. Among the drugs available to relieve symptoms were quinine (cinchona bark) for malarial fevers, digitalis for heart failure ('dropsy') and opium for pain relief. James Lind had demonstrated that fresh fruit and vegetables prevented scurvy. Smallpox vaccination was not yet widely available and mercury was of doubtful efficacy for syphilis.

The surgeon, Richard Smith of Bristol thought *'pharmacopoeias were loaded with a useless farrago of useless trash…the great bulk of bottles were mere placebos.'*[17] Then as now, many doctors were sceptical of their own effectiveness. Many would have concurred with Marryat, writing in 1764, who opined that:

'With respect to the mode of operation of medicines it must be confessed we are somewhat in the dark…Nature is often very unmannerly to theories…Would it not be more ingenious to acknowledge that medicines do generally produce effects, though we cannot satisfactorily account for the manner in which they act?…When a person is ill, he naturally and justly looks for the restoration of his health from a physician, and the number of those who are disappointed is exceedingly small.'[24]

Therapeutic nihilism was a luxury no practitioner could afford to confess - or any patient to face. He had the strongest incentive to promote faith in the remedies he dispensed, however secretly sceptical, because they were the main source of income. There was a mixture, draught, bolus, pill or lotion for every disorder known to medicine. Pharmacy was a necessarily major part of practice.

This may have been, in Richard Smith's phrase, the 'Golden Age of Physic'[25] but an awareness of the need for critical enquiry was dawning. *'Unless we can calculate with some degree of precision the extent of powers of nature (to cure fever), we shall find it impossible to assign what is due to them and what to the agency of medicine…and we run the risk of congratulating ourselves on a great cure when there may only have been a lucky escape.'*[26] Thankfully, patients were as yet less discerning.

Some similarities with the practice of today would have been evident in the fields of surgery and obstetrics. In addition to bloodletting and cupping, doctors lanced boils and drained abscesses, extracted teeth, set bones and dressed wounds. Accidents and injuries were commonplace in an agricultural community.

Though village women and midwives assisted most normal deliveries, the practice of routine obstetrics had changed little. It was a hard way to earn a living, requiring attendance for hours or even days, always with the dread of losing patients from puerperal fever. One John McCulloch earned £248 over the year for an average of six deliveries/week around 1800.[27] Midwifery came to be regarded as the province of lower ranks of the profession and, by default, associated with the GP. Man-midwifery was poorly paid but satisfying, and important for the building up of a practice.

Environmental health

As we have seen, the Hippocratic works associated epidemics with a combination of environmental and individual factors. The putrefaction of organic matter (rotting vegetation, excrement, decaying corpses, etc.) was thought to create an evil air or 'miasma', the medium through which pestilence was propagated. Post-Galenic physicians were mindful of how environmental factors affected the body's humours. Such understanding helped to determine what illnesses afflicted individuals in particular geographical places. Marshy locations, for example, were particularly linked with fevers. Environmental factors informed the regulation of the six non-naturals through regimen. Much of the advice offered by individual physicians concerned diet but air quality was also regarded as central to the maintenance of health.[28]

Writing in the seventeenth century, Stephen Bradwell had suggested that plague was spread by invisible, often air-born, poisonous particles. This challenged the Galenic emphasis on humoural balance.[29] He urged his readers to clean and ventilate their surroundings and each to *'keep oneself as private as he may'*. Bradwell provided an early illustration of Anti-Contagionism. Similar strictures were adopted by later health boards regarding urban cleanliness and the segregation of the sick. Over time these notions would be replaced by a primary concern with external agents in Germ Theory (see chapter 5).

In contrast, other parts of the natural world were beneficial to health. Wells, hot springs and waters were celebrated by both laymen and physicians. Widely believed to relieve a range of ailments, they were often associated with the cults of various saints. In early modern times, scourges like the Great Pox were still seen in religious terms as divine punishment for moral transgression. In Catholic countries urban morality and public health were thus promoted through penitential rituals, processions and prayers.[1]

More generally, plague shaped attitudes towards poverty over the seventeenth century. The perceived links between the practices of the poor and sickness provided the basis for much policy to contain outbreaks. Instead of being seen in a religious light as a vehicle of salvation, the poor came to be regarded as 'degenerate'. Epidemics were used to impose social control and exclusion in both Catholic and Protestant countries.

Poor Laws

The first Act for the Relief of the Poor was passed by Parliament in 1601. Its origins extended back into the 15th century with the decline of the monasteries and the breakdown of medieval social structures. Charity was gradually replaced with a compulsory land tax levied at parish level. The Elizabethan Poor Law formalised earlier practices of relief distribution in England and Wales.

This 'Old Poor Law' was not one law but a collection of laws passed over the seventeenth and eighteenth centuries. The system's administrative unit was the parish. The 1601 Act saw a move away from the more obvious forms of punishing paupers under the Tudor system towards methods of 'correction'. Relief took one of two forms - indoor relief inside a workhouse, or outdoor relief in the form of money, food or even clothing. Inmates of the new workhouses were subjected to bureaucratic oversight, discipline and moral reproach. As the cost of building these institutions was great, outdoor relief continued to be the main form of relief in this period.[30]

Relief for those too ill or old to work, the so-called 'impotent poor', was in the form of a payment or items of food ('the parish loaf') or clothing also known as outdoor relief. Some aged people might be accommodated in parish alms houses. In theory, this system allowed greater sensitivity towards paupers whose overseers were supposed to differentiate between the 'deserving' (innocent victims) and 'undeserving' poor (beggars, vagrants, prostitutes). Country doctors were sometimes employed by the parish to assist in the administration of poor relief.

Apothecaries' incomes

Provincial practitioners have sometimes been lowly regarded. They often combined their work with another occupation such as farming. The traditional, semi-literate, shop-keeping apothecary has been contrasted with the arriviste proto-GP visible in English society by 1730. Surprisingly little is known of ordinary practitioners but it is likely that the dictats of Colleges or the Society of Apothecaries were largely irrelevant to their day-to-day activities. They worked from their shops (or 'surgeries'). The counter, as later the desk, constituted a barrier between doctor and patient but such social niceties declined with the steady expansion of home visiting. Thus began to evolve a more intimate perception of doctor as family confidant.

Waddington describes a two-tier system: doctor-led care available to a minority for financial reasons while the poorer majority sought domestic remedies or the services of apothecaries and irregulars.[31] This is rather contradicted by evidence from contemporary sources (diaries, case-books and doctors' ledgers) that evidence expansion in the numbers of rank-and-file practitioners and the widening variety of patients they treated.[32]

The profits of pharmacy were substantial. Prices doubled around the middle of the eighteenth century on account of rising demand and the status of medical care.[27] There was a similar rise in charges for visits and journeys but doctors' increasing prosperity was mostly pharmacy-related. Though often criticised for their exorbitant charges, the apothecary's profit received an unexpected endorsement from none other than Adam Smith. In his *Wealth of Nations* (1776), he wrote that *'the skill of an apothecary is a much nicer and more delicate matter than that of any artificer whatever; and the trust that is reposed in him is of much greater importance…Though he should sell his drugs…at a thousand per cent profit, this may frequently be no more than the reasonable wages of his labour charged in the only way he can charge them…wages described in the garb of profit.'*[33]

Such an affirmation of the rising status of the apothecary and surgeon-apothecary provided little defence against the dilemma which was to haunt future general practitioners in their bid for respectability. The taint of trade and shop-keeping impeded their social advance. Mercenary stigmata linger today though the public are largely ignorant of the profits accruing from practice dispensaries.

Practitioners in London and other fashionable urban areas in the 1750s could achieve incomes of over £1000/year. By comparison, the country apothecary and surgeon-apothecary earned but £400-500/year once well established. This compared with £100 for superior clergy and the law, £150/year for richer farmers. By the end of the century the trade of surgeon-apothecary was better paid.[32]

Other essentials for success were a good reputation and a good horse. The latter needed to be *'neither highly bred, elegant or expensive but reliable and possessed of unusual stamina…ready for work at all hours.'* For early GPs like my ancestors had to rely on the wisdom of horses, trundling home with their exhausted master fast asleep in the saddle.[34] This required between £10 and £30/year, more if two horses were kept - for use by day and night. Indeed, William rented a three acre paddock (the 'East Field') and stable within a short distance from Ship Lane to meet these needs. GPs have always set much store by their transportation. The bewildering choices of coaches, broughams, carriages and other accoutrements - each with their distinct social significations - make today's automotive options seem mundane by comparison.

With increasing numbers of practitioners, competition grew fiercer towards the end of the eighteenth century. This period saw major changes in education and prosperity that yielded increasing commercial opportunities for medicine as both a business and a profession. However, increasingly critical consumers accorded less respect to the moral and legal rights of trained practitioners. Faith in progress sat alongside lay scepticism towards the efficacy of physic. The Enlightenment drove a new more rigorous epistemology of science along with a new consumerism and rising expectations. Health was becoming a more important public and private issue.

Untrained irregulars still flourished. Their pills and potions remained popular and many adopted smarter personas to promote them. They were assisted by the birth of newspapers and magazines allowing them to advertise to new consumer markets, and new modes of mass production of their remedies. Apothecaries benefited also from the growth in commercial medicines. Any distinction between the organisation of medicine in theory and the reality in practice was increasingly blurred.

Conclusion

Growing consumerism over this period helped sustain the commercialisation of medicine and a rising demand for care. Distinctions between the diversity of practitioners were breaking down. An increasing proportion of the rank-and-file were combining medical, surgical and obstetric skills as *de facto* general practitioners. This made good business sense in a crowded marketplace.

Apothecaries had long defied the law, practising physic in increasing numbers, and decisively shaped the future divisions of medical practice in England. Like the first William, they learnt their business as apprentices, on the job. The Rose case of 1704 had important implications for general practice: perpetuating the inferior status of apothecaries and promoting over-prescribing practice. However, the Rose case did give legal confirmation to the role of apothecary as medical practitioner, not tradesman.

The range of afflictions presenting to William the Older at first sight seem very distant. His practice and those of other surgeon-apothecaries were entirely unregulated. Yet the prominence of the prescription is somehow familiar. And, if the fevers are foreign, many of the practical rituals involved in attending to those who consulted him would be recognisable today. Then as now, the doctor's most valuable tasks were to listen, to bear witness, *'to cure sometimes, to treat often and to comfort always.'*[35]

William the Younger was faced with a dilemma. The more profitable direction of travel for an aspiring doctor was plain. His two younger brothers left home for university never to return. After training in Edinburgh, William opted for the security of his father's established business. Filial responsibility was no doubt a factor in his decision. The same tricky choices were to face many of his descendants.

Chapter Two – Upward mobility
(1800-1830)

'How frail the bloom, how short the stay
That terminates us all!
Today we flourish green and gay,
Like leaves tomorrow fall.'
John Clare

The second generation

William the Elder and Elizabeth prospered. Five children survived into adulthood - a relative rarity itself in those days. The Skrimshires were a close family and William's passions were duly passed on to his children, notably reflected in their lifelong interests in botany and entomology. They were well educated at Wisbech Grammar School. During a critical period for the development of general practice, the careers of two medical sons were to take rather different trajectories.

Figure 2.1   Family tree of the Wisbech Skrimshires

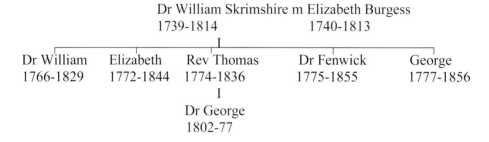

William Skrimshire, the Younger

William was informally apprenticed to his father in the early 1780s. He qualified as a doctor in Edinburgh and moved back to Wisbech. By 1796, he was in partnership with William senior and had taken on apprentices of his own. In time, he followed his father as Commissioner for Sewers, but he was more widely known as a botanist. In those days, as we have seen, study of the natural sciences was an integral part of medical training. His painstakingly catalogued collection of dried plants can still be seen in the Wisbech Museum. Yet this scarcely does justice to a substantial herbarium which continues to constitute an archive of considerable value (figure 2.2).[1]

William was a *'very accurate and attentive observer of nature'*, qualities which no doubt served him well as a doctor. His manuscripts delightfully detail excursions to adjacent counties in search of specimens. His interests were wide-ranging to judge by his published articles. These concerned flora and fauna, phosphorescence and even the weather.[1,2] He was the first to record that the roasted seeds from *Iris pseudacorus* could be used as a substitute for coffee.[3] He was a focus for many other amateur naturalists living in the area.

Figure 2.2 WS Herbarium - specimen

As an entomologist, he and his brother Thomas published papers in various scientific journals including the Transactions of the Entomologists' Society. He contributed to William Nicholson's Journal of Natural Philosophy and its successor, the Philosophical Journal, between 1806 and 1818. His partner (formerly his apprentice), John Rose Weatherhead, was another major contributor to the Wisbech collection, and he too later qualified MD at Edinburgh University.

His brother Thomas returned home from Magdalene College, Cambridge, with a law degree and opened a school locally - but he faced stiff competition. The Rev Martin Coulcher, recently appointed Master of the Grammar School, gave notice that he intended *'admitting 20 boarders and instructing them in the Classics, the French Language, Writing and Arithmetic (Algebra and the principles of mathematics) at 25 Guineas per annum 2 guineas Entrance.'*

William the Younger showed rare displeasure for he considered this *'poaching'*. He wrote to Anthony Hamond, an influential local businessman involved in Coulcher's election to the Mastership of the Grammar School: *'He will evidently interfere with my brother Thomas's pursuit in the same line in the same town...'* He suggested he might *'make us some amends by using (his) influence with Mr C to think of my Father and myself in his new establishment & create us Apothecaries to his household.'* Mr Hamond wrote in support of the Skrimshires: *'They are men of good character and knowledge in the practice, and my friends, the Peckovers* (a well-known banking family in the town) *are particular friends.'* This Dickensian correspondence sheds light on small town professional rivalries, as well as on the place of private education, alongside established schools. Brother Thomas left anyway in response to a different calling.

William the Younger never married but continued to nurture a range of interests. With other worthies, he established a local branch of the Auxiliary Bible Society. This was a charitable and non-denominational organisation, devoted to publishing and distributing bibles at affordable prices. No doubt that met with fraternal approval but he was not unworldly. He demonstrated a surprisingly entrepreneurial streak with his partner, John Weatherhead. They concocted a product they called *'British Salop...as a substitute for cocoa, chocolate, tea and coffee.'* According to an advertisement in the Stamford Mercury of November 1815, it was *'one of the most nutritious preparations ever offered to the public'*, and *'as useful in the sick chamber as at the breakfast table.'* It was apparently sold *'by appointment by vendors in London, Stamford, Spalding, Peterborough, Norwich, Lynn, Fakenham, Cambridge and Bury, and by most country dealers - at three shillings per pound.'* How profitable was this venture is not recorded.

In 1818, William took on a rather special apprentice - *'in Consideration of the Sum of one penny'*. The Deed of Indenture for his Apprenticeship committed his nephew George to five years of sober living: *'Fornicating he shall not commit, nor matrimony contract, Taverns, Inns or Alehouses he shall not haunt; at Cards, Dice, Tables or any other unlawful games he shall not play; nor from the service of his said Masters Day and Night shall absent himself... His said Masters the said Apprentice in the Art of Surgery and Pharmacy which they now useth shall teach and instruct...allowing unto the said Apprentice, sufficient Meat, Drink, Washing, Lodging and other Necessaries during the said term of five years.'*

Family history does not relate what demands these injunctions made of either party. They certainly suggest that William took his responsibilities *in loco parentis* with all due seriousness.

In later life he moved to Bushy Place, a house on the edge of the town with a large garden. There he cultivated among other things a large 'peppermint plantation', distilled for medicinal use. It is pleasing to imagine the old man, pottering about among his plants and lepidoptera. He died on 22nd July, 1839 and lies buried near his father under a monumental stone in the Lady Chapel of St Peter's Church, Wisbech.

Righteous reverend
Thomas Skrimshire was ordained as a deacon in Norwich in 1798. In the seventeenth and eighteenth centuries many priests held a number of benefices. One stipend was often insufficient to support a family. Thomas lived before the first Pluralities Act was enforced (footnote 1). His first church appointment was at Whissonsett, where he had 'married well' - on June 17th 1797, to Rose Raven, daughter of Robert Raven of Whissonsett Hall.

Footnote 1. Dispensation enabling a clerk to hold several ecclesiastical benefices dated back to the Ecclesiastical Licences Act of 1533. Many incumbents were non-resident and delegated their spiritual duties to assistant curates. The system was widely exploited. The Pluralities Act 1838 therefore required that no person should hold more than two benefices and only if both parishes were within 10 miles of each other.

By the turn of the century, Thomas and Rose had established a small *'academy for young gentlemen'* in Fakenham. Fees for each of the parlour borders were as high as 35 guineas a year. They instituted the first public library in the town. The Skrimshires later moved their operations to Syderstone where Thomas was now the vicar. The vicarage there was more spacious.

At the same time, they were bringing up their own growing family. Syderstone was just one of several parishes in which Thomas was incumbent during his career in the diocese of Norwich. He was among the last to enjoy the privilege of being a 'pluralist'.

Thomas became well-known in local educational circles and championed the teaching of literacy to the poor. In this, he was ably supported by Rose who ran their Sunday schools but tensions were rife. They were frequently obstructed by local farmers opposed to education for the masses. The couple's activities are described in some detail by her aunt, the celebrated diarist Mary Hardy of Letheringsett.[4]

Many local clergy come across as committed if despairing of the constraints they faced. They contributed what they could spare from their meagre stipends to buy books, candles and coals for their scholars. Thomas seems to have been especially driven by Revivalist fervour.[4] In a long, affecting letter to the *National Society for Promoting the Education of the Poor in the Principles of the Established Church in England and Wales* (dated November 14th, 1814), he detailed the challenges they faced and appealed for support. Such activism laid the ground for the later introduction of state-funded public education in 1833.[5] By then, Sunday schools in Great Britain were ministering weekly to over one and a quarter million children, approximately 25% of the population. This must have been a source of profound satisfaction to Thomas at the end of his days. He died in 1836 of tuberculosis.

Fenwick Skrimshire

If William was dutiful and unassuming, his brother Fenwick was in some respects a sharp contrast. He too gained early experience in his father's practice. He too studied in Edinburgh and qualified MD in 1798. He too earnestly pursued the family interest in natural history with a doctoral thesis (entitled *'De Assimilatio'*) concerned with the practical conversion of nutrients by organisms. He was, at the same time, president of the Edinburgh Natural History Society and busy extending his knowledge of general science. Fenwick was extrovert by nature and a natural communicator.

What took him first to Kettering is not known. It seems likely that his first intention was to lecture. His first two published works, *A Series of Popular Chymical Essays* (1802)[6] and a *Series of Essays as an Introduction to Natural History* (1805)[7], were both developed from planned courses of lectures. Both were directed at young people, carefully summarizing a breadth of knowledge derived from learned treatises.

In both series, the practical usefulness of scientific knowledge is stressed. In both, his theological opinions are expressed, as necessary to an explanation of the facts. Fenwick regarded his investigations as part of a wider examination of the divine. Although never himself to go into the church, his writings - over fifty years before Darwin's publication of The Origin of Species - evidence his firm Christian faith, as an extract from this Natural History essay nicely attests:

'The wolf and the fox are classed by naturalists under the same genus as the dog...between which there is considerable similarity of manners, as well as of appearance. But when naturalists or philosophers attempt to prove that some varieties of the human species are nearly allied to the simiae, or apes, I cannot help thinking that such men, propagating such notions, debase themselves thereby, and become more on a level with the brutes of which they speak, than are the poor African or South Sea Islander, whom they endeavour to depreciate. I have heard arguments, founded on such a notion, advanced even by intelligent men, to support the propriety of the slave trade: a commerce that must cause every feeling heart to sicken at the sight... None would be daring enough to assert that a traffic in human flesh was reconcilable to the doctrines of Christianity.'[7]

His first book, the *Chymical Essays*, was dedicated to the Governors of the Kettering Dispensary and other subscribers, *'for their ready and liberal assistance in promoting the establishment.'* Coming later to the notice of a local notable, Earl Fitzwilliam, the book helped to determine his choice of Fenwick Skrimshire to organise the foundation of a dispensary in Peterborough.

In 1806, Fenwick married Charlotte Cobb. She was the daughter of James Cobb, an ironmonger and boot manufacturer. He was also a founder of the Kettering Bank: an altogether useful father-in-law. Three years later, Fenwick settled in Peterborough, attracted by a larger city with more opportunities. He was now moving in Whig circles and became Earl Fitzwilliam's personal physician. He was a Captain in the Volunteer Militia, set up on the Earl's initiative, to defend the realm against a feared Napoleonic invasion (footnote 2). On the conclusion of hostilities in 1815, Earl Fitzwilliam decided to divert unused funds to the establishment of a public Dispensary. He asked Fenwick to publicise the venture and take responsibility for its fulfilment. The history of its first thirty-one years, during all of which time he was its physician, suggests his choice was judicious.

Footnote 2. Notoriously, the East of England always struggled to meet government quotas for military recruitment. Colley attributes this to the region's geographical isolation and strong Nonconformist leanings.[8]

The Peterborough Dispensary and Infirmary

In a letter addressed to local nobility, gentry and other inhabitants dated December 2nd 1815, Fenwick invited attendance at a public meeting in the Town Hall three days later. His aim was to raise additional funds for a new dispensary. He was already an influential figure, having been elected to the Peterborough Gentleman's Society in 1809. He was living in Cowgate, where the first accommodation was found for the dispensary. It opened on May 4th, 1816.

Following the Kettering model, the dispensary was established as an Association of Subscribers, those giving one guinea or more being called governors. They were responsible for the management of the institution and, together with the clergy who made collections at local churches, had the right to recommend patients.

Fenwick's annual report, for the First Anniversary meeting held in January 1817, listed the number of patients treated. This rose, with some fluctuations, from 706 in the first year coming from 36 parishes, to 1223 in 1833 from 60 parishes. The reputation as well as the need for the institution was felt to be reflected in these statistics. A resolution passed the following year shows how the dispensary was being financed: *'A triennial Summer Meeting shall be arranged when a Procession of Officers and Governors shall take place, a Sermon preached and a collection made.'*

The demand for contributions increased as accommodation was needed for patients too ill to return home on the same day. A commodious lodging house was therefore established, where the patients would receive lodging, nursing, firewood and candles free of charge. Separate accommodation was also sought for fever patients.

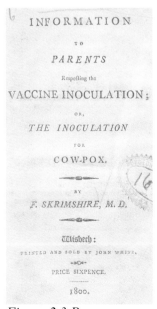

Regrettably, at the Third Anniversary meeting in January 1819, it was reported that suitable premises for the fever cases had not been found. Earl Fitzwilliam ordered the construction of a new building. A resident nurse was employed to act as matron and servant. A surgeon, Dr Thomas Walker, was appointed in 1819, though it was not until 1823 that he was recognised as equal in status as a governor with the physician. These two, with three other worthy citizens, signed the financial reports which were then produced triennially. In his report of July 1825, Fenwick expressed his satisfaction with the progress of both dispensary and infirmary.

Vaccination against smallpox was an important feature of their work, though it had only recently become routine practice (and did not become mandatory until 1863). Fenwick produced a detailed pamphlet and argued

Figure 2.3 Provaxx

audaciously that no child should be accepted at school without a certificate confirming successful vaccination (footnote 3). He faced his own local Antivaxx and felt his authoritative statement was *'calculated to render its introduction less liable to objection, and its introduction more general'*[10] (figure 2.3).

As well as vaccination, 40 to 50 trusses for hernia were provided annually, and about 260 surgical cases were treated. A medical library was established, with thirty-five members, which possessed over 1000 books. Despite all this additional activity, in 1825 Fenwick pronounced that the financial situation, *'the pivot on which all their operation must hinge'*, was satisfactory. The triennial sermon had attracted a collection of £95-10-5d. The total expenditure for medical and surgical attention, vaccination, the supply of trusses and the medical library had not exceeded £650/annum.

In this report he introduced a tabular record of prevailing disorders such as the remittent and intermittent fevers believed to be caused by malaria, common in the Fens on account of the stagnant water where mosquitoes bred. Though the causes of these diseases were not yet known, the number treated rose from 148 in 1819 to 527 in 1827.

Fenwick's annual reports were characteristically crafted. In his triennial report of July 1834, he once more listed the number of patients treated each year. The totals of all the years showed 16,652 cured, 891 relieved, and only 481 mortalities. 97 parishes were recommending patients. His tabulations of patients' needs resulted from his daily contact with impoverished families. He appreciated their way of life and concerns, and this fuelled other interests of his own.

Popular writing

If his main achievement was to establish the first infirmary in Peterborough, he continued to build a personal reputation through his writing. In 1834 he published, for sale at 1/-, *Letters on the consumption of Malt*, addressed to the *'Farmer, Labourer and Labourer's Friend!'* In the same year, for a mere 3d, or 2/6d a dozen, he brought out *Every poor man his own brewer*, a letter addressed to the same *'Labourer of every class.'* Accompanied by clear practical instructions, he calculated that home-brewed ale could be produced for 2 1/2d a quart, compared to the average 5d payable at an ale house. *'For 1/6d a week, every married man may allow himself a pint and a half daily, and half a pint for his wife.'* The pamphlet sold well.

His connection with one particular patient should be mentioned, since Fenwick is notorious for having declared him insane in 1841. He had first attended to John

Footnote 3. The compulsory vaccination of schoolchildren remains a contested issue today - resisted on libertarian grounds in the UK. Perhaps surprisingly, the evidence suggests that linking access to primary education to compulsory completion of immunisation schedules does more harm than good.

Clare, the 'Peasant Poet', at Earl Fitzwilliam's request in the 1820s. Born into an impoverished family, books became Clare's life after he had, by his own endeavours, bought himself rudimentary schooling. His poetry evoked country scenes, with highly personal descriptions of landscape and place. Born at Helpston, a few miles from Peterborough, he saw the change wrought by the enclosures, and his poetry is a lament for the death of rural England.

Through a Stamford bookseller, his first volume - *Poems, descriptive of Rural Life and Scenery, by John Clare, a Northampton Peasant* - was published in London in 1820. It was an instant success. Earl Fitzwilliam sent him £100, to add to the same sum forwarded by his publishers. The Marquess of Exeter allowed him an annuity of 10 guineas, and Earl Spencer a further £10.

For a while he lived comfortably in a humble dwelling lined with books, but speculation in farming brought him ruin, and aggravated what was described as *'nervous despondency and despair.'* His behaviour must have been extreme, since it led to him being committed to a private asylum in Epping Forest in 1837. Four years later he escaped and walked back to Northamptonshire, deluded into thinking he would re-discover a wife, Mary. This relationship had in fact broken down long before he had married, in the early 1830s, one Martha Joyce (to whom he is said to have been a 'dutiful husband').[10]

As a patient of Fenwick's, he wrote in 1824: *'I forgot to tell you Dr Skrimshire has set me on my legs.'* In the same year he referred to him, in a letter on natural history, recognising his continued interest in ornithology, as *'a curious man, who collects the eggs of English birds.'* At another time, he wrote, hinting some disenchantment: *'Dr Skrimshire has been four or five times. I don't know which but I am almost sure it is no more than four. I have now done with him.'* Nevertheless, in 1841, Fenwick together with Dr William Page certified that Clare was insane. This resulted in his spending the last twenty years of his life in the Northampton General Lunatic Asylum.

Fenwick was asked on Clare's admission papers if his breakdown was *'preceded by any severe or long continued mental or emotional exertion?'* He replied: *'After years of poetical prosing'*.[11] The cause of insanity was, however, described as *'hereditary'*, so perhaps his doctors were aware of a familial predisposition. At all events, John Clare was fortunate in that the Director of the Asylum, Dr Thomas Pritchard, believed in the humane treatment of his patients, freedom from restraint and decent living conditions. He was able to continue writing up until his death in 1863. The admirable Earl Fitzwilliam had undertaken to support him after his breakdown.

In 1835, Fenwick first published by subscription his most popular work: *'Letters to a young clergyman, his son, on entering the duties of a Parish Priest.'*[12] In thirteen letters, he described commonplace ailments likely to be encountered, taking care not to *'introduce more professional terms than are absolutely requisite.'* There was no mention of mental afflictions but perhaps he regarded the clergy as ready-equipped in that regard. He sought to facilitate *'...an interchange of kindly offices that would both generate, and be generated by, the affections of his flock.'* The appendix includes a revealing table of essentials for the pastor's medicine cupboard (table 2.1). With the exception of quinine, they would have relieved symptoms rather than effected cures.

Familiar Names.	Druggist's Names.	Convenient Quantities.	Dose for an Adult.	Dose for a Child 5 years old.
Antimonial powder	Pulvis antimonialis	2 ounces	4 grains	2 grains.
Arsenic—or ague-drops	Liquor arsenicalis	4 ounces	8 drops	4 drops.
Blue pill	Pilula hydrargyri	2 ounces	5 grains	3 grains.
Calomel	Hydrargyri submurias	2 ounces	6 grains	4 grains.
Dover's powder	Pulvis ipecacuanhæ compositus	1 ounce	12 grains	3 grains.
Epsom salts	Sulphas magnesiæ	2 pounds	1 ounce	¼ ounce.
Goulard	Liquor plumbi subacetatis	½ pint	With 40 times of water as a lotion.	
Jalap powder	Pulvis jalapæ	¼ pound	20 grains	8 grains.
Ipecacuanha powder	Pulvis ipecacuanhæ	2 ounces	20 grains	8 grains.
Laudanum	Tinctura opii	2 ounces	40 drops	8 drops.
Opium in powder	Pulv. opii	¼ ounce	2 grains	¼ grain.
Quinine	Quinia	¼ ounce	2 grains	½ grain.
Rhubarb powder	Pulvis rhæi	4 ounces	½ drachm	10 grains.
Soda powder	Pulvis sodæ carbonatis	4 ounces	6 grains	4 grains.
Tartar emetic	Antimonium tartarizatum	1 ounce	2 grains	½ grain.

It will be desirable to have a good supply of calico bandages of various sizes rolled up, old linen, and adhesive plaster spread on calico, and some white leather for blisters; scales and weights.

Table 2.1 Essential medicines for the village pastor's medicine chest.

The list of nearly five hundred subscribers included many gentry known to him through his work (Earl Fitzwilliam, Viscount Milton, the Marquess of Exeter), doctors and academics. By this time, he had been physician to the infirmary for twenty years and was held in much respect. The *Letters* are surprisingly detailed. Four of Fenwick's sons ultimately entered the church. No-one could have been more aware of the extent of overlap in the pastoral roles of priest and doctor. In those days transferring from one profession to the other was not uncommon.

Figure 2.4 Family of Fenwick and Charlotte Skrimshire

Dr Fenwick Skrimshire m Charlotte Cobb
1775-1855   1785-1866

Susan	Charles	Rev Henry	Dr Arthur James	Charlotte	Frederick	Edward
1808-68	1809-32	1810-61	1814-1906	1815-43	1816-91	1820-96

The medical clergyman

Fenwick's third son, Arthur James, went first into medicine. He followed his father to Edinburgh University. He qualified MD in 1838 with a thesis with the long-winded title, *'Observations on Chronic, Remittent and Intermittent Fevers and on the tendency to Remittent and Intermittent Paroxysms in various diseases, both acute and chronic, as occurring in Marshy or Fenny districts.'* It seems he had conversed with his father and taken note of his grandfather's Wisbechian workload.

In 1840 he was appointed House Surgeon at the Peterborough Public Dispensary, when he still lived at home. In those days, nepotism went unchallenged.

He moved to practice at Sudbury. An energetic man with wide interests, Arthur involved himself sufficiently in local politics to be elected mayor in 1850. He also contributed to the Proceedings of the West Suffolk Archaeological Society, an article on *'Original Documents relating to Sudbury.'* By 1854 he had received the 'Call'. In that year, he went to St Bee's Theological College in preparation for ordination. His father, who had retired in 1846, was firm of faith and strongly approved his decision. Fenwick died at Paston Hall, Peterborough on 11th June, 1855. Sadly, he did not live to see his son's ordination in Norwich, as deacon in 1856 and priest the following year.

#   #   #

The advent of the modern hospital

Fenwick Skrimshire was far-sighted. He was a generalist who anticipated the rise of hospital medicine. He derived his influence and prestige from these coming institutions. Today's hospitals have medieval origins. Typically, they were supported by the church. As an example, the Great Hospital at Norwich was founded in 1249 by the Bishop of Norwich, Walter de Suffield. They began as small multifunctional buildings accommodating pilgrims and travellers, sheltering the poor, treating the residents of monasteries and the local sick. They were, in other words, avowedly religious establishments.

Expansion in hospital numbers across Europe began in the seventeenth and eighteenth century as productive populations were seen as key to national prosperity in accordance with the mercantilist political theories of the time.[13] In 1800, there were only five hospitals in Britain and all of these were in London. Over the next few decades a wave of new voluntary hospitals was constructed funded by charitable subscriptions. Doctors like Fenwick were often the driving force behind these institutions and they fell under medical control. Infirmaries served the sick (and 'deserving') poor and elderly. The wealthier classes were still treated at home. There was a dramatic increase in the number of specialist hospitals (66 in London alone by the 1860s) and dispensaries.

The nineteenth century also saw the creation of small 'cottage' hospitals serving towns and villages. They offered little in the way of specialized care, only basic facilities and nursing, but provided an important service in rural areas.[14] The later doctors Skrimshire oversaw similar in-patient care for the inhabitants of Holt at nearby Kelling Hospital which was originally built as a TB sanatorium.

By the late nineteenth century and following the Poor Law Amendment Act of 1834, the state became the major provider of hospital care. Hospitals were also transformed architecturally. In addition to the growth in bed numbers, their size and complexity increased to accommodate operating theatres, specialist wards, labs, x-ray facilities, outpatients and waiting halls.

In social terms, hospitals can be viewed as a medium of exchange. The poor received free care in return for submitting to be teaching material; practitioners like Fenwick gave their services but gained reputation, contacts and potential custom through doing so. As in Peterborough, new hospitals embodied civic pride bringing benefits, for example in terms of jobs, to local economies. Initially, subscribers (i.e. the wealthy who supported their local hospital) controlled admission rights. Increasingly, these rights were ceded to doctors on the basis of medical need. Doctors were also playing a larger managerial role in their administration.

Foucault, Jewson and others have argued that modern hospitals 'silenced' and 'objectified' their patients but this is hard to evidence from personal accounts. McKeown's analyses suggested that nineteenth century hospitals did positive harm as 'gateways to death' but hospital mortality rates were highly variable.[15] In any event, from the eighteenth to the twentieth century, hospitals moved from being marginal places of succour to representing the pinnacle of medical attainment. Today they continue to serve both a medical and a welfare function sheltering the weak and elderly (if they have nowhere else to go).

Dispensaries and outpatient services
Hospitals came also over time to be major providers of primary care through their outpatient departments. Dispensaries such as those in Kettering and Peterborough began to be set up in the nineteenth century and also supplied medicines, often free-of-charge, for the poor.

Treatment in both settings was similar to that in a GP's surgery - rapid examination after a long wait and a routine prescription, though some patients were referred on to specialists or even admitted. Think of today's casualty departments. There was sometimes a small charge in order to reduce demand. They were frequently staffed by general practitioners.

Charitable dispensaries, funded by wealthy donors, were an increasingly important source of care for working class patients - and lost earnings for GPs (footnote 4). By the end of the century, they inspired the creation of provident dispensaries which operated as a form of health insurance. In return for a small weekly subscription (typically 1d for adults and 2d for families), members received basic medical treatment at the dispensary's premises.

Footnote 4. A major gripe of GPs in these cost-conscious days remains the dispensing of expensive drugs at discharge on short-term hospital prescriptions. The long-term financial burden is thereby transferred onto GP drug budgets.

Founded in 1788, the York Dispensary provides a well-researched example. About 5000 patients were attending per year in the 1880s. Attendance peaked at 9000/year before the advent of National Health Insurance (see chapter 5). Thereafter, it provided services for women, children and the elderly who remained uninsured. The dispensary also provided dental and maternity services.[16] From around this time, other specialized dispensaries and clinics opened their doors. These dealt with specific conditions such as tuberculosis and venereal disease.

Later on, with rising costs, most patients were expected to pay towards their care. Hence arose a plethora of regular contributory schemes. The Norfolk and Norwich Saturday Fund, for example, was established in 1919. It provided regular donors and their families with free treatment as long as they had been referred by their GP and held a voucher from the fund secretary. Thus by 1900, voluntary hospitals had changed their status from charities serving the poor to institutions selling their services directly to the rich and indirectly to the working classes through such proto-insurance schemes.

The roots of 19ᵗʰ century medical reform

The causes of the intra-professional acrimony of this period sound familiar: the struggle for position, status and power between a new majority and the old reactionary minority. They coincided with growing national prosperity and the birth of 'consumer society'. Paradoxically, the resulting reforms followed a period of economic contentment when established practitioners' incomes increased and younger ones improved their educations.

There is little evidence that reform was promoted for the improvement of public health, despite the rapidity of societal change and the crisis in health for which profession and institutions were ill-prepared. There was little association between reformers and political radicals or religious dissenters. The public were uninvolved in medical politics. In other words, the reformers were inward looking with few connections between medicine and the state. As one perceptive physician opined:

'...*so strangely perverted and unharmonized has the whole medical profession become in this country that it is impossible to conceive any change that could be as productive of equal recriminations. The surgeon exclaims against the apothecary, the physician answers both, the apothecary retorts…mutually exasperating each other by every vilifying epithet and opprobrious insinuation until… the strongest feeling of every liberal mind must be to escape forever from the profession and its bickerings.*'[17]

Pressure was growing up from below. Medical education was a thriving industry but chaotic. Organised training and qualifications did not distinguish regulars from irregulars. Aspiring doctors' increased financial expectations were some compensation for the initial outlay but their livelihoods were threatened still.

A major driver for change was thus the rise of dispensing druggists (footnote 5). Like many apothecaries before them, they served their apprenticeships as grocers or tea dealers but observed the profits to be made from pharmacy. In 1775, there was one druggist to every 17000 inhabitants. By 1794, there was one to every 4000. Surgeon-apothecaries were each now losing £200/year to druggists. There is some similarity here to the earlier dispute between apothecaries and physicians except that, following the Rose case, apothecaries were never stigmatized as quacks. Rather these developments paralleled the earlier rise of the apothecaries.

A striking feature of proto-GPs' surviving accounts and workbooks is the vast quantities of medicines dispensed and their financial dependence on prescribing.[18] An increase in the number of dispensing chemists undercutting regular practitioners prompted the formation of the General Pharmaceutical Society of Great Britain in 1794. This was a confusing name for an association formed by medical men to protect their monopoly on dispensing. Founded *'to remedy the evils of chemists and druggists'*[19], the association was ineffective and short-lived but ushered in a period of significant reform.

The first detailed proposals for changes to medical training were published in 1806.[20] They were promoted in the medical press by Dr Edward Harrison from Lincolnshire and garnered much support. The resulting Bill was finally stymied by the obduracy of the Royal College of Physicians (RCP).

Next into the fray, Dr Edward Barlow published his own *'Fundamental Principles which should guide the Legislature in Regulating the Profession of Physic'* anonymously in a series of essays.[21] He was much less bothered about irregulars being more concerned about the chaotic state of medical education. He sought to transform *'that excellent species of practitioner, the surgeon-apothecary'* into an educated generalist. *'On the competency of this class must the great mass of the population rely for the preservation of health and removal of disease. To by far the greatest portion of society they are the sole physicians, and even the highest ranks are known to depend with fullest confidence on their skills and ability.'*[21]

Barlow's agenda for reform was to recur constantly in acrimonious debates over the next decades: the justification for generalists; the corresponding decline of physicians; the need for comprehensive education, examination and licensing; and the desirability of greater uniformity among medical corporations. He believed the College of Surgeons was the most appropriate institution to take on responsibility for training and oversight.

Footnote 5. The druggist too has more distant roots. In *The Alchemist* (1610), Ben Jonson uses one such to satirize men's follies. Abel Drugger is a gullible tobacconist with an eye for greater profits. Druggists were also colourmen and suppliers to the building trade. The latter's decline in the 1780s may have driven them to seek other outlets.

The anguished birth of 'general practice'

'And it is the business of the judges (the Court of Assistants), so to construe the Act, as to suppress the mischief and advance the remedy.' Thus, quoting Judge Blackstone and with a characteristic flourish, did George Man Burrows conclude *A Statement of Circumstances Connected with The Apothecaries' Act, and Its Administration.*[22] Published in 1817, this intriguing document provides insights into the history of general practice that resonate today. While Fenwick was raising his professional standing at a local level, Burrows was advancing it nationally. Burrows is nowadays chiefly remembered as an expert on insanity. He is strangely neglected for someone sometimes revered as the 'father of general practice'.[23] Why does he merit such claims? To what 'mischief' does he refer and what were his remedies?

Burrows was born at Chalk, near Gravesend, in 1771. Educated at the King's School, Canterbury, he was then apprenticed to an apothecary in Rochester before completing his medical education at Guy's and then St. Thomas's Hospitals. He entered general practice in London where he became deeply embroiled in political disputes over the future legal status of the medical profession (figure 2.5).

Figure 2.5 George Man Burrows

The first association properly to address the needs of general practitioners was founded - in the best professional traditions - at a meeting in the Crown and Anchor in the Strand on 3rd July, 1812. A protest had been called in response to a rise in tax on glass by which apothecaries had been hard hit. A new Association of Apothecaries and Surgeon-Apothecaries of England and Wales was proposed. Its object was to improve the education and status of the profession. Burrows accepted the chair reluctantly, later writing that he would have declined had he known the work involved.

As chairman of this body Burrows was indefatigable. Over the next three years he attended 130 committee meetings, answering over 1500 letters sent to him as the membership rose to over 3000.[22] The growth of the Association reflected changing attitudes among rank and file practitioners. The surgeon-apothecaries of the eighteenth century - individual entrepreneurs with no particular corporate allegiance - were morphing into a more self-confident profession with a growing sense of collective identity and determination to reform.

With great perseverance Burrows led the production of a Bill that combined idealism and self-interest. The Association's aims were, firstly, improved training and examination based on a broad curriculum and, secondly, a licensing process that clearly distinguished irregular practitioners from the formally educated. It proposed that future general practitioners be examined and licensed by a 'fourth body', that they be required to hold a diploma from the Royal College of Surgeons and that a new London-based school of medicine be founded for their training. In this manner, the surgeon-apothecary would gain legal status as a generalist licensed in medicine, surgery and midwifery while unlicensed practitioners would be liable to prosecution.

The idea of a fourth body (or College of General Practitioners) was, of course, anathema to the other Colleges and duly suppressed. The Association had originally intended to provide its nucleus. Instead, the RCP re-opened negotiations on condition that key responsibilities were handed to the Society of Apothecaries. As a representative association, the latter was ill-equipped to oversee the training of future general practitioners. Burrows nevertheless felt that concessions were necessary if progress was not to be deferred indefinitely.

The Apothecaries Act had received its first reading on January and was eventually passed by the House on 11 July, 1815. The Society of Apothecaries was to be responsible for the examination and licensing of future general practitioners and for prosecuting the unlicensed. Candidates for the Licentiate of the Society of Apothecaries (LSA) were required to have spent six months at a recognized hospital or dispensary. The penalty for practicing without a licence was £20 but 'Pre-1815' medical men were exempted. Membership of the Royal Society of Surgeons (MRCS) was not compulsory but the diploma was so frequently taken that the dual qualification MRCS LSA (colloquially known as 'College and Hall') became our hallmark.[24]

One further amendment was particularly hated. The physicians inserted a clause compelling new licensees to compound and dispense their prescriptions. Symbolically, this was viewed as belated retaliation for the Rose case (see chapter one). Comparing the final Act with the Bill originally proposed it is not difficult to see why no one was really happy.

Implementation - and the fall of GMB
Appointed to the first Court of Examiners, Burrows was astonished to find that many of those elected knew nothing of the Act. Over the next year his usual patience and diplomacy deserted him. Early in 1817, following a protracted dispute with his colleagues, he resigned in bitter disillusionment.

His *Statement of Circumstances* was both an act of exoneration and a settling of scores. He began by reminding readers how sedulously he had laboured to improve the lot of his fellow professionals before announcing the need to narrate circumstances the concealment of which *'must be a crime'*.

Burrow's concerns were of three sorts. First, there were fundamental flaws in the original Act. These included the infamous clause 15: a requirement that all entrants to general practice be required to serve a five-year apprenticeship to an apothecary. The absence of effective controls over druggists and midwives was another notable omission.

Secondly, he detailed the defective constitution of the Society whose senior officers seemed barely to understand their new responsibilities. In particular, he considered the dependence of the Court of Examiners on the Court of Assistants, the main governing body, to be wholly egregious. He listed major defects in the administration of these committees - closed selection procedures, the absence of written minutes, inappropriate cross-membership, etc. His earlier experiences had plainly left him with an eye for bureaucratic detail.

Finally, the Statement provided dismal insights into the true workings of the committee. Burrows exposed the ignorance and ineptitude of his fellow examiners. Despite his judicious tone, they come across as self-seeking time servers, more interested in their own remuneration than fair stewardship of the certification process.

He reserved particular disdain for the nepotistic, self-appointed chairman of the Court of Examiners and sometime Master of the Society, William Simon. In a lengthy, somewhat obsequious letter, Burrows advanced arguments for opening up membership of the Court and reducing emoluments, *'with the truth of which I expect you will coincide.'* Suffice to say that he didn't.

Already strained relations took a sharp downturn when a candidate who had been apprenticed to a chemist, and not an apothecary, presented for examination - in flagrant breach of the rules. Burrow's objection to his admission was overruled by the Court of Examiners. A formal protest was similarly ignored. When his subsequent letter of complaint to Simon was leaked to the medical press, Burrows found himself arraigned before a disciplinary committee. He described this minor melodrama in major detail. *'Extremely hurt'* by the manner of his treatment, he soon after resigned - ostensibly *'to return to that privacy and quiet, to which so long I have been a stranger.'*

It is hard not to pity Burrows, caught between *'shameful dereliction of principle and… service to a cause for which so many had so long and so zealously laboured.'* Yet re-reading the Statement, and even allowing for the quaint epistolary conventions of the time, it is hard not to feel sympathy for his fellow examiners also. His tone is sometimes sanctimonious and egotistical. *'Painful as it is to be the narrator of circumstances wherein self must always appear so prominent'*, this was a one-sided account.

Medico-political lives often end in failure also. Burrows suffered for ideas ahead of their time. He was steeped as no other in the arcana of the Act and mindful of its deficiencies but had fatally underestimated opposition to his remedies. The *'tergiversation'* he encountered was not to be dissolved through reasoned argument.

Retiring from general practice, Burrows devoted himself to the treatment of the insane, keeping asylums in Chelsea, then Clapham. He became a leading authority, publishing several treatises on insanity.[25] His *Commentaries on the Causes, Forms, Symptoms, and Treatment, Moral and Medical, of Insanity* (1828) received widespread acclaim as the most complete and practical guide yet published in this country. Burrows was made a Fellow of the Royal College of Physicians, ironically, in 1839. He died on 29 October 1846 (footnote 6).

Consequences of the Apothecaries Act

On one hand, the Act added compulsion and examination to the pre-existing educational framework and was a step forward towards full professionalization.[26] The term 'medically qualified' at last had a clear meaning. As Dr Jobling told his audience in Martin Chuzzlewit: *'We know a few secrets in our profession, sir. Of course we do. We study for that; we pass the Hall and the College for that; and we take our station in society by that'*[27] (footnote 7).

New exam regulations were formulated. Chemistry, *materia medica*, and medical botany were the most important things to learn. Insufficient Latin became the commonest reason for rejecting candidates for LSA. The College of Surgeons covered surgery in much more detail than average GP would require and this formed a major part of the oral exam. Midwifery, paediatrics and public health by contrast were generally ignored - *plus ça change*.

On the other hand, the Act was undoubtedly muddled with no clear definition of an apothecary or what constituted illegal practice. Unsurprisingly, it failed to outlaw irregulars. The continuation of apprenticeships was condemned on two counts: it did not provide relevant practical experience and it lowered the status of practitioner. Apprenticeships were defended as a route into practice for those who could not afford full medical education, i.e. those of less wealthy parentage. The last thing the College of Physicians wanted was recruitment from a broader social spectrum. The five-year apprenticeship was also justified as exercising moral control. It filled the gap between school and an age when it might be safe to turn lads loose as medical students in London. It was only abolished in 1858.

Footnotes 6. Sadly, Burrows' career ended ignominiously. His reputation was gravely damaged when he ordered the compulsory admission of a young man thought to be dangerously insane. Though acting in good faith, he gave orders for detention without having seen the patient.

7. *Martin Chuzzlewit* is more particularly famous for the colourful character of bibulous Sarah Gamp - a midwife.

The ever-irascible editor of the Lancet was Thomas Wakley. His hatred for the Society of Apothecaries ('Rhubarb Hall') was only exceeded by his loathing of the Royal Colleges. He continued to challenge the Society's right to prosecute irregulars or surgeons by pointing out deficiencies in the Act. The Society seemed hardly to know the important powers and duties devolved upon it. Blame for the degraded position of GPs lay squarely, he felt, with the Colleges. They were concerned only with threats to their autonomy and certainly not with providing medical care for the population as a whole.[28]

Conclusion

Was the Apothecaries Act among the great reforms of the nineteenth century or a degrading compromise in the face of reactionary opposition from the Colleges of Physicians and Surgeons? It was certainly monopolistic in intent and ran counter to the *laissez-faire*, liberal spirit of the age. Medical historians are divided.[29] Certainly, few general practitioners were satisfied with the outcome. They had started out with a sense of optimism and energy. They deserved to be represented by a body sharing these characteristics. They ended up with an Act designed by other Colleges for their suppression and administered by a society unfit for purpose.

Nevertheless, GP numbers grew rapidly over the first decades of the nineteenth century. This reflected changing attitudes and expectations among the rank-and-file. The Association which had played an important role in the development of general practice lived on until 1827 and voted Burrows 500 guineas on its dissolution. It morphed into the Associated General Medical and Surgical Practitioners, specifically to introduce amendments to the Act.

William the Younger ended his working days as a 'classic' general practitioner as we would understand the term. However, the momentous intrigues described above made little immediate mark on his professional life. His distinguished sibling was, in Anne Digby's parlance, rather a 'GP surgeon'. Fenwick undertook general medicine with a hospital appointment. He died just as these distinctions between different branches of medicine were to be forever formalised.

Chapter Three – Years of Transition
(1830-1860)

'There is no human bliss equal to twelve hours of work
with only six hours in which to do it.'
Anthony Trollope

The third generation

From the first Dr William onwards, the Skrimshires demonstrated admirable civic responsibility. Altogether they were a family seemingly steeped in the concerns of their fellow citizens. They kept in close touch with one another in an age when this was more difficult than today. They shared hobbies, interests and ideas. Yet strangely, the great debates and upheavals of the times rarely feature in family correspondence. Once the talking is done, how many of us want to write about Brexit?

This after all was an era convulsed by disputes over electoral reform and free trade. Shortcomings in the electoral system had long been evident. Some of the more egregious abuses included 'rotten boroughs' and bribery for votes. Calls for reform in the 1790s were initially inspired by radical ideas about sovereignty and democracy emanating from America and France. Early measures were blocked in Parliament but the Reform Act of 1832 doubled the size of the electorate and redistributed seats in favour of urban centres. The Skrimshires may have been whiggishly disposed but did they support the Chartists? How did they view further extensions of the franchise?

They initially favoured the Corn Laws which, after all, enhanced the profits and political power associated with land ownership (footnote 1). Yet viewing at first hand the consequences of high food prices and agrarian poverty, later generations joined the clamour for their repeal. Agricultural wages were low in the early decades of the century. 'Print capitalism' had yet to permeate north Norfolk and they lived in relative political isolation (footnote 2).

The Skrimshires seem rather to personify the later 'age of equipoise'. The period between about 1850 and 1870 was one of stability and calm in contrast to the political tumult and anxiety of the years before and after. These were times of

Footnote 1. The Corn Laws imposed tariffs on imported food and grain between 1815 and 1846. They were designed to keep grain prices high to favour domestic producers. The laws raised food prices and the costs of living for the British public. By reducing disposable income, they hampered the growth of other economic sectors, such as manufacturing. The laws were opposed by urban groups who had less political power than rural areas. The first two years of the Irish Potato Famine of 1845-1852 forced a resolution because of the urgent need for new food supplies. The Tory Prime Minister, Robert Peel, finally achieved repeal with the support of the Whigs, overcoming opposition from his own party. This marked a decisive shift towards free trade in Britain.

optimism, economic and technological progress. This mid-Victorian generation was one *'in which the old and the new, the elements of growth, survival and decay, achieved a balance which most contemporaries regarded as satisfactory.'*[1]

George Skrimshire

Figure 3.1 The family of Thomas Skrimshire

```
                    Rev Thomas Skrimshire m Rose Raven
                    1774-1836                1773-1829
```

Elizabeth	William	Dr George	Anne	Jane	William Wright	William Price
1798-1857	1800-01	1802-77	1804-83	1805-74	1809-48	1836-96

We pick up the medical baton with the Norfolk dynasty of Fenwick's elder brother, the Rev Thomas (see chapter two). Among his descendants are counted sixteen doctors. George was the third-born; his older brother William had died in infancy. He followed his grandfather and two uncles into medicine, via the old-fashioned route. As we have seen, he had been apprenticed to his uncle, Dr William the Younger and his partner, John Weatherhead in Wisbech.

On March 31st 1823, he received his Certificate of Satisfactory Apprenticeship, *'having conducted himself with great proficiency and as far as respects his moral conduct entirely to (their) satisfaction.'* He then moved to London, to walk the wards at Guy's Hospital and prepare for his Licentiate of the Society of Apothecaries. This entitled him to practice as a doctor. There too he met his 'London Lady'.

He was gaining further experience with a Dr Olliver, at Stilton in Cambridgeshire, from where his father wrote him a touching letter. Thomas begins by assuring him he is often in their thoughts. *'When the stormy winds are blowing and the rain is battering against our windows, often does your mother exclaim, I wonder whether poor George is riding about on this dark and dreary night. When we are sitting round our social fire your sisters observe you are wanting to make up the circle and to join in with your flute in the harmony of the evening.'*

He moves on to write of the arrangements for his fiancée's stay. *'You know we have invited your Lavinia to come and stay with us in the spring...We shall invite*

Footnote 2. 'Print capitalism' refers to the mechanised printing technologies which encouraged mass literacy, broadened communication and started to shape national identity.[2] Petitioning, peaceful protest and the formation of political organisations, all supported by printed publications and propaganda, were being used to achieve reform. Print outputs across the British Isles rose exponentially at the end of the eighteenth century.

the Metcalfs to come over and spend the first fortnight of the holydays with us and then we hope Mr Olliver will have the goodness to spare you for a short time to come and see us.'

Thomas then switches to entomological topics, encouraging George in the shared family interest. *'I am glad you think of attending a little to Entomology this next summer for you are in a very favourable situation for many rarities.'* He asks him to collect specimens of various species for friends, with instructions as to their presentation. *'Should you procure any, let some be laid underside uppermost. A set consists of four, two males and two females, one of each upperside and one of each underside.'* He continues by referring to his belated Christmas present enclosed - a sovereign. He apologises on behalf of Farmer George (his uncle at Kettlestone) for not sending a turkey and tells of how he and William the Younger joked about his 'London Lady'.

Lavinia Truscott was the daughter of a London builder and they were evidently eager to marry. Their wedding took place, by special licence, on July 11th, 1826 at Syderstone with his father officiating. George is described as *'of the Parish of St George in the borough of Southwark in the County of Surrey'*; Lavinia, rather mysteriously, as *'of the Parish of Syderstone in the County of Norfolk, a spinster of the age of eighteen years'*. Was she by now in some way attached to the school?

Early years
By now, George was an assistant in a practice in Surrey, though there was some discussion about his continuing the Wisbech practice. There were two obstacles to this idea. One was that William's partner, John Weatherhead, was now well established in the town. A second was that Lavinia, then only 18, did not wish to be cut off from her parents. They were to give the family much financial support over the years. Their early married life was lived very close to John and Lucy Truscott - first in Southwark where twins George and Anne were born in 1829, and then in Camberwell where followed the next four children.

Several factors precipitated their move to Loddon, Norfolk in 1839. Like so many young parents, they needed more space. They aspired to leave London and raise their family in a more rural, small town environment. John and Lucy had moved to Bexley and Lavinia no longer felt the same need for her mother's help. George's father, Thomas, had died in 1837. He wanted to be closer to his sisters, most notably Elizabeth who lived in Sculthorpe. She had lost seven of her children between 1834 and 1836.

Loddon is a picturesque little town on the river Chet, a tributary of the Yare, with a population then of around 1200. Three surgeon-apothecaries were already well established there, one of whom ran the local asylum. Competition for custom was intense. The Skrimshire family soon outgrew their new accomodation. The census of 1841 shows Thomas, aged 9, and John Truscott, aged 6, to be at Bexley in Kent, with their grandparents and their great grandmother, Ruth Parnham. Theirs was a fertile union and three more boys joined the throng: Edmund Browne in 1839, Henry in 1842, and Charles Parnham in 1844.

One indication that they may not have been entirely satisfied with life in Loddon is that none of these three children were baptized there. Nonconformity was prevalent. Perhaps George and Lavinia never found a local church where they felt comfortable. In any event, when an opportunity arose to purchase another practice in February 1847, George appears to have jumped at it.

Holt

Exactly why George came to link his family's fortunes with north Norfolk is unknown but he was certainly familiar with the patch. His mother's sister Rose had married one William Hardy in 1819. The Reverend Thomas officiated. William's sister Mary Anne was married to Jeremy Cozens of Letheringsett. Their children were playmates and holidayed together. George later became the Cozens-Hardys' doctor. The two families were to remain on close terms across several generations.[3]

Holt stands on rising ground looking out over the wooded countryside that earned its name in Saxon times.[4] It is an attractive place, in part because of the 'Great Fire' of Mayday, 1708 which devastated much of the town. Georgian houses thereafter lined the High Street which runs from Obelisk Plain to the Market Square (figure 3.2). However, Holt in the first half of the eighteenth century was

Figure 3.2 Holt High St, circa 1900

impoverished, struggling to fund its own renovation. £1229 was required for the rebuilding of Holt church and steeple. In 1723 Henry Briggs, Chaplain in ordinary to George II, obtained 'letters patent' empowering the church wardens to *Ask, Collect, and Receive the Alms, Benevolence, and Charitable contributions of all Our Loving Subjects'*, i.e. to crowdfund the work. Thereafter, the town and its population of some 1600 souls slowly began to thrive.[5]

We think of north Norfolk today as rural, even remote. In reality, the locality was densely packed with little villages and ports, feeding bustling market towns within a dozen miles of one another (p 286). Twenty-five parishes lay within five miles of Holt. This unusual parochial profusion is owing to the pattern of its settlement by Anglo-Saxons and Danes.[6] Goods and livestock were brought in from neighbouring villages to the busy, weekly market up until 1960. There were many hot summers and good harvests in the mid-1700s. On the heath to the south of the town was a racecourse where an annual meeting was held.

Sir John Gresham, Lord Mayor of London, gave Holt the school which bears his name in 1555.[4] This establishment has always been a major player in the local economy. The education it provided seems also to have served many of my predecessors well.

Towards the end of the century, as a result of wars, prices rose faster than wages entailing much poverty. Local death rates were high. Parson Woodforde wrote that *'Holt stands well and is a good and decent town.'* However, the district *'presented to the eye of the traveller but a wide waste of brown heath, over which the north and north-east winds blow with all their chilling violence.'*[7]

A stage coach (or post coach) left twice a week for Norwich - and then onto London - from the Feathers Inn. There was room for six inside passengers paying 5s each. The Norwich-Holt road was once a turnpike, though often in poor repair. In winter time, many local roads were impassable for wheeled traffic. Jane Hales tells of a local apothecary who found himself sinking into the mire but was reassured by a lad in an adjacent field. Deeper and deeper he sank. *"I thought you said the road had a good bottom!" "So that have"*, replied the lad, *"but you haint come to it yet."*[8]

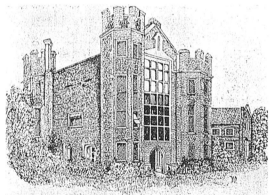

Figure 3.3 West Beckham Workhouse

Dominating the skyline were the church of St Andrew the Apostle, less magnificent than its rivals in nearby Cley and Salthouse, and a windmill on the Cley road. Less conspicuous on the eastern edge of town was the new workhouse or 'House of Industry' erected in 1779. It replaced the first *'houfe for the poore builded by the Towne'* in 1599, according to parish records.[9] In time, Holt and other surrounding parishes were grouped together under the Erpingham Union. A vast new workhouse was constructed at West Beckham housing 600 paupers separated into sections for men, women and children. Today it is a ghostly ruin (figure 3.3).

Enclosures aggravated rural penury from 1810 onwards. The poor lost their commons on which to feed livestock and became landless labourers. In the name of economic advantage, an old and happier way of life was lost. The heaths were replaced with fenced farms.[7]

Hill House

Whether Holt was well chosen for the medical opportunities it presented is open to question. John Truscott, George's father-in-law and a businessman, described it later as *'perhaps not first-rate'*, and Lavinia herself writes of *'a very sad year, no sickness scarcely at all'*. For there was no lack of competition.

Intriguingly for one so small, Holt appears always to have been a 'medical town' (footnote 3). Various barber-surgeons still plied their trade on market days. According to White's directory, there were two doctors: John Banks and John Thornton. With the latter retiring, there was scope for George to develop his own practice in the town, particularly in view of his social connections. Another advantage that Holt held over Loddon was the presence of the Gresham Grammar School.

Doctors Thornton and Ellis, his assistant - both with their own families - were sharing the practice premises before George's arrival. Thornton had recently agreed to sell the practice to Dr Peter Parlett Ransom and to spend six months introducing him to his patients. Ransom had paid Thornton half of the purchase price of £550 up front and was due to pay the remainder on June 30th, 1847. What induced Thornton to change his mind and sell the practice to George Skrimshire is not clear. Perhaps William Cozens-Hardy did his share of arm-twisting in favour of his more experienced second cousin.

Figure 3.4 Holt practice contract, 1847

Negotiations were protracted. In the event, George agreed to pay £275 to John Thornton and £325 to Ransom for *'certain fixtures and other articles connected with the practice'*. George was assigned the right to practice as a *'surgeon apothecary and accoucheur'* and the tenancy of Hill House, the practice premises. (Even then, the term GP was not in general use.) William Cozens-Hardy was the witness to his signature on the contract (figure 3.4).

Thornton agreed to do his best to persuade his patients to transfer their business to George - and justify his outlay. Peter Ransom moved down the road to practice at North Elmham.

George and Lavinia moved to Hill House in the summer of 1847. The author's home today, it lies at the bottom of the High Street. Just beyond its front gate

Footnote 3. Holt remains well supplied today: eight doctors, three opticians and a host of popular, latter day 'irregulars' at the Holt Holistic Centre and the Holt Consulting Rooms.

stands an obelisk where once stood a gallows. Within its walls lie some three acres that include an orchard and vegetable garden, a paddock and small wood. The latter looks out over the Spout Hills whose springs long supplied pure water to the town. (The Spout Hills were left as commons by the 'Inclosure Commissioners' and were still used as such when I was a child.)

George must, therefore, have been carrying a sizeable debt at the same time as supporting his growing family. Although his six sons received free education at the grammar school, they and his youngest daughter Emily, were living at home. His was a one-man practice and he set about establishing a foothold in the community. He became Medical Officer for the Erpingham Union but life in those early years was a struggle.

This struggle was initially compounded by two family tragedies. First in 1848 came the sudden illness and death of George's brother William Wright Skrimshire and his wife. George became the guardian of his nephew William Page, then aged just 11. They took the boy in at Hill House and sent him to Gresham's. In a touching letter written when he was 18, William Page thanks George and Lavinia for all they had done for him.

In 1854, they lost their own daughter, Lavinia, shortly after her twenty-first birthday. The cause of her death was recorded as 'Marasmus Phthisis 10 months'. Hers was the paradigmatic death of the day: slowly wasting away from the ravages of TB. Both parents were at her bedside. Her burial ceremony was conducted by Rev Edward Brumell who had recently arrived in Holt from

Figure 3.5 George, Lavinia and family, 1867

Northumberland. The Reverend offered George and Lavinia much spiritual comfort at that time. His influence on other members of the family was to be significant also (see chapter four).

George and Lavinia were to live, work and raise their family in Hill House over a period of 30 years. Frederic William was born in 1848, Ernest in 1850, Emily arrived in 1852 and, finally, Arthur in 1855 - 13 children in 27 years. Lavinia was a strong woman. Their only surviving photo shows the couple in what must have been a rare moment of relaxation with six of the children on the lawn at Hill House in the summer of 1867. The boys pose self-consciously; George leans back wearily to read from a family bible (figure 3.5).

For much of this period, the house must have been very crowded. On the day of the 1871 census, for example, they were living with five teenage and adult children, George's sister Anne, a cook and a housemaid. A schoolmistress Sarah Silcock occupied another part of the house, with an assistant, two domestic servants and nine school children between the ages of 8 and 14: a total of 23 people. At that time, the house accommodated a small school, as well as a doctor's surgery and numerous residents.

George and Lavinia both died in 1877. Four years later, their son John Truscott Skrimshire bought the house from William Cozens-Hardy. At this time it was described as 'two dwellings' and remained congested. The Cozens-Hardy family, who built the Methodist Chapel next door, made sure to reserve a section of the house for the Minister. Mr Buck, a solicitor, is described in Kelly's Register as 'of Hill House', and Charles Knowles, father of a local tailor, was also a lodger in residence in 1881.

Hill House represents more than just a backdrop for the humdrum events described later. As a constant reference point and the setting for clan gatherings down generations, it has moulded my family's culture and shaped its collective unconscious. The layout of the house also illustrates how general practice was delivered in the 1800s.

Figure 3.6 Hill House, Holt

Early in the century, the house had been extended. To the left of the main front door, a second less imposing door allowed entry to the surgery (figure 3.6). Regular patients queued for attention in the cramped hall. Grander patients were admitted through the grander entrance and were permitted to recline in a front sitting room.

Domestic ideology
'Lavinia was a strong woman.' The invisibility of women in these pages, other than as mothers, is shocking to contemporary sensibilities. Families were the means through which a growing middle class could secure property and capital. They were also a space through which to inculcate values and culture. Domestic ideology

was infused by evangelical religion that preached separate roles.[10] Men were required to protect and provide as breadwinner. Women nurtured husbands and children; thus were they supposed to provide spiritual rejuvenation for society at large.

However, the separation of work and home was less and less absolute. Women were a 'hidden investment' whose labour was essential to the success of many small businesses.[11] They 'kept shop' and undertook administrative tasks. General practices were no exception. Wives could bring capital to businesses - as later did my grandmother and great-grandmother.

The middle-class home prepared the next generation. Girls were generally trained for domestic life. The boys in these pages followed predictable paths in their teens: grammar school education and medical training while still dependent on their parents. Marriage and the extended family developed networks of support. Wills and inheritance transferred wealth unto the next generation.[12] Sentimental images of nineteenth century family life belie how strategically complex was the maintenance of class and professional privilege.

\#   \#   \#

Continuing 'professionalization'

Medical training and practice were transformed in the nineteenth century but these changes have been interpreted in different ways. Standard sociological accounts associate professionalization with social progress. The accumulation of particular features supposedly distinguish professions from other social groups (table 3.1). These provide a framework for summarizing changes that took place over the next two generations.

Table 3.1   Characteristics of a profession (after Friedson[13])
- Possession of a body of specialised knowledge.
- Professional unity and a strong ethos of public service.
- A monopoly of practice.
- Professional autonomy.
- High social status.

Until the eighteenth century, surgeons received a practical training through apprenticeship while physicians learned medicine via university courses. Subsequently, they began to train together in universities and hospitals. New medical schools followed curricula that spanned both disciplines as well as emerging new specialties like paediatrics and ophthalmology.

In continental Europe, governments took over responsibility for licensing. Broadly speaking, there emerged an elite of university-educated practitioners and an underclass of general practitioners educated in medical schools. The exact divisions between different cadres varied from country to country. In Britain, training standards came under the supervision of the General Medical Council (GMC), established in 1858 (see below).

Across Europe, a university degree eventually became the first qualification for medical practice. Medical schools closed or merged with universities, many of which established their own medical faculties. These changes were thus part of a wider expansion of university education as degrees became a pre-requisite for many careers.[14]

Governments also sought to protect the health of their nations for economic reasons. The provision of good health care required well trained practitioners for military and civilian service.

Another driver for change was demand from students and practitioners who were investing in training that would allow them to meet the requirements of an increasingly prosperous, expanding middle-class. Across Europe, overcrowding in the medical marketplace meant competition for fees and heightened the value of reputable training.[15]

Educational and licensing reforms undoubtedly fostered professional unity. A sense of identity was strengthened by the formation of new medical societies and journals in the nineteenth century. These promoted the exchange of ideas but also provided political focal points. The Lancet, for example, was launched in 1823. The Provincial Medical and Surgical Association (PMSA) was founded in 1832 by Charles Webster.

While practitioners were no longer divided by their qualifications, across Europe there remained medical hierarchies. In the UK, the hospital-based elite did not yet specialize in the manner of today's consultants. Distinction from the rank and file general practitioner was rather a matter of access to wealthier social classes.[16]

As we saw in the preceding chapter, conflict was inevitable given the disproportionate power exercised by this elite, often clustered around the Royal Colleges of Physicians and Surgeons. The latter disdainfully defended existing economic interests through nepotism and the control of licensing arrangements. A residue of past struggles between Colleges and the trade union endures to the present day.

Various groups of unorthodox healers - herbalists, homoeopaths, hydropaths and hypnotists - flourished until the mid-nineteenth century.[17] Then as now, they offered 'natural' remedies in contrast to the allopaths' chemicals and minerals with their attendant side-effects. Thereafter, orthodox practitioners sought to suppress their irregular competitors. New licensing laws helped to enforce their monopoly though the two groups were not as clearly differentiated as historians sometimes imply.[18]

The concept of professional autonomy is often conflated with the ability of its members to police themselves. The GMC was to be run by and for doctors. However, the notion that self-regulation was granted by governments in recognition of the profession's possession of esoteric knowledge is easily refuted. In many countries, governments retained responsibility for licensing. Self-regulation was rather the gift of more *laissez-faire* governments, as in the UK, in contrast to those governments that exerted strict control over other aspects of social and political life.[19]

Furthermore, 'autonomy' is political and economic as well as clinical.[20] Later accounts have stressed the inherently self-interested and elitist nature of professions.[21] Professionalisation can be seen as a less benevolent occupational strategy whereby knowledge, training and medical organisations secured a market monopoly.

Rising status, falling self-esteem

Many doctors in the early nineteenth century felt they were held in low esteem by a public happy to employ the practitioner charging the lowest fee. Cartoonists and commentators lampooned incompetent doctors and drunken medical students. Dickens's humorous portrayals of Bob Sawyer and Ben Allen were particularly cruel.[22] As a release from long hours and the brutalizing nature of their training, students seem always to have taken refuge in rowdiness and hard drinking. However, one should be wary of imagining such stereotypes to be ubiquitous. Writers from Chekhov to Trollope portrayed doctors in more flattering terms.

Status came to rest on acquired standards of behaviour rather than superior knowledge. In the latter part of the century, medical schools were seeking to inculcate ethical standards of compassion and altruism that the public were perceived to desire. If Fildes' familiar painting of *The Doctor* (1891) is representative, medical practitioners' status had certainly risen over the

Figure 3.7 Luke Fildes' The Doctor

preceding decades (figure 3.7). This was no linear progression but as much the result of hard work and cussed determination.

The concept of status has to be considered from both without and within. Peterson describes a 'social chasm' between medicine and other 'liberal professions.'[23] Less than 20% of practitioners came from the families of gentry or other non-medical professionals. This was reflected in an educational grammar versus public school divide. Doctors were regarded as inherently subservient (to governors, sick club committees, bureaucrats) and engaged in menial physical contacts.

In the Gazette of Health, Medicus coarsely caricatured the country practitioner as the farmer's son who drinks and wenches his way through a dissolute apprenticeship and a spell in London where he cuts lectures to follow low pursuits. He nevertheless obtains his certificates which are *'stuck up in a conspicuous part of the surgery'* to impress the neighbours when he returns home.[24] George's Deed of Indenture suggests his employers were mindful of the stereotype.

Historians are less harsh. *'The lawyer and the doctor took the lead amongst the middle classes of Middlemarch, or in the suburbs of London…'*[25] For in the first half of the nineteenth century, specialisation had not yet become the pathway to prosperity or high status. The distinction between medicine and surgery was blurred with the consequent equalization of rank. The Select Committee on Medical Education (1834) lauded the high level of GP education.[26] Within the profession, GPs were plainly gaining kudos and acceptance.

There was perhaps a difference between London and provincial market towns like Holt where GPs occupied a higher, more secure social position as sole medical attendant to all social classes. Like Fenwick Skrimshire, they were also the driving force in newly established dispensaries and small local hospitals. This was born out by the houses they lived in and their family histories.

Why then did these reliable all-rounders not establish themselves as equals? In large part, it was because the practice of pharmacy was a reminder of their original trade and the apothecary's shop. It blurred their distinction from the reviled druggist. Then as now, many GPs felt that to become a 'physician in ordinary' and a respectable member of the medical profession, they would have to abandon pharmacy while others defended the right to dispense as a skill best performed by one with a medical education and the opportunity to observe the effects of their actions.

The social insecurity of the GP was aggravated by continuing acrimony within the profession. *'The way things are constituted the general practitioner finds himself treated rather as a tradesman than a gentleman.'*[27] They were criticised as *'imperfectly educated…engaged in the money-making parts of the profession and not one of them distinguished by anything like science or liberality of mind.'*[28] They seem to have been regarded with a sort of good-natured contempt. Medical etiquette reinforced these attitudes. It was considered deplorable taste to call yourself 'Dr'; the title 'Mr' was only later confined to surgeons. Some of this disdain lingers today in the commonplace perception of GPs as financially motivated businessmen by comparison with their supposedly more altruistic consultant colleagues.

As for the much-maligned Society of Apothecaries, reformed committees went on to administer their examinations efficiently enough. By the 1840s, general practitioners formed over 80% of the profession but overcrowding was detrimentally affecting their income. They alone had no college or institution to defend their interests. With his habitual causticity, Thomas Wakley lampooned the Royal Colleges: *'With them, the chief qualification for eminence in the healing art is ignorance of one or the other half of it…but a general practitioner - a man so preposterous as to understand both physic and surgery - is fit only to become a subordinate.'*[29]

Competition
Old-fashioned travelling quacks like Dr Dulcamara (footnote 4) gradually disappeared but complementary therapies maintained an enduring popular appeal. Proponents of homoeopathy and mesmerism (footnote 5) considered them to be as intellectually and scientifically respectable as the mainstream. Though conflict re-surfaces periodically, conventional practitioners have long been resigned to the presence of alternative medicine. Then as now, doctors recognize their own limitations and the public's distrust of 'pure science'. The relationship has always been as much symbiotic as conflictual. After all, campaigning against quacks helped fashion the superior GP's professional identity.

Edward Harrison's survey of 1802 suggested a ratio of irregulars to regulars of over eight to one but many druggists worked part time and he had reason to inflate their numbers. GPs were more concerned about competition from their own colleagues on account of overcrowding. The distribution of doctors across the country was reasonably even, though it tended to be lower in rural counties. In Norfolk, the GP to population ratio was 1:1300 as compared with 1:1185 across England and Wales as a whole.[30] The present-day ratio is approximately 1:1900 but a much smaller proportion of the population was able to pay for health care in the 1840s. The corresponding ratio for druggists was 1:1762.

Footnotes 4. His 'elisir d'amore' is central to Gaetano Donizetti's popular opera. In truth, his potion is more effective than some: cheap wine. Indeed, 'real' doctors in opera are generally somewhat flawed as role models.[31]

   5. Franz Mesmer (1734-1815) believed all living beings to be possessed of an invisible natural force which could promote healing. This could be manipulated with magnets and the laying on of hands. Mesmerism's popularity declined in the nineteenth century. Its principal benefit was on the wallets of its practitioners.

The care provided by irregulars probably represented only a small loss of income for GPs but the numbers attending dispensaries and hospitals for primary care was increasing steadily (see chapter 2). Consider the steep rise in outpatients treated at the London Hospital: from 3000 in 1750, 7000 in 1840, 52000 in 1870, to 200000 by the end of the century.[32] Overloaded urban casualty departments are not a new phenomenon but in those days this represented lost business for local GPs.

By 1847, the terms 'apothecary' and 'surgeon-apothecary' were obsolete but the public could be forgiven for terminological confusion. Many doctors styled themselves as 'physicians or surgeons in general practice'. Ten per cent of GPs held other honorary appointments, mostly at dispensaries. There remained a bewildering variety of different qualifications though more than half were 'College and Hall' (MRCS, LSA).[33]

GPs increasingly came to be distinguished from surgeons on three grounds: first by the nature of their practice in all four branches of medicine, secondly by dual qualifications, and thirdly by lower income. While the idea of a consultant physician existed before 1850, their numbers were very small. The distinction in practice had more to do with their refusal to undertake pharmacy or midwifery, and on the income or class of their patients. The degree of overlap remained greater in the provinces - and towns like Holt - than in London.

GP Income
Private practice was the main source. Although reliable data are limited, between 1781 and 1819 doctors improved their financial position to a greater extent than other groups (table 3.2).[34] Thereafter, it declined due to overcrowding and market forces. Like students today, they were under early pressure. Between 1815 and 1850, around £1000 (four years' income) was needed to cover an apprenticeship.[33] An 1842 guide to parents reminded them that *'by the time when a physician earns his bread and cheese he has no longer the teeth to eat them with.'*[35]

Their most important additional appointments were as 'parish surgeons' before and 'union surgeons' following the Poor Law Amendment Act of 1834. As 'union surgeons', they were paid less for looking after larger numbers of sick poor. The status of medical officer was degraded and GPs suffered financially as a consequence.

Under the original Poor Law, the medical fees approved were the same as in private practice but item of service payments were gradually replaced by salaries. Lower pay led to lower quality as Poor Law relief degenerated. There was a reduction of posts and from the average salary of £69 per annum practitioners had to provide drugs and dressings.[36]

Table 3.2   Annual earnings of various occupational groups, 1781-1851[26]

Occupation	1781	1819	1851
	£	£	£
Farm labourers	21.09	39.05	29.04
Non-farm common labourers	23.13	41.74	44.83
Clergy	182.65	266.65	267.09
Solicitors and barristers	242.67	447.50	1837.50
Engineers and surveyors	170.00	326.43	479.00
Surgeons and doctors	88.35	217.60	200.92

There were thus three clearly defined levels of patient-related remuneration: poor law, 'hospital class' and private provision, supplemented by various medical benefit clubs. There was more extensive provision for the poor in the south east as compared with the industrial north but a third of the working class were not club members and received no relief. Poor Law medical relief was widely regarded as ineffective because of the low financial incentive to provide good care. The perceived stigma increased the resistance of many poorer people to applying for relief. The burden of morbidity was overwhelming a system which was degrading for provider and recipient alike.[37]

While the new Poor Law legislation was designed to make life unpleasant for the able-bodied pauper (less eligible), it was never intended that conditions for the sick, aged and infirm should be harsher. The Poor Law Medical Reform Association produced three highly critical reports in late 1850s. Many practitioners hoped that the state system would be abandoned in favour of a system of relief based on provident dispensaries. These had expanded rapidly and provided good income for the medical officers appointed to them.

There was a wide range of institutions dotted rather haphazardly around the country; an inverse care law operated even then. The proportion of the population covered by sick clubs varied; e.g. in 1830, from as little as 8% in industrial areas such as Liverpool. Levies were deducted from weekly wages as a form of compulsory insurance, e.g. 1d in pound for accidents, 2d for full attendance on the whole family. Frequent complaints from patients, subservience to administrative committees, and low pay made sick club posts unpopular. GPs put up with such pay and conditions as a means of introduction to the family and friends of members - as a way, in other words, of getting known.

Dr Henry Rumsey and others began to argue that Poor Law medical relief should be available to all who could not pay for medical care (footnote 6). GPs knew well

Footnote 6. Henry Wyldbore Rumsey (1809-76) practised in Cheltenham and is one of the unsung heroes of this piece. As Honorary Secretary to the Poor Law Committee of the PMSA, he became deeply committed to improving the care of the poor. He was convinced of the need for state medicine.

how egregious was the pretence that the deserving could be clearly distinguished from the undeserving poor. However, abolition of the indefinable grades of pauper opened up the possibility of increased costs on a huge scale and was resisted by government. Nevertheless, in these early skirmishes can be discerned the roots of universal state provision under the NHS.[38]

Overall, GP incomes therefore changed little between 1820 and 1850. Indeed, taking the costs of living into account, the eighteenth century surgeon apothecary was more prosperous. A minimum of £200/year was needed for a way of life that included domestic servants, private education for children, the necessary standards of house, furniture and dress. Most commonly, income during this period was between £150-200 in the country, £300-500 in larger towns. The relative sparsity of data raises the suspicion of deliberate concealment. Income tax was re-imposed by Robert Peel in 1842 for incomes over £150 and this may have prompted reticence. GPs came under schedule D and could deduct all expenses incurred in the course of work. Creative accounting has always been a useful skill in general practice.

If real incomes were lower in mid-century, buying into a successful practice or succeeding father or uncle was the surest route to prosperity. More than half the population and more than half of all GPs lived in rural areas. Country practice was generally less well paid. GPs in villages or market towns like Holt whose practices involved long journeys on horse to cottages, farms and villages were the rule rather than the exception. They often hovered for years on bare subsistence.

Little changed either in the practice of dispensing and book-keeping between 1750 and 1850. Medical time had yet to be monetized. When the surgeon-apothecary James Handey successfully sued for remuneration of time in attendance, his peers arranged a celebratory dinner (footnote 7).

To achieve prosperity, a GP needed at least three things: 15-20 visits/day, an efficient pharmacy run by his apprentice or assistant, and the minimum of 'bad debts'. Complaints of bad debts were endemic but sympathy should be tempered in the light of the treatment of some assistants who were often paid well under £100 per annum. However, generalizations about the nature of general practice remained mostly true until early in the twentieth century: this was a hard, wearying and (relatively) poorly paid occupation.

Associations
The strengthening sense of corporate identity among GPs found expression in the

Footnote 7. James Handey treated the family of Mr Henson (an attorney) over a period of seven weeks in 1829. He charged £2.10s for medicines and £4.10s.6d for the visits. Henson cited the Rose case in refusing to pay. Handey's suit provided a rare victory for the medical over the legal profession.

growth of medical societies and associations. They served both educational and material purposes. Local associations of GPs provided networking and educational opportunities. They also began to draw up fee scales to reduce 'undercutting'. These were based on custom and competition.

The Metropolitan Society of General Practitioners set up a protection and benevolent fund. It was welcomed by the Gazette of Health but spurned by Thomas Wakley who hated the term 'general practitioner'.[39] He formed a rival London College of Medicine which lasted two years. He then threw his weight behind the PMSA which was to morph later into the British Medical Association (BMA). An attempt to establish a College of GPs was rebuffed by the Royal College of Surgeons (RCS) in 1843 but led to the formation of the National Association of General Practitioners (NAGP) on 7th December, 1844. A recommendation for a charter of incorporation to the Surgeon-Apothecaries under the title of the Royal College of General Practitioners seemed finally to be agreed in February 1848. However, it was further resisted by the RCS on account of an infamous clause that required surgeons to have dual qualifications though this was probably a bureaucratic oversight. The optimism among practitioners of the 1820s had faded away by 1850.[26]

In part, the failure of plans for a GP College was due to simultaneous movements to introduce a bill for medical registration. Wakley was viscerally opposed as were other potential supporters such as the PMSA which viewed the idea as divisive at a time when professional unity was needed. GPs were, after all, asking to be divorced from physicians and surgeons and for complete control over training and examination of future GPs. Ultimately, given the forces ranged against the NAGP (and the apathy of most GPs), only a post-graduate institution might have been acceptable. This was what indeed emerged a century later.

The Medical Act
An Act to Regulate the Qualifications of Practitioners in Medicine and Surgery was passed by Parliament in 1858. Its principal legacy was the establishment of the General Medical Council to regulate doctors in the UK. Describing its purpose, the Act notes that *'it is expedient that Persons requiring Medical Aid should be enabled to distinguish qualified from unqualified Practitioners'*. Until recently, the Medical Act has been seen as the defining advance whereby the education and ethical behaviour of medical practitioners finally came under firm control.

The Act created the position of Registrar of the General Medical Council - an office still in existence today - whose duty is to keep up-to-date records of those registered to practise medicine and to make them publicly available. It stated that, under the Poor Law system, Boards of Guardians could only employ those qualified in medicine and surgery as Poor Law Doctors. Under a clause in the Act that recognized doctors with foreign degrees practising in Britain, Elizabeth

Blackwell was able to become the first woman to have her name entered on the Medical Register on 1 January 1859 having qualified in Edinburgh. (The original Act has now been almost entirely repealed. The current law governing medical regulation is the Medical Act of 1983.)

Was the 1858 Act the great landmark of popular acclaim or was it another example of self-interested professional consolidation? Did the concept of the 'safe general practitioner' confer benefits to the public and the profession? Loudon is dismissive of its impact on medical education, professional unity, material wellbeing or GPs' status. Waddington argues that doctors rather than the public were the main beneficiaries of the Act which marginalized unqualified practitioners and increased medical incomes.[40]

The Medical Act resembled the 1815 Apothecaries Act in one respect: to the majority of practitioners it was a disappointment. In particular, it failed to outlaw quackery and control druggists. The profession wanted a clear definition of medical qualifications, a register, a representative medical council, rationalization of the chaotic state of education and a 'single portal of entry'. There was no single entry point and the Act perpetuated the partially qualified doctor. Compulsory examination of all students in medicine, surgery and midwifery was only introduced in 1886. However, the Act was of benefit to patients. Its disciplinary powers exercised a powerful deterrent effect and medical registration was important even if it did not unify the profession.

Overall, the Act was as much the consequence as the cause of changes in the medical profession. GPs gained little beyond ensuring their subordinate grade but subsequent developments provided GPs with economic security in laying down the principle of referral rights. The growing tendency of physicians and surgeons to practice as consultants in hospitals depended on a solid stratum of GPs in the community. Over time this enshrined the principle that access to a consultant could only be obtained after first seeing a GP. In the oft-quoted aphorism: *The physician and surgeon retained the hospital but the GP retained the patient.*[41]

The rise of laboratory medicine
Alongside these political developments, scientific discoveries were to change medical training and practice over the next two generations. The term 'laboratory' refers not just to physical space but to associated attitudes and methodologies. In the advancement of basic medical sciences - physiology, biochemistry and the development of diagnostics - German universities led the scientific research community from the mid-nineteenth century. The advent of medical microscopy gave rise to competing epistemologies of disease. Traditional diagnosis based on histories and observation was displaced by a new 'rational medicine' based on histology. Medical authority shifted to the pathologist as the final diagnostic arbiter

and the laboratory came to be regarded as the source of most fundamental, reliable information on the workings of the body.

Medical knowledge was thus transformed in the nineteenth century as attention shifted from structure to function; from anatomy to physiology. This changed the way practitioners thought about disease - as a manifestation of disrupted underlying physiological processes.[42]

The work of Claude Bernard (1813-78) perhaps best exemplifies this transformation. He championed laboratory medicine and research skills as central to medical training. He suggested the use of blinded experiments to ensure scientific objectivity. In his *An Introduction to the Study of Experimental Medicine* (1865), he wrote on authority versus observation, induction and deduction, cause and effect, verification and disproof. To these ends, he was notoriously pro-vivisection. He originated the term *milieu intérieur* and the associated concept of homeostasis. He is often described as the father of physiology (especially digestion) being the first to elucidate the role of the liver and pancreas. Increased standards of proof heralded the large-scale reorganization of the research process.

That disease might be caused by micro-organisms rather than miasma had been proposed in 1546 by Girolamo Frascatoro. The first 'animalcules' were observed microscopically by van Leeuwenhoek in the 1670s. Louis Pasteur's fermentation experiments debunked the notion of spontaneous generation. His rival Robert Koch demonstrated the cause of tuberculosis in 1882 and forged his famous postulates (footnote 8). Together they ushered in a golden era of bacteriology.

The development of new staining and culture techniques (e.g. by Richard Petri) hastened the rapid identification of agents responsible for diphtheria, typhoid, leprosy, plague and syphilis. Pasteur's anthrax and rabies vaccines fuelled expectation of more breakthroughs though the discovery of infective agents did not necessarily lead to more effective treatments. Another forty years were to elapse before the availability of antibiotics, following Fleming's discovery of penicillin.

In the meantime, laboratory researchers began to explore the effects of drugs on body function. The embryonic discipline of pharmacology advanced on the basis of theories associated with Paul Ehrlich (1854-1915): that drug molecules act by locking onto receptors on target cells and microbes. He tested over 600 compounds for therapeutic properties. Salvarsan (number 606) was to transform the treatment

Footnote 8. Robert Koch (1843-1910) was a German physician and microbiologist. His 'postulates' link a causative organism to a specific disease: the microorganism must be found in all organisms suffering from the disease but not in healthy organisms; the microorganism must be isolated from a diseased organism and grown in pure culture; the cultured microorganism should cause disease when introduced into a healthy organism; the microorganism must be re-isolated from the diseased host and identified as being the original causative agent.

of syphilis (1907) but there were to be no similar 'magic bullets' till the advent of prontosil for streptococcal infections in 1935. However, deficiency diseases such as rickets and beriberi were being linked to vitamin deficiencies. Effective treatments followed.

The laboratory's champions viewed medicine as moving from art to science - from the qualitative to quantitative - with novel diagnostics and measuring techniques. The regular use of new equipment such as the thermometer, spirometer, kymograph, polygraph and electrocardiogram (footnote 9) dates from the second half of the nineteenth century.

Medical education

As we have seen, until the 1830s medicine was still largely based on Greek and Roman ideas. Little was known of the causes of disease, and enquiring doctors, without university training, looked for explanation by studying natural history and science. Though the expansion of university education after 1830 was not immediately matched by an increase in middle class employment opportunities, increasing wealth led more parents to choose liberal educations for their sons. The expanding medical schools were one beneficiary.

Medical studies were more formally structured after 1858 following GMC guidelines. Potential medical students were required to take a preliminary exam to demonstrate liberal educational attainment followed by a minimum of five years in training. Practice was proscribed before the age of 21. Two or three years of pre-clinical studies were followed by three or four years of clinical training, very much as now.

It was gradually realized that lab-based insights were complementary to traditional bedside socio-clinical skills. Many new labs began to be established within hospital medical schools and experience of lab research was rapidly adopted into teaching and licensing requirements - in London and Edinburgh from the 1870s.

For many teachers, hospitals were now complementary but subservient to laboratories. The latter served professional, educational, social and political purposes in raising medicine's status but did not really yield effective therapies before 1900. Furthermore, the use of laboratory techniques was resisted by some in the medical establishment (who feared erosion of their arts) though GPs were starting to employ newfound skills with diagnostic kits in the community.

Nowadays, GPs frequently acquire half a dozen degrees, diplomas and memberships before they are unleashed upon the world. Educational credentialism

Footnote 9. In 1887, Augustus Waller invented an ECG machine consisting of a capillary electrometer fixed to a projector. The trace from the heartbeat was projected onto a photographic plate that was itself fixed to a toy train. This allowed a heartbeat to be recorded in real time.

has always marked the medical profession. In the late Victorian era, increasingly structured full-time education gave rise to a growing range of available qualifications. To this day, there is continuing debate over the most appropriate sequencing and balance of theoretical versus practical work, and how to accommodate new sciences.

The education of GPs has always been vitiated by the needs of specialists. Students often gain more experience of 'serious' (rare) illness in hospital rather than common conditions found in the community. In some respects, training before 1850 had been more practical - with advantages for the GP. London dispensaries were a useful training location. From the earliest days, there were concerns that factual cramming restricted the professional's outlook. *'There is…no profession in which it is more essential that those engaged in it should cultivate the talent of observing, thinking and reasoning for themselves, than it is in ours. You have done not much more than learn the way of learning. The most important part of your education remains.'*[43]

The recognition of what are nowadays called 'consultation skills' date from this period. A good bedside manner was seen as financially expedient too. A liberal education would fashion the interpersonal skills suitable for a gentleman and facilitate communication with more affluent patients.

The expansion of hospital-based training in the nineteenth century helped to improve the image of medicine - and parental willingness to pay for it. Though some students may have been coarse and lazy, most were well-mannered and conscientious. These institutions inculcated a professional ethic. Then as now, there were the initiations of dissecting room and theatre - experiences that toughened the emotional carapace for the rigors of the job (footnote 10).

After 1858, the process of medical training and socialization was the same for the future physician, surgeon or general practitioner. All were branded with loyalty to their teaching hospital and the role models within. London was popular as a world where connections could be made with many peers and famous names of the time. Then as now, it was not necessarily the source of the best training experience.

The rise in the standing of London medical schools was followed by expansion of provincial schools. European centres sharply declined in popularity. The number of applicants for places rose in the early twentieth century and competition for women was particularly intense.

Footnote 10. When I undertook anatomical dissection as a student 150 years later, I am ashamed to recall a small intestine being used as a skipping rope. Sport provided an outlet for youthful energy but study was unfashionable until around 1900 when a more serious and committed attitude became evident. Needless to say, women students have always been described as more assiduous.

In the decade leading up to the Medical Act, 44% of GPs were LSA/MRCS, 25% MRCS only, 6% LSA only. The remaining quarter had MDs, Scottish, Irish or other qualifications. After 1858, practitioners had to be qualified in both medicine and surgery. Twenty licensing bodies across the British Isles dispensed a veritable alphabet soup - some 61 qualifications. There thus remained many different routes into practice.

Key questions for educationalists concerned the character of pre-clinical education, the location of training, curricular content, the relationship of surgery to physic, the place of anatomy and dissection, and the relationship of bedside medicine to experimental science. A century and a half on, we wrestle with the same dilemmas but the roots of present practice were firmly in place by the middle of the nineteenth century.

Conclusion

General practitioners failed to achieve parity with physicians and surgeons for multiple reasons. Voluntary hospitals dominated medical education and general practitioners were entirely divorced from teaching. Their leaders were constantly outflanked by the persistent obstructionism of the Physicians and Surgeons. Many of these barriers persisted till the recent past. GPs' hoped-for prosperity was not achieved due to the costs of education and overcrowding. Consequences included competition, fee-cutting and recruitment from 'lower levels' of society.

The Medical Act is hailed both as a landmark through which the profession put its house in order and as a prime example of monopolization. From this time dates the second of the three pillars of modern-day general practice - the concept of referral rights. The first was the notion of generalism itself; the third being the registered list which emerged early in the next century.

The notion of Georgian country life as remote or unchanging is exploded in diaries of the time.[3] Itineracy for curates, doctors like George and other tradesmen was a way of life. No wonder they opted to establish roots when possible. As for my forebears, the Industrial Revolution had as yet made little mark on their daily lives. Rather, George was coming to correspond to a cameo of the typical country doctor from The Times of 1851. *'Dr Camomile is well with the squire: a sound churchman, and on dining terms with the Rector... He occupies a square white house neatly slated... Behind the house is the stable with two stalls. Commensurate with his increasing status, of all the houses in the town, the medical practitioner's is the largest.'*[44]

Chapter Four – Ebbs and Flows
(1860-1890)

'Conscientious people are apt to see their duty
in that which is the most painful course.'
George Eliot

The fourth generation

Of George Skrimshire's ten sons, four went into medicine. Unsurprisingly, those that did not are among the more individual and interesting participants in this saga and some merit a mention below. This was an age of expanding opportunities for the enterprising or adventurous. Numerous letters survive this generation; it too was close knit.

Figure 4.1 George and Lavinia's children.

George Skrimshire m Lavinia Truscott
1802-77   1807-1877

Dr George	Dr John Truscott	Dr Charles Parnham	Dr Frederic William
1827-82	1835-1912	1844-1912	1848-99
(London)	(Holt)	(Clydach)	(Morpeth)

(The four doctor sons of Dr George)

Other sons

Thomas	Edmund B	Henry T	Ernest	Arthur
1831-63	1839-1913	1842-1910	1850-1931	1855-1932
Chemist	Draper	Master Mariner	Rev Canon	Various jobs
(Aylsham)	(London)	(Retd to Liverpool)	(Llandaff)	(Liverpool)

Daughters

Anne	Lavinia	Elizabeth	Emily m Dr Alfred Whitlock
1829-1906	1833-54	1837-84	1852-1904

Young George

Born in 1829, George followed firmly in his father's footsteps. He qualified LSA in 1853, having been supported while at King's College Hospital by his Truscott grandfather. He settled in a practice at 6, Crescent Place, New Bridge Street, Blackfriars which his grandfather described as 'run down'. There is no record of him qualifying MRCS, which had become usual, and as his father did while at Loddon in 1845. However, he acquired an MD from St Andrew's in 1862, a few months after his brother, John Truscott Skrimshire ('JTS'). As this was by recommendation and required the support of two eminent physicians, it must be assumed that he had a good reputation. He subsequently married, had four children and spent most of his career as a GP in Paddington.

The nearly man

Born in 1832, the next brother Thomas also considered medicine as a career. In 1851 he was working as a Surgeon's Assistant in Finsbury. By 1857, however, he had re-joined the family in Holt - working and living with Mr Craske, a chemist. His mother wrote of how she enjoyed his Sunday evening visits to Hill House. Unfortunately, he had to leave Mr Craske in 1860 as a son-in-law was joining the business. By this time he had developed an 'intimate friendship' with a Miss Kendall of Stody. On February 8th his mother wrote to her son John Truscott:

'Miss Clara Kendall came to tea for the first time and we had a pleasant evening. She is a fine girl and very quiet, of course rather timid, rather a formidable affair to be introduced to eleven members of a family at one time…they both play and sing and we are all so fond of music. Her father seems to have given up all opposition and Thomas spends his Sunday afternoons and evenings there. We shall be very sorry for Tom to leave Holt. He is a good quiet fellow and, of course, at present we have no idea where he will go or what he thinks of doing. He forms plans and we are as ignorant of them as if we lived on the Moon!'

More was revealed when Tom wrote to JTS, in a letter from Aylsham on November 10th. He was seeking another chemist's apprenticeship. Though he refers to previous happenings obliquely, it is possible to piece the story together.

'You will be perhaps surprised to hear I have now left Holt. I have been here a fortnight tomorrow and am able to say, I think, I shall like Aylsham when I get more used to the people. I think I told you in my last (letter) about Foulsham and that we got as near as twenty pounds. I have since heard that he would have said yes if I had gone ten more but I thought and still think I offered quite enough. I have taken another situation, whether it will be for long, I cannot say. For my own part I shd like to get something of my own but I find a difficulty in making up my mind to take the step.'

Sadly, his friendship with Clara did not survive the move. In the meantime, he had begun discussing prospects with Mr John Symonds, a chemist in the Market Place.

'I was told yesterday that he wished to sell out but to take his house, business, stock, and fixtures and goodwill would require £1500. He does a nice business and the premises are very compact and convenient, in fact as nice a little crib as any man could wish for, but as his wife and he lately lost his only daughter, and has sufficient to live on of his business, he does not care about it - in fact he has no reason for continuing it…You would have thought he would have been rather shy

of taking me on that account, and I might soon leave him, or even set up on my own in opposition if I came to get a little known.'

He referred somewhat plaintively to regrets at leaving Holt. *'Of course, I find it extremely awkward being 12 bad miles from Stody. Some people would say good miles but I cannot think so - in fact they must be Irish ones for I have not been able to get over yet since I left.'* Notwithstanding regrets at leaving Clara, by Census day in 1861 he was lodging over Mr Symonds' shop. Tom had returned to the family's apothecary's roots. He remained in Aylsham, was married briefly, and died young of tuberculosis in 1863. His father George was present at his deathbed.

The genial black sheep and a Master Mariner

The weight of history can burden the next generation in different ways. Striking out against the prevailing expectations requires energy and individualism. Several letters to JTS paint a cheery picture of his younger brother, Edmund Skrimshire. He was looking for an opening in London and his social life was evidently full. On this occasion, his reason for not writing sooner

'...was a correspondence which I have been carrying on with une chère amie, which, I am happy to say, has just come to an end and I have received back no less than thirty-three letters - a few! Since I wrote I have not been quite so dull having made several friends, male and female. One, Harry Lloyd, the son and partner of a chemist, visits with several good families. Their apprentice, Sherwood, I have known since I came here. He is a tried friend but rather wild. Then there is another chemist's apprentice, a recent acquaintance, Birch, a very good fellow and likely to prove a very agreeable companion.

I have been out to two parties, one a Ball chez des amis de ma chère amie at Camberwell. I enjoyed myself very much. We danced all evening, with short intervals of singing and refreshments, until five o'clock, when, the company having departed, the fairy hands or rather fingers of some six or seven Young Ladies enveloped me in sundry shawls, mantles and furs and I took my seat in a large easy chair where I slept until I was awoken by one of the ladies. Having arranged my toilet and taken a little breakfast for which I had no appetite, I returned by an early train. The other was just a small party of friends just to have a dance. We broke up early and I returned the same night.'

Fortunately, he describes more healthy pursuits to his rather solemn older brother:

'This evening I have been to have a bathe. I am learning to swim and am getting on very well. I have had one game of cricket this summer, even got up at five o'clock one morning and played till seven, but it made us all so stiff that I cannot persuade anyone else to get up again!

It is some time since I went to see Grandpapa and Mama, but in all probability I shall go before my next monthly (allowance) comes round...'

He was eventually to embark on drapery but his business failed, involving his father in some expense. He married young, at St Matthew's Church, Westminster on November 11th, 1862 and raised a large family - four boys and four girls. Unfortunately, he deserted his wife after 27 years to move to Australia with another lady. There he seems to have reformed enough to work for one firm in Melbourne for twenty-five years before his death in 1913.

His wife had a difficult time, however. In an undated letter to her brother-in-law JTS, by then in the practice at Holt, she explains her predicament. Trade was poor, and she was relying on two of her sons for support - Albert, a portmanteau maker, and Sidney, a draper, were both struggling as well. She had written to all Edmund's brothers, suggesting that as little as 6d a week would help greatly. History does not relate how they responded.

A younger brother, Henry, chose to go to sea. Born in Loddon, on a river with boat building yards, his earliest memories were of ships taking shape with their sails. His interest was further stimulated by visits to Blakeney and Wells, still active ports with a thriving coastal trade. He too shared his plans with JTS:

'I suppose you already know how averse Grandpa is to my choice. From what I hear I shall not meet with a very warm (or perhaps a rather too warm) reception from Grandpa, who, Pa thinks, takes a rather one-sided view of the case...'

All went well, however, although his mother expressed anxiety when she heard nothing from him for long periods. By 1881 he was in West Derby, Liverpool, a Master Mariner, with a Yarmouth-born wife and three children, one born in India, the younger two at sea. He named his own son George, appropriately enough.

In 1882 the two brothers were forever tied in tragedy. Edmund's son of the same name went to sea on Henry's vessel, 'Hannibal', aged just 19. On November 15th, he fell from the mainyard to the deck and was killed.

In 1889, Henry's ship the 'Scotsman', went aground in fog and sank off Newfoundland. Ten lives were lost and some fault was found. Though his actions after the accident were said to be 'praiseworthy', his Master's certificate was suspended for nine months.

John Truscott, cleft rock
My main focus in this generation is the second Holt-based Dr Skrimshire, my great great grandfather, born in 1835. Eventually to succeed his father in the practice, he is recorded in the 1851 census as a 'medical pupil', living at Hill House. From

surviving letters, he seems to have adopted a paternal role in relation to his younger, often less dependable siblings.

He passed the preliminary exam for admission to the Society of Apothecaries in 1851, at the age of sixteen. The syllabus included Virgil's Aeneid, Book 1, the Gospel of St Luke (in Greek), Cicero's *Oratio Pro Milone*, Algebra, Euclid Book 1 and Xenophon's *Anabasis*. Thus equipped, he had to bide his time before starting at medical school in London. In 1854 he joined Dr W. F. Tuckett, Surgeon to the Blaenavon Ironworks at Clydach in South Wales as an assistant for four years.

A notable event during his stay was a lecture he gave to the Clydach Reading Association. A notice announcing it survives:

On Monday Evening, April 28th 1858.

By MR J.T.SKRIMSHIRE

Subject: GREAT MEN

Who have Risen from Humble Positions.

An interesting, handwritten script, not always easily decipherable, suggests a well-informed, earnest young man of strong convictions. He gives the historical outline of the lives of his subjects in some detail, interspersed with moral reflections and literary quotations, and concluding with a religious message confirming his own faith.

His first 'great man' is James Cook, from whom he moves on to James Watt. If their names were likely to have been familiar to his audience, those of Henry Kirke White and Guillaume Dupuytren, were probably less so (footnote 1). His subjects were varied: from Martin Luther he goes on to Cardinal Wolsey and Thomas Cromwell. Throughout he extols the virtues of perseverance and self-improvement at all stages of life, whatever the circumstances. He reminds his hearers that John Dryden embarked on a translation of the Iliad at 68, and that the elder Cato taught himself Greek at the age of 80. His message is directed to the ladies, too. *'Wives, sisters, mothers, all must influence others to develop their talents.'* Having quoted Longfellow's verse from Autumn:

> *Oh what a glory doth this world put on*
> *For him who, with a fervent heart, goes forth*
> *Under the bright and glorious sky, and looks*
> *On duties well performed, and days well spent!*

Footnote 1. By coincidence, Kirke White was at St John's College, Cambridge, with which JTS was later to have a close connection, and Dupuytren's earliest position of importance was at the Paris Medical School as Prosector, a job later JTS took on as a medical student at King's. Baron Guillaume Dupuytren (1777-1835) was an anatomist and military surgeon, esteemed for treating Napoleon Bonaparte's haemorrhoids. He was first to describe a deforming contracture of the hands associated with his name.

JTS concludes with his own fervent hope: *'Let us not forget daily to ask the assistance of that Great and Wise Being without whom we can do no good thing, that He will bless all our thoughts, words and works, that what we think, say or do may be done with Him, for Him and through Him.'*

His work for the Reading Association was appreciated. The Members of the Association presented him with a purse of £12-1s-9d, *'with much regret in parting and sincerely hoping he may prosper in his future career.'* They wished it could have been larger but hoped he would receive it as a token of their approval of *'his uniform good conduct and services, during a stay of four years in the neighbourhood.'*

A model student

He had some savings after four years with Dr Tuckett but, even with the purse from the Reading Association, he needed to subsidise his way through medical school. Before starting at King's College Hospital he approached his grandfather John Truscott for assistance. The latter had seen JTS's elder brother George through medical school single-handedly and, once prevailed upon, was unwilling to help again:

'I naturally assumed they would at least have assisted in the payment of George's college expenses, but they, your parents, never provided one penny.' He told JTS that a loan could be procured, though repayment might be difficult, and went on: *'I was induced by these means to provide £200 to enable George to buy Burt's rundown practice, and since then I have been called upon to assist him, largely to enable him to keep his position.'*

He commented at the start: *'It may be true that the Holt practice is not first rate'*, but concluded - after advice on prudence and forethought - by expressing the belief that George (his father), *'well knowing the sacrifices he had made, would assist him by every means in his power.'* How much he was helped by his parents is not known, but JTS was resourceful. Towards the end of his time as a student, he took on extra work, as an Assistant Demonstrator, and as Prosector for Primary Exams. Testimonials from the Principal and senior surgeons attest to their high opinion of him.

The Principal, R.W. Jeff, DD, had much pleasure, *'in very warm terms in bearing witness to his exemplary conduct and diligence.'* Wm Fergusson, FRCS, Surgeon and Professor of Anatomy, recommended him *'very earnestly and strongly'* for an appointment as Assistant House Surgeon to the Liverpool South Hospital. *'In every capacity Mr Skrimshire has shown himself to be able, attentive and trustworthy. I should add that he is a gentleman of irreproachable character and habits.'* Finally, a handsome scroll printed for the President of the Royal College of Surgeons, requested by the Court of Examiners, expresses *'their best thanks for the efficient services rendered while acting as Anatomical Prosector for their primary Examinations for the Diploma of Member during the years 1859 - 60 at six different examinations terminating in May 1860.'*

Perhaps these account for the suggestion, in an obituary notice fifty years later, that he could have continued in hospital work rather than in a country practice: *'At King's College he was regarded as a student of great capacity, with aptitudes marking him out for a professional career. Some surprise was shown, therefore, when he chose to return to Holt to assist his father in the labours of a large and burdensome country practice.'*

It is unsurprising that he found supporters when he applied for an MD (by recommendation) from St Andrew's University in 1862. But how much risk did he take in joining his father's practice - and would he ever really have considered an alternative?

Starting in Holt

JTS was always imbued with a strong sense of family. Although separated from his parents during schooldays, he chose to return at the age of 16 and observed at close quarters his father at work. He joined him in the practice shortly before his marriage. A letter from a former patient after his death suggests he had a sympathetic bedside manner. The writer describes being visited as a boy by old George and JTS: his *'heart rose when he saw the younger doctor approaching!'* His arrival must have transformed his own father's working life.

There was another father-son practice in the town, the Doctors Hales on the Norwich Road, but there was plenty of work. Holt was a flourishing market town and its tradesman benefited from the arrival of the railway in 1847. The population increased from about 1,000 to 1,500 between 1800 and 1850. Then as now, Holt was a shopping centre for outlying villages. With the social reforms of the age and after the creation of the General Board of Health in 1848, there were official posts in the Poor Law Unions of parishes. JTS was appointed Medical Officer of Health and Public Vaccinator to the Walsingham Union. His Contract for Vaccination in the Blakeney District of the Walsingham Union, dated August 21st 1863, lists his 'Days of Attendance, for Vaccination, and a week later for Inspection' at five different 'stations' as well as at Hill House:

> *'At Blakeney, for Blakeney, Wiveton and Morston;*
> *At Langham, for Langham, Saxlingham and Field Dalling;*
> *At Sharrington, for Sharrington, Brinton and Bale;*
> *At Gunthorpe, for Gunthorpe and Swanton Novers;*
> *And at Briningham, for Briningham and Melton Constable.'*

For each successful performance he received two shillings, or three shillings if the vaccination was performed at more than two miles from a station.

These were modest rewards for tasks which involved many miles trotting in a pony trap along the country lanes. However, they were the necessary bread and butter of

practice through which he built up a 'panel' of patients, mostly members of Friendly Societies. His father, before his death in 1877, had been Medical Officer of the Erpingham Union and of the Reedham Providential Society. Later, with the establishment of sanatoria and the development of Gresham's School, more public appointments became available. The practice grew significantly during the forty-two years in which JTS was a partner before ill health necessitated his retirement in 1905.

JTS was undoubtedly a talented and hardworking man (Figure 4.2). He did not allow himself to stagnate in his rural backwater. The Norwich Medico-Chirurgical Society was founded in 1867; he was its President in 1886. He is recorded as having been in

Figure 4.2 JTS, 1882

correspondence with the BMJ in 1875. By this time, he was married and already father of three children. But if he was professionally successful, his personal life was full of sadness.

A troubled life

Sometime in the early 1860s, John Truscott met Lizzie Finch at the local rectory. She was the third daughter of a dedicated curate based in Morpeth. Her mother, Jane, was visiting her brother, Edward Brumell, then vicar of Holt. Lizzie had already shown herself vulnerable to what was described as 'intermittent dementia' - presumably dementia praecox or schizophrenia. JTS was a compassionate man and clinically experienced. Her parents made him aware of earlier episodes of psychotic illness but his devotion to Lizzie led him to take the risk. She and JTS were married in Morpeth on September 29th, 1869.

His sister Emily wrote a charming account of the celebrations that took place at Hill House:

'My dear John,

   We are all very glad you and Lizzie are enjoying yourselves so much, and also to hear from all sides that the wedding passed off so nicely. I must also add that we also enjoyed the day very much. The Grammar School had a holiday, for which I hear they are very much obliged to you.

We had a little party and went blackberrying in the afternoon and returned to a substantial tea. Then in the evening we had some music, games and we also acted some charades. Then we had supper, a little music and our happy little party broke up, but I dare say you will wonder who came, so I will tell you…Minnie, Charlie, and Jessy Bull, John Burrell, best known to you by the name of Jacky, Charley Bray and Fanny Roberts - but I must not forget to tell you that at several intervals during the day our bells in the house rang forth a merry peal (for you), I dare say that will make you laugh.

And now I think I have nothing else to say except that the house begins to look very much like being finished and I think it will look very nice.

With love from all to Lizzie and yourself and the same from myself,
Believe me to remain Your Affect. Sister,
Emily J Skrimshire.'

The couple spent the first years of their married life at Wansbeck House in Holt. These were mostly happy years, though, as early as February 1870 while pregnant with her first child, Lizzie appears to have fallen ill. Her sister, Dora, came down to help out. Over the next years three children arrived: Dorothy Jane ('Dolly') in 1870, John Fenwick ('Jack') in 1872, and Henry Finch ('Harry') in 1874. A second girl born in 1876 died in infancy.

Their life continued to be fruitful. Family correspondence reveals mutual interest in family affairs - birthdays acknowledged, loans or gifts bestowed, bouts of illness stoically borne. *'We are very sorry to hear John is laid up with a boil, and hope he will soon be better. You must feed him well, as I am sure that is the great thing to do with boils. Give him port wine and beef tea…'* Over time, occasional references begin to be made to Lizzie's 'breakdown'. Her third daughter, Amy, was born in 1879 in the Heigham Asylum, a private establishment. By now, she was unable to cope with the strains of family life. JTS decided that she should be permanently committed. Incarceration of the insane (following the 1845 Lunacy Act) required certification by another medical superintendent[1] but JTS shared responsibility. It was the great sorrow of his life.

Lizzie was to spend the remaining 43 years of her life in various asylums and guesthouses. She was first admitted to Craighouse Royal Edinburgh Asylum for the Insane early in 1879, aged just 31. Established for paying patients on the initiative of the eminent psychiatrist, Dr Thomas Coulston, it would have been known to JTS. Records show that she was there, with occasional spells 'on parole', until at least 1903. Her letters show clear comprehension of the world about her and she received periodic visits from the family but they make no mention of her husband. She spent her last years at St Andrew's Hospital, Northampton, and there she died on October 29th, 1923 (footnote 2).

Did her derangement justify her long separation from the family? Would she have been contained today at home? JTS appeared to believe that her symptoms would be aggravated by the stress of living at home. Mental illness was stigmatizing and poorly understood. He was a strong personality occupying a prominent local position. Though hard to square with what we know of JTS, self-interest may have contributed to his detachment. He kept only one of her letters - from 1881. Perhaps they were too painful for him. The reasons for her incarceration went with him to the grave.

For twelve years he had rented Wansbeck House, so named by Lizzie after the river running through Morpeth. Alone now, he quickly finalized the purchase of Hill House. According to an Agreement between William Cozens-Hardy and John Truscott Skrimshire dated 15th August, 1881:

'The Vendor will sell and the Purchaser purchase, free of all incumbrances (but subject to an annual land tax of £1 and a tithe rent of 12/6d) all that capital messuage or mansion now divided into two dwelling houses, together with the offices, chasehouse, buildings, yards, walled in and other gardens orchards plantations and shrubberies, land and thereto belonging containing by estimate two acres and a half or thereabouts situate in Holt aforesaid now in the respective occupations of Anne Skrimshire, William Henry Becken and Charles Knowles, except and reserved the right of the vendor, his heirs and assigns and his and their tenants and occupiers to pass and repass with or without horses carts and carriages along the existing carriage drive and roadway from the street to the piece of land retained by the vendor lying between the property hereby agreed to be sold and the chapel and the land belonging to the Trustees of the United Methodist Free Church for the sum of £850...' Rather less than a third of today's annual council tax.

A developing practice

A Victorian medical career was a means to maintain social prestige, rather than gain higher social standing.[2] JTS built on his local connections to consolidate his place in the local community. The employment of a steady stream of assistants indicates the practice's growing prosperity. A surviving contract signed by JTS requires *'John Joseph North Emerson of the same place Surgeon to serve for six calendar months from the sixth day of June 1878 at the yearly salary of One Hundred and Twenty Pounds to be paid by monthly instalments of Ten Pounds on the fifth day of each month, the first of such instalments to be paid on the fifth day of July 1878 and for six calendar months from the sixth day of June 1878.'*

Footnote 2. Previously called the Northampton General Lunatic Asylum, it had opened in 1838. Its first medical superintendent was Thomas Octavius Prichard, a pioneer in humane treatment of the mentally ill. As we have seen, John Clare was one of his earliest patients. The Asylum was renamed in 1887, having been built on land once owned by the Cluniac Priory of St Andrew's.

Whether he stayed for more than the six months is not known, but in 1881 one Dr Alfred Whitlock came for two years. He left to set up on his own at Wells-next-the-Sea, having married JTS's sister, Emily. Others followed but the next significant appointment was that of Joseph Beckett Gillam, the first doctor from a farming family at Gimingham (my great grandfather). He joined as an assistant in 1892 straight after qualifying from Cambridge and St Thomas's Hospital. He became a partner on the 21st March, 1895.

The Articles of Partnership required Joseph to pay *seven hundred pounds by way of premium and as consideration for the purchase of one third part of the present value of the horses, carriages, harness, surgical instruments, drugs, bottles and other effects'* of JTS. The latter *'reserved to himself the general Control over and regulation of the practice and business of the partnership'*, as well as the right *'to introduce either of his sons…into the said business.'* Joseph was to work seven years to parity, earning £140 per quarter.

The early years were demanding but, in the meantime, he too joined the family. At a large, fashionable wedding on July 25th 1901, he married JTS's daughter, Dolly. His father-in-law was gratified to look down on a practice no more run-down; one that could finance two sons through Cambridge and London medical schools.

Outside his doctoring life, JTS was much respected. As a trustee of the Loyal Alexander Lodge of the Independent Order of Oddfellows, his advice was considered, *'always sound and carefully thought out.'* He was a foundation governor of the Church School, a long-time member of the church choir and, from 1904-07 a church warden.

The new century had started well for him. Jack and Harry completed their training, and Dorothy's marriage was opening up new prospects but JTS began to find life more difficult. Perhaps keeping up with younger, dynamic partners placed pressure on him. Later that year he was sent to the south coast for a change on account of depression. Subsequently, he was unable to resume working. He had lost all of his sisters - Anne, the last, in 1906. Of his brothers, Tom died in 1863, George in 1882, Fred in 1899 and Henry in 1910. His last years continued to be a struggle. He had in February 1912 learnt of Charles's death. He had lost his son-in-law, Joseph, a year previously and Jack was in hospital for a second major operation. He and Lizzie had been living apart for over thirty years.

By April 29th his state of depression led Harry to take him, for a change of scene, to Aylsham. He stayed in the house of Dr Little, where his treatment was supervised by Dr Barton-Fanning. There, although his behaviour had seemed undisturbed, he contrived to take a bottle of strychnine from the surgery cupboard and put an end to his life. He was 77 years of age.

The Eastern Daily Press (EDP) reported on the inquest at which the jury found that he had poisoned himself whilst in an unsound state of mind. A warm tribute was then paid to him: *'He knew and was known by everybody, and it is not excessive to say that most of the people amongst whom he dwelt regarded him with a warm personal attachment. He was an admirable type of country practitioner, capable of a weighty opinion, and endowed with the best of personal qualities. His townsmen always recognised in him a man of sound business capacity, punctilious and methodical in the extreme. A thoroughgoing Churchman, he sang in the choir for many years and interested himself practically in the affairs of the church…In politics, a moderate Conservative, but seldom seen at public meetings…his views certainly not obtrusive.'*

JTS had led a full and responsible life. He chose to join his father's practice after qualifying with distinction, largely paying his own way through teaching hospital. Through his connection with Edward Brumell he found his wife in Morpeth, and, with her passed eleven years at Wansbeck House which saw the arrival of four children. He had seen two sons qualified and launched into his own profession, indeed now as partners in his practice. His eldest daughter, though now a widow, had given birth to four grandchildren.

He was a tower of strength to every one of his numerous siblings, and had managed to buy Hill House, previously rented by his father. From the Literary Society at Clydach, through King's College to the Norwich Medico-Chirurgical Society, his professional life had earnt him respect. It was also profitable. At his death, probate on his estate was granted on over £4,000 - equivalent to around £500,000 today.

Perhaps the nicest piece about him appeared in the Gresham magazine for June, 1912:

JOHN TRUSCOTT SKRIMSHIRE
Died May 5th, aged 77
On Sunday, May 5th, went to rest John Truscott Skrimshire.

He had been for many years the School Doctor, but retired some five years ago owing to advancing years and indifferent health. Still he ever felt a great interest in the school, and he was a familiar figure to us all on many occasions. A man of great ability he was wholly unpretentious; all who knew him felt the influence of his gentle lovable nature; less known because he made no show of it, was the deep, quiet courage with which he bore the burden of a life that was troubled beyond the common lot of man. He was kind to all in word and act, and beloved of all, for in him was a great store of Christian charity.

JTS is remembered still in one small photograph. He stands under a sycamore tree on the lawn at Hill House: a strong, slightly stooping, dignified elderly gentleman with a carefully groomed white beard looking firmly into the camera. His daughter Dolly looks on. It is her wedding day (figure 4.3).

Charles Parnham

The next medical brother went on from Gresham Grammar School to train at St Bartholemew's Hospital. He was described in a rather stodgy obituary in the BMJ as the senior scholar of his year, before embarking on 'an eminent and successful career' in Wales. Introduced by JTS, he joined the same Dr W F Tuckett as a partner married his daughter and eventually

Figure 4.3 JTS and Dolly, 25th July 1901

succeeded him. As well as being head doctor for the Blaenavon Iron and Steel Company, he held several other public appointments: as Medical Officer of Health for Brynmawr Urban District Council and Llanelli Rural District Council, as Medical Officer to the Crickhowell Union, Public Vaccinator for Brynmawr and District, and as Medical Inspector of Factories for the Blaenavon Company. A member of the British Medical Association, he was President of the Eastern Valley Medical Association. He was described as '*earnest in everything he undertook.*'

Outside medicine, he was a Volunteer Brigade-Surgeon of the South Wales Infantry Division, and Surgeon-Lieutenant-Colonel of the 1st Brecknockshire Battalion. He was a prominent Freemason, having been Worshipful Master of the Kennard Lodge. He died, having retired to Weston-super-Mare, on February 22nd, 1912.

Frederic William

Fred's career progression was also supported in various ways by JTS. He followed his older brother to King's College where his letters suggest he was assiduous in his studies: '*I answered Mr Partridge my first question this morning at Anatomy Exam. The fellows all stamped as applause but Old Dicky told them they had much better find reasons for their answers as Mr Skrimshire did instead of applauding him! Of course this sounds very wrong from me, but I hope it will please you to find that I am getting on a little, though slowly yet. I have not yet got a part for dissection and do not stand much chance before Christmas.'*

He was for a while Assistant Demonstrator of Anatomy at the medical school, before further developing the Morpeth connection. After three years as a house surgeon to the Dispensary there, he went into practice with Lizzie's uncle, Dr Matthew Brummell.

His letters suggest financially straightened circumstances but a few contain medical snippets: *'Clarke of Dalling got his foot into a thrashing machine (steam) which was fortunately going slow. There were two wounds, one above the ankle, a contusion but as it has continued fairly quiet to the present we shall not have much suppuration.'*

He too retained a keen interest in his siblings. In an intriguing letter to his father, for example, Fred writes: *'I am sorry indeed to hear of poor Ernest's crisis of affairs, but I hope they will look favourably upon his youth and his being led astray as he was by one much older than himself.'* Whatever scrape Ernest had got into, he proceeded on to respectability as a priest, ending his career as a canon at Llandaff cathedral.

Fred's letters generally suggest solemnity:

'Morpeth Dispensary
Feb 24ᵗʰ 1871.

My Dear Father,
I've been trying not to let your birthday slip by forgotten and I think I have succeeded so far as to send you a few lines wishing you many happy returns of the day. Every year as it passes leads us naturally to think that the many are gone by and that to all of us the few are to come, but as we must all thank God that you have been spared to us so long, and hope that by God's will you will yet stay to set us on our road, I cannot but be thankful that since your last birthday I have been launched in the world and have become less burdensome to you and my dear Mother.
I am getting more work now and have several good cases in professional parlance although bad enough for the sufferers. I have a case of smallpox but trust it will not become epidemic here.
I had the honour of dining with Lord Richard Cavendish, brother of the Duke of Devon, who said he knew Dr Skrimshire of Peterboro. He used to meet him at Sandon or some such place. And now with love to all the house circle.
I remain your affectionate son,
Fred.'

In his public appointments he paralleled Charles in Wales. Medical Officer of Health to the Morpeth Union District, Medical Officer and Public Vaccinator to one of the Districts of the Union, even a Certifying Factory Surgeon. He too was

Surgeon-Lieutenant to the 1st Volunteer Brigade of the Northumberland Fusiliers and a Master of a Freemason Lodge.

Music was his particular passion. For the last two years before his death he was churchwarden, having been for many years a member of the choir, and was described as a *'singer of taste, a pianist of skill, and composer of no mean ability.'* His sister, Anne, moved up with him as housekeeper until his marriage to Eleanor Bradley in 1883. This was a happy occasion. The Rector, the Rev the Hon Francis Grey, travelled all the way to Reading to conduct the service - an honour that indicated Fred's links with the church.

#   #   #

Health care across East Anglia
Between 1860 and 1911, the average number of people per doctor rose from roughly 1,300 to around 2,000 in rural counties like Norfolk, though most could not afford a GP's services.[3] Early-nineteenth century medical clubs began in market towns such as Wymondham and Coltishall and nearly half the region's poor law unions offered such schemes in the 1830s. Roughly one-quarter of doctors had friendly society work in the two counties by 1880; most ran their own sick clubs and some 60% were involved in poor law medical work.[4]

Over 300 rural cottage or village hospitals were established between 1860 and 1900, more than 20 of them in Norfolk and Suffolk. Around one-quarter of rural GPs were therefore involved in hospital work. The influence of professional medicine in the countryside increased from the 1860s, with implementation of the 1858 Medical Act, belated application of sanitary legislation (see below), a surge of cottage hospital building and Poor Law reform.

Armstrong's study of rural Norfolk suggested declining infant mortality rates, from 164/1,000 live births to 131/1,000 between 1851 and 1881.[5] Rural Norfolk's crude death rates were 10-12% below the national average. However, local Medical Officers of Health also alleged parental negligence, variously citing the reluctance to have children vaccinated, insufficient provision for medical attendance, drinking from contaminated ponds or wells, and resort to opium to relieve marsh fever in low-lying areas. Their work involved notification of infectious diseases (with local school closures for measles, diphtheria, whooping cough), inspections of slaughterhouses and dairies, and improvements to wells. 'Stinking old middens' were superseded by 'dry pail' systems burying excrement away from water courses. *'...quite a lot of people in rural Norfolk stood to benefit...from the measures of rural district councils by the early twentieth century.'*[5]

Central state influences upon rural sanitation and health were partly mediated by Poor Law authorities and later local councils. These were essentially more concerned with economy than with reform. In practice, the part-time Poor Law doctor frequently became the district Medical Officer of Health (MOH).

The part-time MOH in a rural area like Norfolk was in a weaker position compared with the full-time urban MOH, who had greater resources and influence. Rural guardians, often local farmers, were slow to link disease prevention with long-term economies as opposed to short-term costs. Excepting limited numbers of 'model' cottages, rural housing was scarce and defective. The latter tended to be the property of landowners. They were strongly represented in local government as well as being the principal wealthy patient clientele for medical practitioners. In other words, a rural GP with a mission to reform faced political constraints and delicate financial considerations in the medical marketplace.[6]

Health care arrangements among the rural poor still included herbalism, self-medication and healers, but increasingly involved qualified medical practitioners. Yet the lack of money for the doctor's fee and fear of stigmatisation within Poor Law institutions were restricting factors concerning modern medicine for most people in rural areas. The country doctor was not necessarily an authority figure or one closely identified with scientific medicine.

Mental illness

Psychiatry was then emerging from a 'dark age'. The madness of King George III is sometimes credited with having helped to raise public awareness a generation earlier. If this seems far-fetched, how was my great great grandmother's 'schizophrenia' regarded? What treatments might she have received? What services would JTS have sought in caring for her, or indeed for other patients with mental afflictions?

The first half of the nineteenth century certainly marked a watershed for care of the mentally ill. The opening of the York Retreat heralded more compassionate institutional care backed up by mental health law and parliamentary interventions. A confident new psychiatric profession was starting to develop its own specialised body of knowledge. However, most medical care of mental illness still fell to general practitioners.

Prior to the eighteenth century, the immortal soul was inviolably synonymous with the mind. It was difficult to conceive of the mind as diseased. The very term 'mental illness' is a product of the Enlightenment. There are pitfalls in retrospective diagnosis. Contemporary descriptions of insanity do not always correspond with modern psychiatric categories. We need to accept what is culturally and historically distinct at face value.

Richard Napier (1559-1634) was an English country physician whose case notes of over 2000 'obscure rustics' have been painstakingly analysed. They show how contemporary definitions of madness were rooted in the social, material and cultural world of the time. They illustrate the role of family and religion in genesis and care of mental illness. Life was oppressively public. Secular and ecclesiastical courts, local customs and neighbours upheld common moral, sexual and social standards of behaviour. Napier's notes suggest a high incidence of disturbance among women and young people that probably reflected social pressures such as early marriage, childrearing infant mortality and economic hardship.[7]

The causes of madness might be natural or supernatural. The former included social factors, the latter spirit possession, witchcraft or religious enthusiasm. Excessive imagination or inappropriate passion could impair reason. Categories included lunacy, mania, distraction, lethargy and melancholy. Symptoms are familiar - anguish, grief, insomnia, anxiety and self-harm; so too are the limited range of cures: astrological cures, herbal remedies and Galenic methods (e.g. purging, bleeding).

The language of mental illness
The term *melancholy* as a diagnostic label was increasingly popular from the sixteenth century onwards. This related to its popularisation in medical circles. *The Anatomy of Melancholy* by Richard Burton (1628) was a best-seller and described its different facets: e.g. *'jealousye, solitarinesse, hypocondriacus, superstition.'* Melancholia became a fashionable affliction of the superior ranks in contrast to the 'mopishness' of lower classes.[8]

Hysteria is another familiar term with an extended history reflecting changing aetiological theories. Originally, symptoms were attributed to the diabolical possession of women. Later, the word related to another cause: 'wandering' wombs leading to 'suffocation' of the mother. Thomas Willis thought hysteria to be a convulsive distemper of nervous system (1667). Later still, William Cullen reclassified hysteria under a new category of ailments, the neuroses (1769) - no longer gender-specific.

The emerging language of modern psychiatry explained the origins of mental illness in physical terms. Nerves had been understood as hollow ducts distributing animal spirits to sustain sensation and motion. Albrecht von Haller argued that nerve fibres possessed an intrinsic quality of 'sensibility' while muscles exhibited 'irritability'. William Cullen viewed these as the most important qualities of individuals. These notions were popularised in literature of the period.

Samuel Richardson's *Pamela* and *Clarissa* provide examples of popular 'novels of sentiment' whose heroines exhibit high sensibility as their emotional adventures unfold. They provoked heightened feeling in their avid new readership. Writers such as Laurence Sterne and Henry Mackenzie also drew on contemporary medico-physiological notions in their writing.[9]

Origins of the asylum movement

Prior to 1700, any care was provided in the community. Later, the insane might be hospitalized, for example in converted monasteries, but early modern care was often repressive, removing the morally and socially disruptive from open society. Slowly, specialist institutions began to emerge along with a climate of greater therapeutic optimism.[10]

In London, the Bethlem Hospital was originally founded in 1247 as the Priory of the New Order of Our Lady of Bethlehem. It was largely supported by the church and charitable donations. In 1546, the Lord Mayor, the same John Gresham, successfully petitioned Henry VIII to cede administration of the hospital to the City of London. As the only state institution caring for the insane, it was a source of notoriety ('Bedlam'). Its nickname derives from its early associations with the worst excesses of early care for the insane. In the seventeenth century, many inmates were forcibly restrained and casual visitors were admitted to raise hospital income. (Think William Hogarth and *A Rake's Progress*.) Whether its open-door policy created a chamber of public horrors or was beneficial in raising public awareness remains contested.

By contrast, the new St Luke's asylum pointed to a different future. Its superintendent, William Battie (1703-76) championed clearer definitions (distinguishing 'original' and 'consequential' madness), a therapeutic environment and high quality care. With the advent of 'moral therapy' and the growth of 'asylumdom' in the nineteenth century, the Bethlem Royal Hospital was re-located to Southwark and retained a pre-eminent place among psychiatric training institutions.

Social historians such as Michel Foucault have bracketed asylums with prisons and workhouses as the state's solution to controlling deviance but there is no evidence for a 'golden age' or 'great incarceration' in the eighteenth century.[11] The main expansion took place in the following century; by 1890 over 70 mental hospitals housed 53,000 inmates. This paralleled the growth in voluntary hospitals for the sick poor. Across Europe, state legislation governed care of the insane. The UK saw Lunacy Acts passed in 1808 and 1845.

What drove this expansion? Contemporary accounts ascribed rising admissions and confinement of the mad to various inter-related factors. These included an increase in pauper lunatics rather than epidemics of mental illness. Industrialization and the rapid growth of cities generated its own pressures. Overcrowding and squalid living conditions, then as now, were associated with depression and unhealthy behaviours such as alcohol misuse. The costs of care were too burdensome for many relatives. The commercialisation of social relationships may have weakened the bonds between upper and lower social classes and the willingness of the former to support the latter.[12] In general, there was reduction in the tolerance of strange behaviours that had characterised earlier times. And then there was the growing willingness of a new breed of doctor to certify patients.

Medical developments

These too underpinned asylumdom. Madness was re-defined in terms of diseases of the brain - witness the vogue for phrenology or Francis Galton's emphasis on the role of heredity and racial degeneration. Mental illness was increasingly accepted to be chronic and incurable. The boundaries of insanity steadily widened, e.g. to those deemed 'dangerous to self or others.'

Philippe Pinel (1745-1826) was Director of the Salpêtrière Asylum in Paris where he developed a more humane approach to custody and care of the mentally ill. He also contributed to the classification of mental disorders. The knowledge base steadily expanded.

In the UK, 'moral treatment' is first associated with the Quaker's York Retreat founded in 1796. William and Samuel Tuke there championed the re-socialization of patients through work, entertainment, incentives, non-restraint. Purges, exercise, diet and regimen remained mainstays. New therapies included hydraulic chairs and hydrotherapy, e.g. douche contraptions. These 'shock tactics' were designed to expel corrupted matter or jolt out of torpor (and presaged later electro-convulsive therapy). Alternatively, tranquilizers and hypnotics - e.g. chloral hydrate, sulphonal, morphia - were intentionally sedating.

Medical imperialism was manifest in the way asylum doctors promoted their position as arbiters on mental illness. They had evolved from 'alienists' and 'mad-doctors' to psychiatrists by the end of the nineteenth century. The Medico-Psychological Association, forerunner of the Royal College of Psychiatrists, was formed in 1865. This period saw an expansion of education and training as well as a growing influence of psychiatrists in shaping new laws and the activities of the Lunacy Commission. Working alongside magistrates and Poor Law Commissioners, they controlled asylum admissions through their role in certification.

However, some historians argue that the role of medical men in the management of lunacy has been over-estimated.[13] Since the late seventeenth century, Poor Law Authorities - guardians, relieving officers, commissioners - had been overseeing the confinement of lunatics in workhouses, prisons and private madhouses. As we have seen, the late eighteenth century saw a move away from supporting lunatics through outdoor relief towards sending the poor to large institutional establishments. The nineteenth century use of public asylums extended this tradition. If anything, the 1834 Poor Law Act and subsequent Lunacy Acts expanded the role of Poor Law authorities.[14]

And what of Lizzie Skrimshire, née Finch? Her behaviours would once have been tolerated in the community. By the time of her incarceration, asylums were starting to be seen as 'warehouses for the insane'[12]: impersonal and overcrowded. Emil Kraepelin produced his classic clinical descriptions of dementia praecox and manic-depressive insanity in the 1890s. He ascribed psychoses to morbid deterioration of the brain. She may have benefited from new sedatives but the phenothiazines were almost a century away. Therapeutic pessimism prevailed but exactly why Lizzie spent most of her life in custody will never be known.

Public health policy

Periodic epidemics of smallpox, cholera and other fevers in the eighteenth century primed local government agencies for action in tackling outbreaks. For example, charities sometimes organised temporary hospitals and food distribution.[14] Continuing concern over high levels of disease in cities drove the passage of the Public Health Act in 1848. This created the General Board of Health, the first government agency responsible for health issues, and gave local authorities a range of new powers.

A major catalyst was the Sanitary Report on the Labouring Population of Great Britain, undertaken by Edwin Chadwick for the Poor Law Commissioners and published in 1842. This graphically described the appalling condition of urban slums and attributed disease to *'atmospheric impurities produced by decomposing animal and vegetable substances, by damp and filth, and overcrowded dwellings prevailing among the population in every part of the kingdom…'* Solutions included *'drainage, the removal of all refuse of habitations, streets, and roads, and the improvement of supplies of water.'*[15]

The report was an important milestone in social reform but Chadwick argued that there was no point in giving food, fuel or clothing to the sick poor: that would not prevent disease caused by environmental conditions. Commissioners were already obsessed with the costs of the Poor Laws. Given a widespread desire to limit the role of central government, the scope and impact of the first General Board of Health was limited.

Public health policy expanded to much greater effect in the 1860s and 70s. John Simon (1816-1904) is credited with a leading role in addressing sanitary reform. He recognised the role of 'germs' in disease causation and oversaw later government departments responsible for public health. His inspectors' research informed new legislation that gradually changed the relationship between central and local government.

Whereas early Public Health Acts were permissive, later Acts were compulsory. The Sanitary Act of 1866 allowed local authorities to compel property owners to install drainage, and to deal with overcrowded dwellings and smoke pollution. Local government agencies had long been active in removing refuse and other 'nuisances'[16], and in small scale sanitation projects. The 1872 Act required them to appoint Medical Officers of Health - local experts overseeing local initiatives. Many of them, especially in rural areas like Norfolk, were GPs (see above). Their local knowledge was fine grained. As the post was professionalised after the 1870s, these doctors were expected to have diplomas in public health and the proportion of GPs declined.

What was the overall health impact of these reforms? From a life expectancy of around 39 years in the 1800s, life expectancy fell to below 30 years in some rapidly growing cities such as Liverpool and Glasgow.[17] From the 1860s onwards, mortality rates declined. Historians for long attributed this to improved sanitation and living conditions. This assumption was challenged by Thomas McKeown in the 1970s as part of a wider critique of modern medicine (see chapter 7). He meticulously documented declines in the death rates from specific diseases according to their mode of transmission. The greatest declines were in deaths from respiratory diseases like tuberculosis (figure 4.4). He argued that improved resistance to such diseases was more likely to result from improved nutrition and standards of living.[18]

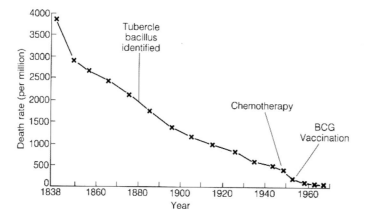

Figure 4.4 Mortality rates from TB, 1838-1970

McKeown's thesis was, in turn, debunked by Simon Szereter who noted the corresponding decline in deaths from diarrhoeal disease, transmitted through contaminated food and water. He concluded that sanitary reforms were increasingly effective as the century progressed.[19] More recent research confirms the considerable effort invested by local authorities in infectious disease control from 1850 onwards.[12] For obvious political reasons, this debate has been hotly contested but the two sides are not mutually exclusive. Overall, both public health measures <u>and</u> rising living standards are likely to have improved life expectancy in the nineteenth century.

Rising status, increasing competition
The law, church and medicine were the three old professions in Britain. The 1870s marked the end of a 'high rectory culture' in Victorian England: materially comfortable, culturally confident, parochially active.[20] Agrarian depression

impacted on rural life and halved clerical incomes. The professional classes lost ground due to the educational expansion that lessened their monopoly of culture or learning.

Recruitment to the medical profession in Victorian times was from people of modest social backgrounds in comparison with law or the church. Victorian medical men were caught in a circular dilemma. Their social origins gave them no claim to gentlemanly status and their activities were inimical to such claims. As Lady Warwick put it: *'Doctors and solicitors might be invited to garden parties though never, of course, to lunch or dinner.'*[21] This inferior status discouraged the sons of gentlemen from entering the profession and thereby raising the standing of the whole group.[22]

Beyond other factors shaping the development of GPs in the second half of the nineteenth century (education, registration, new science and laboratory medicine) was thus their yearning for the accolade of 'respectability' (footnote 3). English society between 1780 and 1880 witnessed profound changes and the emergence of class consciousness. The origin of a new class structure was associated with a struggle for ideals.[23] Beyond aristocratic, entrepreneurial and working class ideals was the non-capitalist, professional, middle class ideal. Perkin argues that the professions - church, law and medicine - were relatively immune from market forces.[22] Certainly, the consolidation of the GP's role as family doctor over this period brought greater financial security.

Within the profession much was made of differences between the ranks of GPs. These concerned matters of professional etiquette and traditions of practice - for example, whether prescribing and dispensing, scale of fees charged, the possession of prestigious degrees. After all, competition with physicians was affected by two conflicting considerations: the need to attract patients in order to survive and the need to follow codes of behaviour that aped physicians of supposedly higher status.

The 1858 Medical Act had given no direct protection from alternative practitioners. It was now a summary offence (liable for a £20 fine) to pretend registration while assuming the title 'Dr', without registrable qualifications, went unpunished. This caused widespread resentment. The public remained poorly protected. The GMC, where GPs were anyway poorly represented, responded mutely. Neither did the BMA see fit to initiate prosecutions. Predictably, the interests of specialists had been better served through the GMC's reforms of medical education. Only hostility to homoeopaths continued unabated after 1858 with the BMA excluding them from membership. They were marginalised through ostracism and defamation. It was,

Footnote 3. These insecurities are manifest today in debates over whether GPs should really style themselves as 'GP consultants' - to improve morale and encourage recruitment. Allsop et al argue that the title better reflects the specialised and supervisory role of today's GPs at the head of multi-disciplinary teams.[24]

however, occasionally difficult to draw a line between the qualified and unqualified because of the acceptance by doctors of ideas first promulgated by the unqualified. Pragmatic GPs sometimes employed their rivals' remedies themselves, much as a few may be dually qualified as acupuncturists or homoeopaths today.

Further legislation in 1875 failed to help doctors against competitors in a notably free medical market as the ratio of population to doctor slumped. Self-medication was widespread and groceries and co-operatives purveyed proprietary medicines. Chemists were perceived to be the doctors' principal rivals. They offered over-the-counter prescriptions, consultations, home visits and even minor surgery.

A new breed of specialist also threatened the economic viability of general practice. Until late Victorian times, consultants were still generalists but scientific advance changed that. Rather as in the US today, middle class patients could be side-tracked away from the family's practitioner to specialist out-patients clinics in hospitals. It was only the evolving practice of GP referral to specialists that helped establish a symbiotic relationship between them.

Training awaited

By the middle of the nineteenth century, medical training was based on a system of apprenticeships, pupillage and unqualified assistantships, succeeded by a period of 'walking the wards' in hospital. Masters accepted £100 to £200 to instruct their apprentices, though these costs might be offset in return for general household duties. For example, Michael Beverley was indentured to Dr W B Francis of Norwich and put to work making oils, compounding medicines, keeping the surgery in good order and visiting patients in a slum area of the city. He went on to be a dresser at the Norfolk and Norwich Hospital and ultimately held a succession of posts there in tandem with local general practice over 60 years.[25]

There was a steady decline in apprenticeships over the nineteenth century before they were supposedly abolished by the GMC in 1892. Unqualified assistantships might give good grounding and shorten training requirements but were outlawed by the BMA in 1894. In the twentieth century, assistantship post-qualification with one or two *locum tenens* provided the same benefits. In both cases, practical training for the GP took place outside medical school.

The rising status of London medical schools was followed by the expansion of schools in the provinces. Correspondingly, European training centres sharply declined in popularity. The focus of hospital training was the 'firm' which consisted of two physicians or surgeons, two house officers and a number of students acting as clerks - 'waiting, listening, learning, helping.'[26] Consultants made typically operatic ward appearances with nurses as handmaidens and students as chorus. However, increasing specialisation continued to thwart many students' need to get the broad experience needed for general practice.

From GP to Family Doctor

In the first half of the nineteenth century, GPs may have struggled individually - complaining about the expense of education, difficulties of establishing a practice, poverty, competition from irregulars, etc - but the profession had become firmly established by around 1850 (see chapter 3). GPs came to dominate the practice of medicine as their rise led to a decline in demand for physicians other than as the more genteel attendants of the aristocracy. Indeed, the provincial GP, like JTS, enjoyed a virtual monopoly of the local health economy. His nearest consultant colleagues were in Norwich.

The Royal College of Physicians remained reactionary, helping to ensure that medicine reached a nadir in the universities. This was illustrated in nineteenth century fiction in the contrast between the adulation of GPs as the family doctor and the unsympathetic view of physicians. Generally, one assumes the novelist to be writing from experience and to reflect attitudes of the time. Eliot's Lydgate and Trollope's Thorne are perceptive, well-informed and sympathetic portraits (though they were provincial physicians as much as GPs). By contrast Trollope's Sir Omicron Pie and Dickens' Parker Peps are notable largely for their social connections (footnote 4).

Loudon has described in detail the fictional stereotype of the early family doctor.[27] He was often poor, shabby and old-fashioned, but always accessible and enjoying the confidence of his patients (footnote 5). A users' guide indeed intoned: *'Let not your doctor be too useful...and avoid the man whose dress and demeanour indicate puppyism...Be not averse to him if he is slovenly in apparel.'*[28]

The ideal of family doctor was thus enormously powerful in shaping public and professional perceptions of nineteenth century medical practice. It provided GPs with a new corporate identity - as neither business-like apothecaries or impassive physicians. In *Loved at Last,* the GP Mr Gregory *'bore with noble courage and patient bearing...broken rest... long rides...exercising a skill and knowledge acquired by years of study and acute observation.'*[29] He was expected to sit patiently at the bedside through long hours and was able to deal with any emergency at any time of day or night.

Footnotes 4. The portrait of Dr Parker Peps in *Dombey & Son* is particularly withering. Sadly, the family doctor is simperingly obsequious in the face of Peps' society name-dropping and obfuscation.

5. Mr Mellidew, in *Paid in Full*, *'wore a cheap heavy hat which was brown from many showers and always carried a stethoscope. He enclosed his feet in clumsy half-wellingtons which were patched...There was generally a button missing from his waistcoat...though a youngish man, he prescribed very much the same remedies which his late employer had been in the habit of prescribing.'*[30]

One practitioner wrote in 1831 of having *'often to soothe and satisfy where no disease exists'* and to advise *'on phenomena little subject to medical treatment.'*[31] The role of the family doctor was increasingly valued for combining a broad clinical approach and a pastoral role but, at its core, was continuity of care. The new GPs' greatest asset was their intimate knowledge of *'the hereditary constitutions, habits and temperaments of their patients.'*[32]

The family doctor had become the secular descendant of the priest as confidant in the sick room, laying on hands, dispensing advice, magical potions - and sick notes.[33] Therapeutic activism augmented the patient's self-belief, promoted confidence and aided the healing process.[34] Fatalism and trust in the Almighty did the same.

Conclusion
The history of psychiatry is marked by serial revolutions: moral management in the eighteenth century linked to the rise of the asylum, the psychoanalytical revolution associated with Freud and latter-day pharmacological advances associated with new psychotropic drugs and deinstitutionalization. All these were to have a major bearing on general practice. (There have been few breakthroughs in the treatment of serious mental illness in the more recent past.)

Little wonder that the GP's stock rose over this period - or that patients feared his demise. The recurrent concern that the family doctor was becoming a thing of the past can be traced back to the 1850s.[35] That this myth recurs at regular intervals is a tribute to its strength and longevity rather than reliable evidence of its decline.[36] Significantly, this professional self-image provided foundations for the later expression of the GP's role, beyond the bio-medical, as 'psycho-social' (see chapter 7).

The role was and remains a demanding one. Poverty, competition, the costs of education and establishing a practice are recurrent concerns for GPs across much of this narrative. Less visible but more corrosive are the emotional and spiritual challenges of the work - the relentless grind of never-ending and unmeetable demands, the exhausting affront of your patients' poverty, hopelessness in the face of incurable illness, bereavement and loss. Professional isolation was even more extreme in JTS's time. He had few tools at his disposal. He would have lost patients young and old to infections on a regular basis.

Mental illness, and what we nowadays call 'stress', have always been common among doctors. Marital disharmony and divorce are the accompaniments. Their suicide rates are among the highest of all professions, facilitated by readier availability of the means (footnote 6). And does this calling not also attract the vulnerable - 'wounded healers' - who imagine they can defy nature's impossible odds? My great great grandfather was in many ways the doughtiest of my forebears. I often ponder the combination of factors that drove him to his lonely death.

Footnote 6. Doctors most commonly take their own lives by poisoning themselves, often with drugs taken from the workplace (or more slowly, using alcohol). The exposure that anaesthetists have to drugs is thought to explain their particularly high risks of drug addiction and suicide.[37]

Chapter Five – State intent
(1890-1925)

'Great things are not done by impulse,
but by a series of small things brought together.'
George Eliot

The fifth generation

My great grandfather was born on the 4th November, 1868. The son of a farmer from Gimingham (Stephen Gillam), Joseph Beckett Gillam was the first of his family to go into medicine. Education was important to his father, and he went with his older brother to St Leonard's School in Cromer before going on to the Paston Grammar School in North Walsham. That he made a promising start is confirmed by a certificate awarded to him at Christmas in 1882 - *'for diligence, good progress and good conduct'* (footnote 1).

His brother, another Stephen, eventually took on the family farm of 350 acres while Joseph proceeded to Cavendish House, Cambridge. This was a non-Collegiate hall where he matriculated in 1885, taking the Natural Sciences Tripos and graduating BA in 1888. He then migrated to Downing College, where after training at St Thomas's Hospital he qualified MB,BChir in 1892. From here he promptly joined John Truscott Skrimshire as an assistant.

His public appointments were to include being Medical Officer of Health: for Erpingham District. for the Children's Sanatorium and for Gresham's School. He threw himself into the life of the community and fell in love with his boss's daughter. Dorothy was lively, attractive and always known as 'Scrumptious Dolly'. He had competition but thankfully his feelings were reciprocated. Her knowledge of the family business must have made her an ideal mate. When they married in 1901, he had been a partner in the practice for three years.

Joseph was the first doctor since Fenwick Skrimshire to demonstrate a more academic interest in his craft, reflecting the rise in research and laboratory medicine. He published in the BMJ: on a 'Case of Ovarian Cyst, Repeated tapping'[1] and on 'Cases of Diphtheria treated with anti-toxin'[2] in a nearby village. The former is a reminder that 'minor surgery' was a core constituent of the GP's daily round (though draining an ovarian cyst using a trocar and cannula under

Footnote 1. My grandfather described his father as another 'egghead' for which there is early evidence. The Thetford and Walton Times for Saturday, 22nd March, 1884 reported on the Paston Grammar School: *'At a meeting held at the school on Wednesday, the Hon Harbord Harbord in the chair, it was resolved that the prizes given by Her Imperial Highness the Duchess of Edinburgh be awarded to J B Gillam (son of Mr S Gillam, Wickmere), he having obtained in the late Cambridge Local Examinations a first class honours, together with a distinction in Latin and French.'*

general anaesthetic with chloroform would hardly nowadays be considered minor). In a rural area like north Norfolk, surgery performed in the home was still the norm.

Diphtheria in those days frequently killed young people. Early in 1905, he noted the feared but pathognomonic membrane coating the throat of a young Gresham's pupil. He promptly evacuated the whole of the Old School House to Sheringham. He was praised for averting a larger outbreak.[3]

AL. SATURDAY. SEPTEMBER 7. 1935

This photograph of Holt United F.C., 1893-4, was taken on the occasion of the first Junior Cup Tie ever played at Holt, and is produced by the kindness of Mr. H. A. Vince, now living at Holt. In that first match Holt defeated Thetford 5-0. The players are (standing)—Walter Palmer (now in America), and brother of H. H. Palmer (linesman), H. Carter Cooper, Charles Pells (now living at Holt), W. Gardner, A. Mansfield, J. Kitterincham (secretary). Sitting—L. Hughes, Horace A. Vince, Dr. J. B. Gillam, K. Groves (now of Briston), Jim Holbrook (now living at Melton Constable). In front—W. G. Haywood, W. Cousins.

Figure 5.1 JBG, seated third from left

He was a sportsman, something which no doubt endeared him to other members of the clan. He played football for the Holt Owls (figure 5.1) and, on the Saturday before his wedding, he captained a cricket team which defeated Gresham's School by an innings and 239 runs. Admittedly, he was able to call on his future brother-in-law, Jack Skrimshire, a distinguished county player.

His wedding to my great grandmother, the ever-Scrumptious Dolly, was reported in detail in the Norwich Mercury. Conducted by the Rev F.C. Finch, Lizzie's uncle, it was *'a very pretty wedding…if the drawback was the state of the weather which was of a most tempestuous nature, lightning and thunder being incessant, with a heavy downpour of rain.'* About 150 guests attended and a detailed list of their presents was printed. Their names indicate the affection and respect in which the family was by now held, including the 'cream' of local society - Sir Alfred Jodrell, various Cozens-Hardys and Miss Lee Warner, many local tradesmen whose names are still familiar, as well as Mr and Miss Howson, Mr J R Eccles, and numerous Gresham's staff. The best man, oddly, was seven years younger than Joseph, one Grote Stirling. How they met is not known but he was later to become a cabinet minister in the Canadian Government.

After a honeymoon voyage in Norway, recorded in a diary kept by Dolly, the happy couple settled in Shrublands, a pleasant house at the other end of Holt, which remained in the family until 1949. Here their union was quickly blessed by the arrival of two boys, John Francis Edward in 1903, and Geoffrey Gerard in 1905. Two daughters followed, Margery Dorothea in 1907 and Josephine Mary in 1910.

Joseph's life was full. He took a keen interest in all that concerned the welfare of the town. A staunch Conservative, he was treasurer of the Holt Association. He was a committed churchman and church warden (1907-8), saying daily prayers with his family at Shrublands. He was a manager of the Church School, and had a seat on the Parish Council and Sanitary Committee.

He had time to relax too. He was a skilful exponent of bowls, and enjoyed an evening game of chess with Geoffrey Shaw, the Director of Music at Gresham's after whom he named his son (footnote 2). Photographs show a dapper, genial pipe-smoking man with an air of some self-satisfaction (figure 5.2).

'Barely 20 years' service'

Figure 5.2 Joseph Gillam, 1909

A cloud nevertheless hung over the family in the form of his father-in-law's health. In 1905, John Truscott suffered a severe bout of depression which necessitated his retirement. By this time his son, Jack, had joined the practice. It continued to expand, in particular towards Melton Constable. There was as yet no room for JTS's second son, Harry, to join the Skrimshire and Gillam practice.

A decade which had started with such hope and happiness was to end abruptly when Joseph contracted pneumonia from one of his patients. In those days before antibiotics, decline could be swift. Medicine was a dangerous occupation as, for different reasons, it still is. He died on February 2nd 1911, aged just 42. The reaction of local people who knew him was well expressed in tributes which appeared in various places, and in two church services which followed.

Footnote 2. Geoffrey Shaw's son, Sebastian (1905-1994), was a sometime director, novelist, playwright and poet. He was most acclaimed as an actor, for many years a mainstay of the Royal Shakespeare Company. He was my father's godfather and we used to visit him behind the scenes at Stratford. He also appeared in *Return of the Jedi*!

The Eastern Daily Press quoted '*From One Who Knew Him Well:*
A sorrow, deep and still, has fallen on Holt in the passing of Dr J B Gillam. It could be felt in the hush that rested on the town on Thursday and afterwards. The feeling rapidly spread to all the villages around, and in some cases further afield. Men of all ranks, from the professional man to the labour-lad, seemed to feel the absence of a personality. Women literally wept in their cottages, and strong men felt themselves breaking down. And then, with the recoil, there welled forth a stream of sympathy converging towards his family, especially to his stricken widow and children, and to him whose shoulders already bear more than their white weight of sorrow. 'Tis well that they should know the affection of the countryside; it might alleviate their sorrow. And the secret of this country doctor's hold on our esteem, with barely twenty years' service, was that the warmth of his heart was as strong, broad and frank as the intelligence of his head, and both were of an order above the average.'

An obituary in The Gresham that spring continued in the same vein: '*'He went about doing good.' One simple phrase and you have the life of Joseph Beckett Gillam spread out before you. Is there a more noble epitaph? He had an unfailing kindness and courtesy, a rigid honesty of purpose, an exceptional clarity of intellect, a shrewd knowledge of men, and a rare sense of humour; these separate qualities of character were welded together into an harmonious whole with a firmness of purpose that is only possessed by an upright man.*
It was my privilege to have him for a close friend; but what he did for me and mine he did for others. All kinds and classes of men mourn for him as an intimate friend, with a grateful remembrance of the countless benefits and kindnesses he bestowed on them; all who met him felt they gained good in doing so. His unselfish career was the finest self-sacrifice.
All mankind should triumph in an individual life so splendidly lived. Sorrow there must be, for the loss is very great; to Gresham's School it is well-nigh irreparable. But let us ever remember to praise God with thankful hearts for the life of this great gentleman.'

He was buried at Gimingham, while simultaneously a memorial service was held at Holt. All the boys at the school lined the road as his hearse passed, as a mark of respect for their school doctor. The Rev F Finch was among the four clergy to conduct the choral service. Joseph's old friend, Geoffrey Shaw, who had now left the school, came up from London to conduct the choir. St Andrew's had '*very seldom been so crowded. Not only from Holt but from all around friends had assembled to pay a tribute of respect to the deceased. Among the large congregation were Sir Alfred and Lady Jane Jodrell, Mr Sydney Cozens-Hardy, Mr Ferneley Cozens-Hardy…and many other well-known Holt families and over one hundred boys from Gresham's School. There were over ninety wreaths, in a rich profusion of floral tributes.'*

An impressive avenue of limes leads up to the church of St Andrew's (figure 5.3). The Great Fire destroyed its steeple but the fourteenth century tower yet presents a pleasing aspect. Older features include a fine Norman font and some beautiful stained-glass windows. As worshippers and wardens, my family have passed many hours in this place. Today, on the wall of the North aisle a simple brass plaque reads:

In memory of
Joseph Beckett Gillam BA MB BC Cantab
Born Nov 4th 1868   Died Feb 2nd 1911
'What I do thou knowest not now
But thou shalt know hereafter'   John XIII 7
This tablet was placed here by his friends.

Figure 5.3 St Andrew's, Holt

What Joseph did not know was that his two sons, John and Geoffrey, then aged 8 and 6 respectively, two grandsons and a great grandson would follow in his medical footsteps. In the meantime, his brothers-in-law were to continue running the family business.

Jack Skrimshire

John Fenwick (Jack) started at Gresham's with his younger brother in 1882, and immediately began to distinguish himself on the sports field. He was a fine cricketer involved in the local Junior League. Happily, Jack was also a surprisingly industrious pupil. His father appears to have encouraged the study of basic science, which was not on the school curriculum. A little botany book still survives inscribed with his name - 'Flowers, Fruits and Leaves', by Sir John Lubbock FRS. Though its title suggests dainty reading for a polite Victorian lady, it contains Lubbock's scientific lectures in print. He was a distinguished scientist, a friend of Charles Darwin, and the content of the lectures provided for the requirements of preliminary medical studies.

In 1891, at the end of a 'gap' year after leaving school, Jack starred in Cromer's cup winning team. Other plans were afoot. Scarcely legible letters were exchanged between John Truscott and Mr Ward, who was to be his tutor. Following a letter of recommendation from Edward Brumell, late Fellow and briefly President of the same college, he started at St John's, Cambridge, that October (figure 5.4).

Figure 5.4 Jack Skrimshire, 1892

The sporting achievements of my ancestors are rather the stuff of caricature. Such prowess is commonplace among medical students, presumably as a consequence of educational advantage. Perhaps too the natural competitiveness of medical students combined with newly encountered stressors favours such outlets. Family legend has it that Jack extended his time at Cambridge in pursuit of a Blue. It is likely that cricketing distractions contributed to his downfall at 2nd MB (his papers were described bluntly by his tutor as *'very bad'*), but he appears to have preferred turning out for the County and inter-College matches (figure 5.5). Any listing of his triumphs conjures up images of drowsy summer afternoons, droning flies, the aroma of linseed oil and the unmistakeable thwack of leather on willow.

He continued to play in the North Norfolk Senior Cup League, helping Gunton to win it in 1894 with the highest score in the match. In 1895 he scored more runs for Norfolk (then a first class county) than any other player, with 332 runs from eleven innings, the highest score being 83. He was also described as a *'more than useful exchange bowler'*. Against Worcestershire in 1896 he took the last four wickets for 15 runs, and against Hertfordshire, the last three for 10.

Meanwhile, he was a stalwart of St John's Long Vac team. Staying up for extra lectures, that year he averaged 35.5 in nine innings - his highest scores being 108 against Trinity and 93 against Pembroke. He was elected to the College's prestigious Eagles Club. He sits, confident and debonair in his boater, in a group photograph of Officers (figure 5.6). Founded in 1870, the Eagles was a precursor by two years of the Hawks, and open to Blues and holders of College colours. Both clubs are still in existence.

In December 1896, he passed Part II of the third year's exams for Medical and Surgical Degrees, and finally qualified BC Cantab (as described on his tombstone)

in 1900. He was able to join his father's practice straight away by opening a surgery in Melton Constable, a growing village on account of the railway. 'Skrimshire and Gillam, Physicians and Surgeons' put up their plate on a house on the Briston Road, and Jack took lodgings in the village.

Figure 5.5 St John's 1ˢᵗ Eleven, Jack (jacketed)

Another practice, 'Kennington and Beveridge', was also operating on the Briston Road. James S Beveridge, FRCS, MRCP Edin, was well qualified for a country GP but, as Jack knew, he was approaching retirement. By 1904 Jack was Medical Officer and Public Vaccinator of the Melton Constable District of the Walsingham Union. By 1913 he was Medical Officer also to the Erpingham Union, to Gresham's School and to the Children's Sanatorium, High Kelling - commitments that rivalled those of his brother-in-law, Joseph.

Like Joseph, he was charismatic. His was a personality which attracted a wide range of people. More sociable than Harry, he was a kind and sympathetic man. In a long letter to JTS, he described his cruise to West Africa in 1909. He was recuperating from surgery for the condition that would cut short his life. He did not suffer from the seasickness afflicting his fellow passengers. *'It is a thousand pities some people are so upset….it utterly spoils their enjoyment of the most beautiful days.'* His readiness to enjoy life's simpler pleasures comes out in this 'travelogue', describing on-board games, charades, and other entertainments. At the time of their father's suicide, he wrote to his brother from London where he was recovering from his second operation:

> *'My dear Harry,*
>
> *This is a terribly sad business and one hardly knows what to say about it. We shall miss the poor old Governor, as Ernest would say, 'above a bit', and it is particularly sad that he should have gone in the way he did. I very much wish I could have been at home to take my share in it all. Still, even this is better than his living to suffer long in the way we know he did at times. I don't think he ever recovered from his attack of five years ago. Goodbye old chap for the present,*
>
> *With love to all,*
> *Your loving brother, Jack.'*

Sadly, Jack too was to suffer an early death following a third operation for bladder cancer, on November 11th, 1919. Harry was at his bedside. Unlike other members of his family, he was seldom solemn as tributes testified. *'(He was) a brilliant conversationalist and delightful companion ...of a singularly generous and loving*

Figure 5.6 Eagles officers, 1895: Jack seated 2nd from left disposition - never courting popularity and unostentatious to a degree...a genuine sportsman.' 'He was a universal favourite, his cheery presence and athletic prowess endearing him to everyone...On every cricket field and bowling green he was a familiar figure, and for a team of boys there was no more popular captain.' 'He was an ideal captain but, greatly as he loved the game and all sports, he did not live for them; he lived for men and in their hearts he will always live.'

Such a man in those days merited another spectacular funeral. From the EDP: *'In a wonderful manifestation of public sorrow, Melton Constable had never before seen such a tribute to one of its residents. The church, not large enough to accommodate all, saw a truly catholic gathering of all creeds and parties and social positions. Gresham's masters attended in cap and gown, Oddfellows in their regalia, the Church Lads' Brigade formed a guard of honour between the church and the graveside. Wreaths included those from the Parish Council, from the Melton Constable Football, Cricket and Bowls Clubs, from the District Choral Society as well as the Burgh Choir; from the Ambulance Corps and the Railway Institute Committee. Present at the graveside, amongst well over a hundred mourners, were Lord Hastings, Lord Cozens-Hardy, Rose and Ellen, and his old nurse, Elizabeth.'* A send-off one fancies he would have enjoyed.

Harry Skrimshire
Henry Finch (Harry) was financially less fortunate than his older brother. He had to bide his time and waited three years after school to go up to Cambridge. He took affirmative action in the meantime, enrolling (on the advice of his uncle Fred at Morpeth) as a student-teacher at the Newcastle School of Science and Art.

His Cambridge days were of great importance to Harry. *'The History of the Jesus College Boat Club'* was a bedside book and, while not quite in Jack's league as a cricketer, in his first year he did score 26 runs for the college 1st team against Caius. He played once for Norfolk, with Jack, in 1896 but rowing was his first love. He was twice in the winning boat in the Fixed-Seat Trial Eights; in 1896 and 1898 he made the Jesus 1st Boat as family photos attest.

Harry was always the more academically ambitious of the brothers (figure 5.7). Of a dozen handsome leather-bound books that adorn the shelves of the Hill House library, only three are inscribed as school prizes for Jack. After his time at the Newcastle School of Science, he was sufficiently confident to take Part I of his MB in his first year. Frustrated by a 3rd, he repeated the exam in the summer. This time, he achieved a 1st, which he gained again in Parts II and III.

He chose Charing Cross Hospital for his medical training and he clearly gained the respect of his teachers. A number of letters survive to his father from his time as a student at the turn of the century. If he is somewhat preoccupied by the need for funds, they are newsy and treat often of topical events.

The letters describe his teachers (*'a very observant old chap, and misses very few things in his cases'*), as well as details of his training. On a visit to the Bethlem Hospital ('Bedlam'), he encountered *a Cambridge undergrad who believed he was Emperor of Austria – and used the Royal person 'We' etc. He regarded Bedlam as a palace, where royal visitors to the English court were lodged... Another man said he was inspired and whereas before he could only speak three languages he now spoke 967 and all 'eloquently'. We also saw the*

Figure 5.7 Harry Skrimshire, 1894

well-known character of the place - an old inmate - who believes she is Queen Anne...'

Politics was another shared interest. *'Did you read Joe Chamberlain's recent speech in the House on the war and settlement in S Africa?...Old Joe seems to have been in great form* (footnote 3). Many letters feature requests for support. *'I shall be glad if you can send me £6. I owe the landlady £2 13sh and also my sub to the Students' Club at Charing Cross which is 30/-.'*

His first appointment in 1902, backed by warm testimonials from senior staff, was as Resident Medical Officer at St Mary's Hospital, Plaistow, for Women and Children. That his work justified their confidence is shown by letters supporting his application for his next post in 1903, as House Physician at the Wolverhampton General Hospital. Cuthbert Lockyer, Senior Physician to Outpatients *'considered any general hospital would be fortunate in securing the services of so well qualified a young surgeon....an agreeable colleague, loyal to his seniors, helpful to his juniors, and endowed with a good address, gentle manners, and a kindly bearing to the patients in his care.'*

By 1905 he was assistant in an upmarket practice at Ascot - to W Netterville Barron, Surgeon to the Household of T.R.H. Prince and Princess Christian. The practice could afford *'an indoor assistant and he did practically all the midwifery work, and did it very well, was careful and conscientious (with) a sound knowledge of medicine and surgery.'*

Harry's early career was necessarily fragmented as there was insufficient work in the family practice after his brother-in-law-to-be Joseph became a partner in 1898. He returned to Holt intermittently, for example at the time of his father's breakdown in 1906, and in 1908, when Jack had the first of his operations. He was briefly at Moreton-in-Marsh in 1910-11 but had returned the following year to manage the Melton Constable surgery. Little did the brothers know how soon they would be managing affairs on their own. They were to work well together in the partnership through the years of the Great War until Jack's own untimely death.

Life at Hill House was austere in the 1920s. Harry, always modest in his own desires, thought it too extravagant to have electricity and the house was candle-lit. (The first small circuit was only installed by his nephew, Geoffrey, in 1950.) He did, however, find the money to buy a new car for the practice in 1926. According to the local garage Elsden's account, he paid £125, which included £4 for delivery from Northampton and £1 for charging the battery. Harry was frugal but not mean, as evidenced in his response to various 'begging letters' from impecunious relatives.

Footnote 3. Joe Chamberlain (1836-1914) was a Liberal MP from a business background with radical views on bettering schools and local government intervention to improve urban living conditions. He was also an ardent imperialist and in this particular speech was arguing for military intervention in the Transvaal to protect British mining interests. The Second Anglo-Boer War (1899-1902) proved in many respects unedifying for the victor.

His annual holiday was a fortnight at Brancaster to play golf on the Links; and he was always ready for a game of tennis. *'As the years went by and he became less agile, he stood at the net and remained a formidable opponent.'* In the twenties he was one of a group who played bowls at the Acacias (The Lawns hotel today), followed by a social glass of whisky.

Figure 5.8 Dr Harry, 1948

On his death in 1953, an article appeared in the EDP - 'Dr Harry' of Holt; an Appreciation. *'He never appeared to be in a hurry, or overburdened with many matters,'* the writer commented. *'He was not an ambitious man.'* His approach to the problems of his day was unflustered, honed by having had to fend for himself from early in his career (figure 5.8). At some stage in his life he developed an interest in the Stock Exchange. Some dishevelled scrap books survive containing cuttings he had kept from financial journals, and a number of bank receipts for interest on investments. This may explain his generosity to his poorer patients, for *'he had become 'Dr Harry' to many people for whom he had risen at midnight and from whom he had never taken a penny.'*

I once encountered an elderly lady sitting by the stream on the Spout Hills gazing up at the wall that bounds Hill House. She had left Holt as a child but did I know that her doctor had once lived there? She remembered him sitting up with her all through the night as she struggled to fight off scarlet fever. As another one recalled: *'None of his patients ever doubted the efficacy of a bottle of medicine off Dr Harry, however nasty it might be.'* A suitable epitaph for a practitioner working through the hard times of the Depression.

Mr R.C. Hunt represented the Letheringsett Bowls Club at this funeral and Mr G.H.C. Byford, the Holt Cricket Club. The Rev C.L.S. Linnell, Rector of Letheringsett gave the address: *'There must be hundreds of people in the town of Holt and in the surrounding countryside to whom Dr Skrimshire was a true friend; a family doctor, a doctor of the old school. One who was always ready to help his patients and did not spare himself in all the many years of his practice in this place…He savoured the delights of the countryside which he seldom left and he had many interests and an eye for its beauty…The view from his window at Hill House, across the garden to Spout Common, was always sweet to him. Flowers, too, were a great delight, especially his bushes of Daphne Mezeron blooming in early spring. They were in flower when he died.'*

Characteristically and with little thought for commercial concerns, when he had had enough and wanted to retire, he simply told his patients to go across the road to *'that other fellow'* (footnote 4). So the fourth of the Holt line of Skrimshire doctors slipped quietly from the scene, 106 years after his grandfather's arrival. A doctor's residence and surgery since the eighteenth century, Hill House reverted to being a family home.

Amy Skrimshire
Described as a music teacher in 1901, Amy was the last of the Skrimshire line. She had co-hosted Dorothy and Joseph's wedding reception with her father, John Truscott, in 1903. Her great misfortune was to go blind in her mid-fifties, but she was a gallant lady. She attended the Chorleywood College for the Blind where she mastered braille. Reading was her great pleasure. She was a lifelong Sunday School teacher and gave support to her brother where she could in running the practice, the source of both their livelihoods.

During the second war, Hill House was a designated collection point for emergency rations. Harry and his sister took in evacuees. Among the first to arrive were Les Allchin and his sisters, June and Eileen. The girls were sent to the Skrimshires while Les went to the Grands in Cross Street. He would recall being allowed to visit his sisters on Saturday afternoons and shared fond memories of their 'kindly' hosts. Les would read to Amy. She would take Les and his sisters out into the garden and point with unerring accuracy with her stick to places beyond Holt like Melton Constable and Cley.

A contemporary remembered her on a visit to Hill House for Sunday afternoon tea. Amy entertained them with rather shaky playing on her recorder, singing in a thin, warbling treble. She had been born with a club foot but, according to a nephew, *'this did not hold her back. Well into her sixties she was a familiar figure on the arm of a Miss Ransom, struggling gamely along the streets of the town.'* Always referred to in the family as BAA (Blind Aunt Amy), she is still remembered affectionately seventy years after her death. Whenever a door opens apparently unaided or there is a creak on the attic stairs, the ghost of BAA is known to be approaching.

Footnote 4. For years, his closest rival was the universally admired Bob Hales who practised on the other side of the Norwich Road. They were longstanding family friends and his daughter, Jane, was a notable local historian.

The advent of state health services

Major developments in the public funding of health care were to take place over Harry's lifetime. Across Europe in the second half of the nineteenth century, national governments began to realize the economic importance of health and welfare for the population at large. A combination of self-interest and an Enlightenment belief in progress and human betterment underpinned these states' increasing intrusion into private spheres.

Simultaneously, the rise of capitalism, industrialization and wealth creation allowed for an expansion of welfare and the provision of 'social medicine' - a range of policies to improve living conditions, health education and new medical services. Established systems of relief and voluntary organisations, such as charities and churches, could no longer meet the demand for support, especially in urban areas. More collectivist solutions were needed.

The first health insurance scheme was set up in Germany in 1883. The Bismarckian model of state insurance was adapted across much of Europe extending access to health care (at least to working families). It covered the poorest workers with contributions from employer and state. Such schemes would over time change the relationship between states and the populations they supported.

In the UK, the Liberal Government of Herbert Asquith was elected in 1904 (footnote 5). It initiated the birth of our modern welfare state through educational reforms, the introduction of old age pensions and, crucially, the National Health Insurance (NHI) Act of 1911.[4] David Lloyd George garnered much of the credit with his 'People's Budget' of 1909 (footnote 6). These reforms had multiple causes including heightened awareness of the causes and consequences of poverty. These had been graphically demonstrated by the poor physical state of working class recruits for the Second Boer War. The 1904 Interdepartmental Committee on Physical Deterioration declared that the vigour of the imperial state depended on the physical health of the citizen (footnote 7).[5] The creation of health insurance followed German precedents and its influence on general practice was profound.

Footnotes 5. Asquith was a bold reformer but proved weak as wartime leader. Lloyd George replaced him as PM in 1916. They became bitter enemies, heading separate factions of the Liberal party. They re-united in 1923 to support the first Labour government of Ramsey MacDonald, only hastening their own party's decline.

6. Lloyd George knew my great-great-uncle (on my paternal grandmother's side). Sir Joseph Davies KBE (1866-1954) was Liberal MP for Crewe and worked in his parliamentary secretariat. Uncle Joe was a statistician with a particular knowledge of transport. Half a dozen other experts in different fields had huts built for them in the garden behind 10, Downing Street. This early forerunner of the No 10 Policy Unit was nicknamed 'The Garden Suburb'. He lost his seat in the election of 1922 (despite a pact with local Tories) by which time the divided Liberal Party was in parliamentary freefall. Building on their successes in 1918, the Labour Party won 142 seats.

The National Health Insurance Act of 1911 established a system of free health care financed by tripartite payment from those in employment, from employers and the state. Thenceforth, general practice covered workers but not their wives and families, whose demands were curtailed by the need to pay fees for service. Access to GP care steadily widened but that care was of variable quality. This drove a rapid increase in the numbers of GPs, out-patients seen and dispensaries providing basic care. Women and children remained poorly served despite more nursing provision. These reforms nevertheless impacted positively on the financial viability of the Holt practice.

Half of the population were on the 'panel' of insurance doctors by the onset of World War II but dependent wives and children were still excluded. The British insurance scheme was therefore less socially inclusive than in pioneering Germany. The politics of poverty determined that friendly societies played a central role as approved societies, given their administrative expertise and experience of dealing with malingerers. This minimized public bureaucratic involvement as an interim stage towards the fully-fledged welfare state of the 1940s.

Inevitably, there was a battle over the NHI Bill. Many doctors saw it as an attack on medical independence, reducing patients' choice of doctor.[4] Incomes in the run up to the introduction of health insurance were often small due to overcrowding and the activities of provident dispensaries.[6] Organized patient power was driving capitation fees down to three or four shillings/head. Reform of the poor laws and competition from alternative practitioners deepened insecurity. The BMA therefore engaged in a 'battle of the clubs' to raise payments given by friendly societies and medical aid societies through collective action.

Conflict with the Chancellor was averted when, following the Plender Report, he bought off doctors' opposition. Overall, GPs gave NHI a cautiously favourable welcome therefore as a lifeline. Not for the last time, the BMA's intransigence was out of kilter with feelings in the profession who recognised its generous terms. They preferred the less obtrusive control of local medical committees in administering NHI benefits to the perpetuation of a system that subordinated doctors to lay control under the hated friendly societies. In particular, there was strong support from younger doctors and those starting out. Critics came from an older generation and those disenchanted with third-party bureaucracy, NHI rules and regulations. (Horror of horrors: prescriptions had henceforth to be signed rather than rubber-stamped.)

Footnote 7. Poor *'national physique'* was ascribed, in part, to a diet of white bread, cheap cooking and tea. *'Adequate'* school meals and regular check-ups were recommended. It has taken the Covid-19 pandemic to prompt comparable interest in the nation's nutrition though, as the 1904 Committee noted, *'popular taste…may take generations of educative influence to correct.'*[5]

The future work of the GP was described in idealistic terms by Lord Dawson in his report of 1920, which laid out the structure a new health service might take.[7] The GP should be accessible, attend patients at home or in the surgery, carry out treatment within his competence and obtain specialist help when it was needed. He would attend in childbirth and advise on how to prevent disease and improve the conditions of life among his patients. He should play a part in antenatal supervision, child welfare, physical culture, venereal disease and industrial medicine. Dawson envisaged that nursing should be available alongside doctors in the primary health centres. This rosy picture contrasted starkly with accounts of life in practice.

Burden of disease
What conditions was my great grandfather encountering in late Victorian times and how was he dealing with them? Childhood infections and respiratory diseases were the most commonplace threat to life, as he was so poignantly to demonstrate. Diphtheria was endemic and every sore throat was viewed with suspicion. Antiserum to the diphtheria toxin provided one of the few curative treatments available; if given within 24 hours of onset, the results were excellent. Otherwise, mortality rates were about 20 per cent. Patients with diphtheria or scarlet fever were taken away in a yellow fever van to the infectious diseases hospital for at least six weeks; no visitors were allowed.

Lobar pneumonia was common; with the more fortunate patients there was a 'crisis' or turning point about the seventh day (footnote 8). It struck terror into the hearts of patients and doctors alike. The mortality was thought to be at least 50 per cent and the first antibiotics were not available until the 1930s. Still dreaded above all was tuberculosis, signalled by blood in the handkerchief after a fit of coughing. Some families were especially vulnerable and it tended to strike young people. The course could be lingering or extremely rapid, with death within weeks. Especially in industrial areas, surgeries were filled with chronic bronchitis and emphysema. Influenza was to kill millions in the global pandemic of 1918-1921. In a rural community like Holt, 'Farmer's Lung' (due to aspergillus exposure) and various occupational injuries were commonplace.

Almost half of all babies were delivered at home, mainly by midwives. Pain relief in labour, although available in hospital, was seldom provided in the home. When things went wrong and for procedures such as breech birth or manual removal of the placenta, the GP would be summoned. Most GPs used chloroform as an anaesthetic but had neither the skills nor the equipment to manage emergencies. Later, in many places obstetric 'flying squads' were established. Based out of hospitals, these could deal with haemorrhage, shock and eclampsia (footnote 9), transfuse patients, give anaesthetics, and undertake operative obstetrics in the

Footnote 8. They provide a staple feature of nineteenth century English literature. Think Jane Austen's Marianne Dashwood in *Sense & Sensibility*.

home.[5] Tales of obstetric disaster were common and puerperal sepsis remained the commonest cause of maternal mortality.[8]

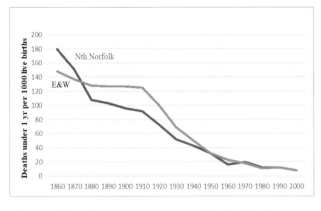

Figure 5.9 Infant mortality rates, North Norfolk

Patterns of morbidity and mortality continued to change early in the new century with rising standards of living. The infant mortality rate in North Norfolk had halved over the previous half century to below 100 per 1000 live births (figure 5.9). Levels of infectious diseases were declining and being replaced by the 'diseases of affluence': ischaemic heart disease, cancer and other chronic diseases. Life expectancies rose over the century to 1950 from 40 in men and 42 in women to 66 and 71 years respectively.[9] This changed the age profile of patient lists. Birth rates and family sizes continued their long-term secular decline as part of this demographic and epidemiological transition.[10]

The early 20th century 'consultation'

GPs in poor, inner city communities recalled the waiting room containing rows of seats for dozens of patients who sat facing a high bench like a bank counter. Behind this counter stood the doctor and behind him the dispenser. The doctor called the next patient to come forward. Having listened to the complaint, he turned to the dispenser and ordered the appropriate remedy. These ritualised encounters of three to five minutes emptied waiting rooms but left little time for preventive advice. Cheerfulness, a hopeful demeanour and sympathy were all important. *'Laying on of hands was the important thing…medicine was 70 per cent art and 30 per cent science'.*[11] There was rarely any attempt at examination. Daily visits often numbered over fifty and were mostly made on a bicycle.

Clinical practice was slow to change and traditional practices endured. Diagnosis was imprecise with little use of examination or instruments and a tendency to over-prescribe. The dissemination of best practice was variable and constrained by the economic and social context of individual practices. Middle class fee-paying patients got more extensive investigations and better medicine. Doctors' expanding knowledge of symptoms and signs aided the diagnosis of common diseases. Other positive advances included minor surgery and the first effective drugs.

Footnote 9. Pre-eclampsia (ankle swelling, high blood pressure and kidney dysfunction) remains common today but can progress to life-threatening eclampsia which causes fits during late pregnancy, labour and the period shortly afterwards.

Successful treatment by the family doctor was accepted with gratitude and their many failures were tolerated with little rancour or recrimination. Patients' expectations were not high. Pain and discomfort were accepted as part of life to be endured with stoicism. The death of children from infectious disease was the way of the world. Mothers of feverish children expected, if the child was not to be admitted to the fever hospital, to be told that bed rest was crucial until the fever had fully subsided. GPs' hours were long, as most practices were single-handed and deputising services were non-existent. Competition for patients was fierce and levels of mistrust correspondingly high.[12] Local rota systems operated on a 'knock-for-knock' basis to make a half-day practicable.

People did not trouble GPs without good cause. Early in recovery patients might dispense with their services as most had to pay for the doctor and the medicines. The professional attitude to working class patients was frequently robust, and sometimes downright rude, but this too appears to have been accepted with tolerance. In middle-class practices there were greater courtesies. There was the ritual preparation of a napkin, a spoon and a glass of water for the doctor's visit. There might be five shillings (25p) on the mantelpiece for the fee; three and sixpence (17½p) if the family was not so well off .[13] Higher up the social scale the doctor was still treated as a rather superior type of servant.

Medical diagnosis was often of academic rather than practical importance. Treatments were still limited to thyroid extract, iron, digitalis, barbiturates, simple analgesics, morphine derivatives and harmless mixtures. Insulin, liver extract for pernicious anaemia and new mercurial diuretics only became available in the 1920s.

The advent in the mid-30s of sulphonamides and then penicillin were to transform the management of pneumonia. Sadly, this was too late for Joseph who would have spent eight to ten days visiting his patients regularly in expectation of 'the crisis'. Henceforth, fewer visits were required as pneumonia's prognosis improved but, paradoxically, the doctor came to occupy a less heroic role in the eyes of relatives.

Earning a living
The gentlemanly pretensions of the medical profession meant that financial concerns were seldom articulated. As we have seen, elevated medical ideals were seen as respectable while mercenary objectives were shameful, even dishonourable. Practising medicine and making money have always coexisted in uneasy symbiosis.

Patients were billed retrospectively for services rendered, on the basis of an individual doctor's assessment of the sum to be charged. Initially, book-keeping was a low priority but inefficiency could affect income. Later, chaotic ledgers gave way to systematized accounts through the employment of book-keepers and, in time, specialist accountants.

At the start of this period, it was customary to dispense; payment for medicine rather than the doctor's skill or time was the economic basis of primary medical care.[14] Dispensing declined with the gradual substitution of alternative payment systems and NHI accelerated this trend. Polypharmacy was the norm in the long-established cultural tradition of compounding mixed herbal remedies for individual patients. Prescription served other purposes - sanctioning the sick role, buying time, as a 'mental poultice.'[15] There was growing official concern post-NHI over the increase in prescriptions per patient and the use of expensive drugs not in the national formulary.

Doctors' accounts with local chemists indicate the extent to which medicine looked to the past as well as the future. Individual prescription was a matter of professional pride and doctors' special mixtures were an asset in building up a local reputation. For example, Dr Bullmore of Wisbech was particularly renowned for his Fenland Cough Mixture made palatable when *'taken three times a day in half a glass of hot milk and a tablespoon of rum.'*[16] Liquid medicines were more popular than pills. Stock mixtures stored in large Winchester bottles were the dispenser's mainstay. Much time was spent measuring different coloured fluids into bottles of varying sizes. The discriminatory nature of clinical practice according to class was often marked with poorer patients receiving a more restricted range of medicines.

There was an important transition over this period from doctors selling one product (medicines) to doctors selling another (professional expertise) for which they had to price their own time. Time management was therefore just one of the disciplines implicit in the development of a branch surgery. GPs were especially conscious of travel time.

A list of 2000 patients was thought to be the optimal size in rural areas; up to twice that in urban ones.[17] Economic survival in the teeth of low fees and unpaid bills was secured pre-1911 by practices operating their own informal welfare state, i.e. cross-subsidizing the care of poorer patients through the fees of richer ones.[18] My great uncle Harry was doing the same for the uninsured a generation later. Gifts in kind were an important alternative to bad debt. Without cash down, GPs needed to extend medical altruism in hard times.

Indicative fee schedules had first been introduced by the BMA in 1870. Fees were correlated with house rentals as a proxy for income. For those paying less than £10 per annum, GPs assumed their needs would be met by collective provision through friendly societies or the Poor Law. This income group constituted just over half the population in 1871 falling to a quarter thirty years later.[17]

Increasing incomes provided more business opportunities for so-called 'shilling' or 'sixpenny' doctors. *'Competition was keen and prices much too low, as little as sixpence for advice and medicine.* '[13] These doctors charged rock bottom fees but relied on maximizing throughput with predictable consequences. The alternative was the free out-patient clinic at the local hospital or dispensary. Sixpenny doctors (about £3.25 in today's money) undercut colleagues but fee levels remained remarkably stable between the 1850s and 1940s as a consequence.

Professional survival

Middle-class parents responded to the demographic transition to smaller families by investing in prolonged education. The resulting oversupply of doctors prior to 1911 increased competition. The profession's responses resulted in major changes in general practice. These included the diversification of career strategies and differentiation of practices according to the needs of their locales. Cultural adaptations included enhanced qualifications, improved practice organisation and the uptake of new technologies.

Urbanisation continued apace. In 1851, one in two people in England & Wales were town dwellers, four out of five by 1901. Rural practices declined in numerical importance and their economic viability was threatened by suburban GPs who used cars and telephones to colonize surrounding villages. Doctors followed their more affluent patients into the suburbs, while city centre catchments became more working class. Industrial and suburban practices tended to be more innovative while single-handed and rural practices remained conservative.

Medicine responded to the market by creating monopolies through educational credentialism, with increasingly high standards of entry and long training, reinforced by the process of referral. An important social constraint on recruitment was the high cost of lengthy training. The medical market in turn stimulated diversification in practice types. Flexible fee schedules and the relentless pursuit of indebted patients were critical. A practice's location and cultural context limited certain practices, e.g. 'patient-pinching', and even surreptitious advertising was frowned upon. The widespread view among my generation that practice management was born in the 1980s is an arrogation. Unsurprisingly, the necessary symbiosis between medicine and business meant that only more efficiently managed practices survived in the 1880s too.

The comparison of practice partnership with marriage is a long-established cliché. Wives were early on employed in a range of functions, constraining the employment of ancillary staff. The role was pressured, combining the duties of receptionist, telephonist and secretary. She was crucial to the practice's success and a spouse chosen from an elite family might strengthen the family socially or financially.[19] Just as Dolly, an established figure in Holt society, eased the path of a newly elevated farmer's son so Amy provided great assistance to her brother, despite her physical disabilities.

Most doctors practiced in the region where they qualified, very often also their birthplace - though the coincidence of all three weakened over time. A practice could be acquired through purchase, partnership or 'squatting' (building from scratch). All three routes were problematic. Medicine is often depicted as dependent on self-recruitment with younger sons following their medical fathers.[20] Though dynasties were conspicuous in small towns like Holt, this stereotype over-estimates the incidence of family-based practice. Before 1910, only one in eight were family practices; after NHI, one in seven. Increasing income was making possible larger partnerships. Two in five GPs had a relative in the medical profession between 1820 and 1850, dropping to one in three between 1890 and 1910 which was a period of unprecedented medical school intakes.[21]

The GP's profile increased with the expansion of their public roles and enhanced technical competence in areas such as surgery, immunisation, public and child health. They started to wield powerful new pharmaceuticals but still faced stiff competition from the unorthodox especially in rural areas. The ban on professional advertising meant that they had to work hard for name recognition. A contemporary guide on *How to Start in General Practice* warned that *'any district is hazardous, as the profession is overcrowded.'*[22] Newcomers were often treated with hostility by professional colleagues.

To establish one's reputation and foster trust, engagement in face-to-face activities in community organisations was vital. Less pressured country GPs could participate in country pursuits such as angling or shooting. The landscape of Britain was becoming fissured by differences of class, gender and ethnicity. Barriers of language and lifestyle militated against too close an integration with the local community. GPs might be in the community but not of it (footnote 10).

Just as now, an important bulwark against the stresses of the job was the space for time away from it. Beginning with the botanists, almost all the doctors described in these pages fostered keen outside interests. Personal protection has always promoted professional durability. Yet some doctors were blessed with boundless energy and worked on in their vocation. The physical topography of the combined home and workplace made withdrawal harder. His relatives recall that my Great Uncle Harry was never really 'off call'.

Woods' study of medical mortality from 1860-1911 shows that general practice was a particularly dangerous trade.[23] The risk of contracting infections such as TB from your patients was ever-present. The dangers of home visiting on horseback, of addiction to drugs and alcohol, of vulnerability to depression and suicide from readily available drugs, all contributed to high death rates. Many doctors could not

Footnote 10. Some of Chekhov's doctors elegantly personify this detachment: educated, locally engaged but isolated. Uncle Vanya's Mikhail Lvovich Astrov is an example.

afford to retire and simply died 'in harness' (table 5.1). The public understood this and appreciated their dedication.

If Fildes and Trollope marked family practice in the late Victorian era, AJ Cronin's vivid account of working in the Welsh valleys defined the hardships of doctoring in

Table 5.1   Outcomes in later life for different qualifying cohorts, 1820-1939 (%)

	1820-39	1840-59	1860-79	1880-99	1900-1919	1920-39
Retired	47	46	29	40	50	46
Semi-retired	4	5	4	5	3	6
Death in harness	38	42	62	46	38	46
Unknown	11	7	5	9	9	2
TOTAL	53	103	138	242	234	168

the early twentieth century.[24] *The Citadel* portrays a voluntary medical association based on the Tredegar Medical Aid Society for which Cronin worked in the 1920s. His experiences in Tredegar where he was born (near where JT Skrimshire had worked early in his career) allegedly provided inspiration to Aneurin Bevin in establishing the NHS.

Thus survival, professional and personal, was determined by both objective factors (location, paid appointments, list or later 'panel' size) and subjective factors (bedside manner, personality and constitution). Confidence in the doctor compensated for his therapeutic deficiencies. Palliation rather than cure was the norm. The turn-out of the whole town for a well-loved doctor's funeral - as for Jack and Joseph - was *'a sure sign that that practitioner had been a prime exponent of the art of manipulating a local environment to construct an ecological niche in the community.'*[21]

Practice organisation

Doctors' management of their practice as the century advanced balanced entrepreneurial considerations against economic rationalism - a trade-off as familiar today. The sheer burden of everyday work and patients' expectations militated against long term vision. Medical education with its focus on science rather than organisational aspects of working life, limited apprenticeships and professional isolation all tended to preserve the status quo. Yet some doctors began to exploit new technologies so that, within a century, the Victorian 'horse and buggy' doctor had been transformed into a purposive partner running a mixed practice of privately and publicly funded health care.

Assistantships were a convenient way to develop a practice. Assistants were low paid, assigned humdrum duties and covered for other appointments, but were a means of accommodating short term fluctuations (e.g. illness, seasonal). They were often taken on to run branch surgeries for working class patients. The expansion of the Holt practice over to Melton Constable is a case in point; the additional income (9s. 0d per patient) helped support the employment of Joseph Gillam.

By the interwar period, assistantship with a view to partnership was the standard route into practice (later a 'probationary' period) but this 'view' could turn to mirage.[25] One in five practices were partnerships by the beginning of the twentieth century (involving one in four doctors). By the early years of the NHS, more than half were in partnership due to the security of income afforded by NHI.[20] Expansion was greatest in urban and suburban areas. Partners provided new stocks of human and financial capital as principals aged. The younger partner served as a workhorse with so many years to work to parity. There was the additional appeal of a second opinion in-house and the leisure time afforded by rotas. Younger doctors were often more market-oriented and adaptable than their older, well-established colleagues.

Partnership agreements were often less a legal document than an 'agreement between gentlemen.'[26] They required prolonged periods of negotiation, reflection, and re-negotiation. The indenture between JTS and Joseph provides an example (see chapter 4). To this day, many go unsigned or unfinalized. Many practices still operate without a legal contract. Practices were often rooted in the household, truly a 'cottage industry'. The doctor's wife was centrally important as a guiding hand: domestically, looking after live-in staff, socially, keeping financial and other records, and in managing resources.

Better, well-located facilities could enhance recruitment. A *'commanding house on the highway'* was a prime asset.[19] Until the early twentieth century, some surgeries were more like shops than consulting rooms with doctors standing behind counters that separated the waiting room from the dispensary. The panel doctor's surgery (figure 5.10) - where the working classes might queue into the street while middle classes were ushered into the dining room - was still a novelty. From the 1870s, a significant development was the branch surgery and lock-up.[27] Way stations might be the front room of a cottage used for a couple of hours on a weekday afternoon according to the GP's rotation of visits round the practice catchment area.

Despite being a service industry supposedly concerned for the needs of potential customers, economic incentives to invest in practice premises were yet limited. The poverty of patients' expectations, particularly in working class areas, retarded progress. Large scale public investment in purpose-built accommodation did not occur till the 1960s.

AT THE PANEL DOCTOR'S.

Gentleman (who has been steadily reading for the last hour). "YOU GO NEXT, MA'AM; I'VE ONLY COME HERE TO FINISH A STORY I STARTED LAST WEEK."

Figure 5.10 At the panel doctor's, Punch 1929

Downward pressure on fees imparted new urgency to time management. A significant shift from the doctor visiting the patient to fee-paying patients visiting surgery was the result, accelerated after NHI. Rural doctors made more house calls due to lack of transportation for patients. GPs made themselves very accessible: *'Twenty four hours of the day and seven days of the week.'*[28] During the first half of the twentieth century, many GPs held two or three surgeries daily, with further surgeries on both Saturday and Sunday. Then as now, Mondays and Fridays were busier than midweek.[29] Appointment systems were only in general use from the 1950s.

There was widespread adoption of the telephone after 1900 as a valuable professional tool. Ownership by patients was a mixed blessing as they inflated workload, through visit requests. Traditionally, diagnostic aids were used only when clinical observation was inadequate.[30] In the 1920s, an advanced practice might be furnished with stethoscope, thermometer, sphygmomanometer, auriscope, ophthalmoscope, microscope and haemoglobinometer.[21] Some of JTS's, Joseph's and Harry's equipment is shown in figure 5.11. These aids began to supplant observation alone. The fruits of laboratory medicine had finally reached Holt!

Record keeping

Victorian records suggest medical officers' diagnostic terminology differed little from that of lay people. Remarkably, poor law doctors in the 1890s were using terminology only a little more scientific, despite the epistemological revolution occasioned by Germ Theory since the 1870s. For four decades from the 1880s, the General Register Office undertook confidential enquiries of medical practitioners for the compilation of more accurate vital statistics. These also served to educate and improve doctors' diagnostic powers.

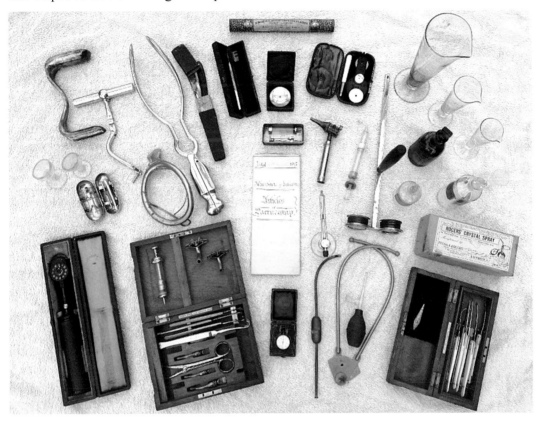

5.11 Medical accoutrements of JTS, Joseph, Jack and Harry

The new 'Lloyd George' record cards introduced with NHI effected something of a revolution in medical note-keeping. Analysis of early cards suggests that clinical notes were made only for the minority of more serious conditions requiring sickness certification, referrals or surgery. Diagnoses were overwhelmingly in physical terms and few clinical measurements or investigations were recorded. These records therefore provide only partial insights into the true frequency of conditions encountered.

The use of 'Lloyd George' record cards eventually improved diagnostic reporting but a proposal in 1920 that diagnoses should be inserted was dropped as expert opinion considered medical work was based on probability, not certainty, in most cases.[31] *'...in perhaps 50 per cent of cases in general practice, you can't make a definite diagnosis, you can only sort of hazard a guess.'*[32] *'Patients do not know what is wrong with them, and often the doctor does not know, but has to give them an expectorant or a waiting treatment.'*[33] 'GOK' was a trusty professional abbreviation for God Only Knows (footnote 11).

Forms have always determined function. The small Lloyd George cards were in time replaced by A4 folders that allowed for the accumulation of hospital correspondence (footnote 12). Doctors were necessarily concise for records had to be stored and transported. Ironically, with the advent of computerised, 'paperless' records most of a century later, many doctors bemoaned the loss of space and flexibility that written records afforded.

Extended roles

There is nothing new about what is nowadays called a 'portfolio career'. External appointments (as exemplified *in extremis* by Charles Parnham Skrimshire in chapter 4) continued to be an important source of income and status. There was a hierarchy of esteem from hospital and government appointments at the top to poor law and club appointments at the bottom (footnote 13). These appointments diversified income and reduced vulnerability to economic fluctuations. The latter affected private fee income and increased the number of bad debts. Poor Law appointments were eschewed by socially well-connected practices because they lowered their social cachet and reduced their appeal to the affluent.

During the four decades prior to 1911, nearly a quarter of the GP's income came from appointments of different kinds. However, as the numbers graduating increased, the proportion holding them declined, especially in urban areas. The support of NHI payments therefore proved timely. More than two thirds of GPs held outside appointments, declining after NHI to one in two. Most widely this was as medical officer to a Poor Law union, especially in rural areas where fewer options were available. Sometimes this was combined with appointment as a public vaccinator. Three generations of my forebears combined these posts with that of school doctor. Ministry and industrial posts were also common (table 5.2).

During the twentieth century, increasing specialisation led to many part-time posts, formerly held by GPs, being converted to full-time appointments. GPs were increasingly marginalised in relation to sanitary work with the coming of the

Footnotes 11. Medical slang is a source of perennial amusement. The use of such terms was mostly apocryphal though I have come across NFN (Normal For Norfolk), FLK (Funny Looking Kid) and even TTFO (Told To Go Away) in rogue records.

12. 'Thick files' have always dampened the doctor's spirits. They generally indicate multiple chronic conditions - or the medically insoluble. GPs of a certain vintage will recall many hours spent trawling through mildewed, folded letters for consultant's nuggets of wisdom - and many more trying to cram them back into the confines from which they were released.

Table 5.2   Non-hospital appointments held by GPs, 1840-1939 (% of cohort)

Type of appointment	1840-59	1860-79	1880-99	1900-19	1920-39
Poor Law	30	40	28	20	8
Public vaccinator	14	19	20	14	5
MOH	14	24	18	12	5
School	5	7	10	10	2
Police	5	10	10	7	8
Post Office	1	11	12	9	5
Military	8	4	7	6	4

Ministry of Health.[34] Enthusiasm for preventive work had seen as many as one in four GPs become part-time medical officers of health in the mid-nineteenth century.[20] In 1933 it became obligatory for a MOH to hold a diploma in public health and most were then full time.[35] A gulf between the disciplines subsequently widened. MOHs were distrusted by GPs as in hock to lay bureaucrats.

Midwifery was another source of income but had declined in the second half of the nineteenth century. The work was seen as a low status GP activity rather than a medical specialism. Competition between doctors and midwives drove down midwifery fees and aggravated a dubious tendency for GPs to intervene more actively with forceps.[8] Though deaths in childbirth could have a disastrous impact on the family doctor's local reputation, 'midder' was still a source of professional satisfaction.

The Midwives Acts of 1902 and 1936 helped midwives achieve professional ascendency in domiciliary obstetrics. In 1880, half of all deliveries were attended by a GP, by 1938 only one third. The proportion of hospital births increased from 15% in 1927 to 54% in 1946.[36] As the number of confinements declined, local obstetric lists were introduced where more experienced GPs (e.g. those with the Diploma of the Royal College of Obstetricians and Gynaecologists) could claim higher payment.

War work
Around half of GPs qualifying between 1880 and 1939 enrolled in the armed services. In Britain before the First World War, doctors were exempt from military service. The enforced discipline, routine and red tape of medicine in the military was frequently regarded with disdain. Involvement in the war did little to improve the lot of GPs.

Footnote 13. Comparable hierarchies exist today. Government advisory posts are more prestigious than managerial roles with academic and teaching posts lower down the pecking order. Work for insurance and pharmaceutical companies is regarded as more mercenary and therefore of lower status.

Conscripted male GPs remained in the lowest classes within the medical hierarchy. Many GPs, under-employed for the most part during the war, found the whole experience a colossal bore. *'I had joined the Royal Medical Core in July 1916'*, one medical officer related to his MP, *'but I had about two hours' work a day until the battle of Arras which took place in April 1917… Since then I have…no medical work to do at all.'*[37] Others enthused about *'the good comradeship, the complete absence of the competitive evil, the living and working at close quarters of friendly teams, the direction of unanimous effort to the one object of doing the best possible both for the Service and the individual sick or wounded soldier…'*.[38] They lamented the lack of such an ethos in civilian practice.

While some impecunious GPs may have welcomed the security of military service, others resented the loss of income and 'stay at-homes' who *'materially improved their financial position, especially if they supported the ill-health pleas of some of their patients of military age'*[39], i.e. aided them in avoiding conscription. Some doctors struggled on return to civilian service.

The inter-relationship of war and medicine is complex. Certainly, war has always helped to advance therapeutic innovations (e.g. in surgery and public health) and service development. Bio-militarism is the language of modern medicine.[40] We *battle* AIDS, wage *war* on drugs, *fight* cancer and restore immune *defence systems*. (The Covid-19 pandemic has provided plenty of recent examples.) Ironically, for many rank-and-file doctors the loss of autonomy consequent on salaried service cemented a distaste for all forms of medical provision involving the state after the Great War.[41]

Changing training
Today's medical schools expect low dropout rates because entrance exams are rigorous. The reverse situation obtained in the late nineteenth century when low entry qualifications were associated with dropout rates as high as a third. This was seen as necessary to maintaining the profession's reputation and usefully reduced overcrowding.[42] Re-examinations (like Jack's) were a commonplace.

All this began to change over the following decades as medicine's status and popularity increased. An associated consequence was a growing moralism in medical education. The concept of a 'gentleman' became synonymous with the concept of duty. Unruly behaviour among students was less tolerated.[42]

From this period dates the recurrent concern to slim down the curriculum and move away from an exaggerated emphasis on knowledge as opposed to reasoning skills. Weaknesses in medical education reflected a traditional bias in British higher education that privileged the academic over the vocational, the needs of an elite over those of the majority. Even in 1935, three quarters of graduates were destined to become family doctors. Graduates felt ill-prepared for practice; few teachers in medical schools had been GPs. General practice was regarded as *'the sum of other disciplines practised outside hospital and at an inferior level.'*[43] Only later did the concept emerge of general practice as a specialism in its own right.

One of the first to bring medical students out of the lecture hall for bedside clinical training was William Osler (1849-1919) (footnote 14). He insisted that students learn from seeing and talking to patients. The idea of the medical residency spread across the English-speaking world; it remains in place today in most teaching hospitals.

Abraham Flexner's landmark report of 1911 stressed the importance of both basic science and inductive learning by doing.[44] It enshrined the division between pre-clinical (classroom-based) and clinical (ward-based) training. Some students struggled with the abruptness of transition between the two and various reviews recommended that they should be brought closer together.[45,46] Debates over the merits of integration continue today.

From this period too date concerns over post-graduate education. The predicament of the 'rusty' GP stimulated provision of short refresher courses from the early twentieth century though pressures of time, travel and utility limited participation. Reading (the BMJ and Practitioner) remained the staple for updating knowledge, alongside the junior partner or the pharmaceutical company representative (footnote 15).

The syllabus was still overloaded. The BMA was among bodies expressing concern at an over-emphasis on curative medicine at the expense of prevention or public health. The Goodenough Report (1944) proposed a radical overhaul of medical education.[46] As well as promoting the broader educational needs of the GP, it recommended that refresher courses be recognised and funded. It also suggested co-education be normal practice (footnote 16).

Women doctors
For arguably the most significant educational development of this period was the admission to medical schools, finally, of more women (figure 5.12). Nowadays, when women form the majority and general practice is thoroughly 'feminised', it is possible to forget how long was their struggle. The mythic belligerence of Sophia

Footnotes 14. Sir William Osler was a Canadian physician and one of the four founding professors of Johns Hopkins Hospital. He created the first residency program for the specialty training of physicians, and has frequently been described as the 'Father of Modern Medicine'. Osler cultivated many interests and, in addition to being a physician, was a bibliophile, historian and author.

15. 'Drug reps' have acquired a dubious reputation in these supposedly purer times. Their *raison d'etre* is the promotion of their own products, usually at the expense of cost-effective, older alternatives. GPs receive sandwich lunches, biros and other bribes in exchange for 'education'. Drug reps are engaging and good at their jobs. There is plenty of evidence that GPs change their prescribing practice inappropriately as a result.

Jex-Blake at Edinburgh University (which for four years blocked her qualification), in some respects, made it more difficult for women inclined to an incrementalist strategy of emancipation.

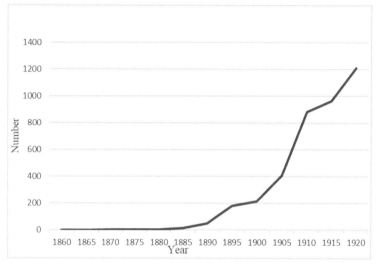

Figure 5.12 Women on Medical Register, 1860-1920

The Society of Apothecaries had closed a loophole through which women could qualify in 1865 and the BMA banned the admission of women until 1892. Male opposition was partly protectionist: the profession was already over-crowded. Obduracy on the part of universities was flimsily justified on the grounds of delicacy. Medical studies were brutalizing and co-education was supposedly indecorous.

The most influential, separatist initiative was the London Medical School for Women which opened in 1874. Under its first Dean, Elizabeth Garrett Anderson, the School came to dominate the early output of medical graduates in Britain. By the turn of the century, medical co-education was beginning to be offered in universities such as St Andrew's and Manchester.

As more male doctors were called to arms, women were presented with professional opportunities during World War I in spheres beyond women's health. These opportunities diminished with the war's ending. Women doctors were forced into retirement or back into their traditional niches such as community child health.

However, the World Wars did speed up acceptance and normalisation of women GPs in the absence of many male doctors. A target of 1 to 4 was soon achieved though women still faced difficulties gaining their first hospital appointments. General practice was thereafter regarded as an especially suitable career choice (footnote 17), albeit heavily slanted towards paediatrics and reproductive health.[20]

Footnotes 16. As one journal wittily opined: *'It is Good, but is it Enough.'*[47] Its proposals should have underpinned a new socialized medical service but they were not implemented due to the power of teaching hospital specialists and the GMC.

17. My mother-in-law, Elizabeth Dallow, exemplified the pragmatism of many women of the period. A star student, she gave up her burgeoning career in obstetrics.

By 1936, two out of five medical women were opting for general practice. Comparing mean income levels in 1936-8, women had little more than half the earning power of men. They worked in smaller practices, held fewer outside appointments, and served more women and children paying lower fees, though their workloads were greater. Women operated in a semi-separate sphere but patients appreciated their commitment and patient-centredness. They were readier to undertake examinations and went beyond a symptomatic approach, customarily seeing a patient's physical complaint within a wider social context.[48]

Nevertheless, medical women remained conscious that they needed to be better than the average male if they were to succeed. Female medical students were advised that in general practice: *'The world in general is in a position to criticize the smallest error with severity...If you choose this exacting branch of practice, you will need a sound medical education, good health, much wisdom and all the virtues.'*[49] Needless to say, male domination continued to characterize most institutions and much medico-political activity.

The impact of National Health Insurance

Medical students at the turn of the century were assured they could look forward to £400-500 per annum, albeit rather less than the £700 thought necessary for a genteel lifestyle. A decade later, NHI and secure capitation payments had eroded income differentials and the search for alternative employment became less intense. Social insurance provided an increasingly important share of income but private fees were growing significantly too (figure 5.13).

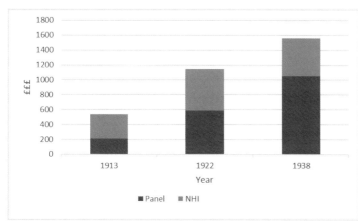

The BMA successfully lobbied for increases in public payments and for the protection of doctors' right to control lists, along with patients' right to choose their doctors. The establishment of partnerships was enabled. Over time, by displacing payments per item of service, NHI capitation payments tended to

Figure.5.13 Avge gross income: private sources/NHI

discourage specialism among rank-and-file GPs.[50] By 1938, over 19000 (three quarters) of GPs were insurance practitioners.[14] There were seven GPs per consultant although their incomes (£1000 to £2000 pa) were typically half those of hospital colleagues.

Altogether, NHI increased financial security and had a knock-on effect on recruitment - possibly attracting those in search of a safe income rather than a vocation. Analyses of the distribution of doctors' capital and of their probates confirm growing medical prosperity in the first half of the century (table 5.3).[51]

Table 5.3.   Distribution of capital in medical profession, 1940-41 (Probates)[51]

Age	No. med practitioners	% med pract	Amount of capital (£000)	% distribn of capital	Average cap (£)
25-34	17,505	38.5	36,900	14.9	2,108
35-44	12,503	27.5	70,100	28.4	5,607
45-54	5,229	11.5	40,000	16.2	7,650
55-64	5,001	11.0	41,400	16.7	8,278
65-69	2,364	5.2	21,600	8.7	9,137
70-75	1,637	3.6	22,200	9.0	13,561
76+	1,228	2.7	15,100	6.1	12,296
N	45,467	100	247,300	100	5,437

Entry into a practice was generally by 'purchase of goodwill', the usual price being one and a half times the annual income. GPs therefore started with a substantial debt but incomes increased relatively and absolutely. On average, 1,000 national insurance patients generated about £400-£500 per year, an income boosted by the care of the families who were not covered by national insurance. A minority of doctors abused the system recruiting as many as 4000 patients, so a ceiling of 3000 was fixed. Large 'specialist' insurance practices maximised income by employing assistants.[14]

The 'statification of medicine' continued in some quarters to be regarded as a source of moral hazard. *'If the advantages which such an acquirement* (health care) *confers can be claimed as a legal right, without having been striven for as a moral duty, then...the certain result must be an increase in the number of those in the community who consider themselves entitled to transfer duties and responsibilities from their own shoulders on to those of their neighbours.* '[52] A century on, Dr James would elicit sympathy among many medical readers today.

If many doctors were ambivalent about the new dispensation, patients were less so. In sleepy Wisbech there were riots in 1913 when local doctors refused NHI patients. Model rules for panel patients were issued: to obey doctor's instructions, not to conduct themselves in ways that would retard recovery, 'not to make unreasonable demands' upon the doctor, to attend surgery 'whenever the condition permits', and to request home visits before 10.00am. As with the NHS, the early demand for free services was high. It was initially predicted that there would be less than two patient-doctor contacts per year; 20 years later there were five.[53]

NHI was perceived as belonging to patients because they had contributed to it. Free at the point of access, working-class patients were not deterred from seeking help at earlier stages of their illness. A report from government actuaries in 1910 had starkly asserted the primacy of male breadwinners.[4] The Royal Commission of 1925 concluded that 'prohibitive costs' continued to justify the exclusion of dependants. However, GPs could run their own clubs for wives and children of their panel patients or enrol them in the Public Medical Service. This service collected 6d per week from each patient who registered with a doctor, covering consultations and medicine.

Were standards of care for panel patients second class? They frequently queued at the back door of a cramped, barely furnished surgery to await appointments while middle classes used the front door at a convenient time. Lloyd George record cards recorded brief, intermittent entries. Complaints related to overcharging or discourtesy. Some insurance committees introduced formularies to limit pharmaceutical range and contain costs. New drugs tended not to be sanctioned for NHI use.

Under the terms of 'club practice' pre-1911, GPs treated patients of friendly societies for a small, defined annual fee. Although payments were larger, they remained modest. They imposed similar pressures on the doctor. Club doctors before the NHI had reduced visits in favour of swift surgery throughput. The new system tended to reward quantity rather than quality of care. A large panel of insured patients necessitated high throughput. Practice was therefore characterised by stock mixtures, vestigial records and restricted clinical procedures. Routinization, over- prescription, and under-investment were other consequences. Doctors were readier to refer where no remuneration was likely. On average, GPs gave three and a quarter minutes to each insurance patient in surgery, four minutes on a visit.[20] Care was henceforth increasingly uniform. In other words, some of the less desirable features of the pre-existing system were systematised.

Patient relations
We know little about sickness behaviour in the distant past - the characterisations of illness, preferences of sufferers or conventions governing behaviour.[54] Then as now, the sufferer made preliminary self-diagnoses and most illness was managed without recourse to professionals. Stoicism and inaction were the order of the day if resources were insufficient to pay for assistance.

Self-medication was widespread with the increasing availability of cheap patent medicines from chemists or grocery stores. From a single shop in Nottingham selling herbal remedies, John and Jesse Boot were extending their business across the land. Little distinction was made between patent medicines and those of GPs. George Bernard Shaw famously depicted the medical profession as a *'huge commercial system of quackery and poison.'*[55] The box of pills was needed, however, to retain the confidence of patients. In truth, GPs frequently bore the costs of care from their own pockets and were paid neither for extensive travel or medicine. Many doctors like my Great Uncle Harry operated an informal welfare state, charging the affluent higher fees so as to subsidize the impoverished.[26]

A competitive advantage in recruiting patients could always be heightened by what would nowadays be called 'communication skills.' The adoption of everyday clothing (in lieu of top hat and tails) by young late-Victorian doctors symbolised their greater social and financial accessibility to working people.

Obituaries could be anodyne and eulogistic but the personal markers of a good GP were unchanging: attention to detail, scrupulous care, sympathy, kindness and generosity. These, it was inferred, earned doctors the devotion and respect of their patients. Occasional 'warts and all' comments provided more interesting insights ('...*loved by his patients, though some found him bluff and he did not suffer fools, or those inclined to swing the lead, gladly*'[56]). Intense, analytic discussion of the dynamics of the patient-doctor encounter and conscious concern for 'patient-centredness' is a feature of the recent past. However, the healing qualities of the doctor's presence and a confidence-inspiring personality were as important then as now. Patient sensitivities were parodied in popular publications of the time (figure 5.13).

Distinguished Physician (*handing prescription to patient*). "IF THIS DOESN'T PUT YOU RIGHT, COME TO ME AGAIN."
Patient. "HOW MANY GUESSES WILL YOU WANT?"

Figure 5.14 How many guesses will you want? Punch, 1926

With the state's growing incursion into health-related matters, GPs developed a multi-faceted gatekeeping role - to hospital, to welfare or insurance-related benefits. For this, they have never received preparation and it inevitably introduced a tension into the doctor-patient relationship.[57] This was illustrated in the work of Poor Law medical officers. County archives reveal that they were often liberal gatekeepers because of their appreciation of the relationship between poverty, poor diet and sickness.[58] Medical treatments for pauper patients were not subject to the same financial scrutiny as nutritional supplements ('medical extras', e.g. mutton, wine, cod liver oil).[59]

Lax gatekeeping - real or alleged - became a more public issue under NHI. The official view was that doctors turned a blind eye to malingering where they were most dependent on panel patients for fear of their deserting their lists. For this there is little hard evidence. Rather, such laxity - as in relation to sickness certification today - was probably a matter of personality and politics. NHI commissioners stiffened GPs' resolve by monitoring returns and using official medical referees to vet certified patients. High certifying doctors were contacted personally. A policy of bureaucratic pressure to erode non-conformist practice was the preferred strategy so only a small number of panel doctors were singled out for financial penalties.[60]

Moving forward

In certain respects, general practice reached a high point in the early years of NHI. Thereafter, the multiple roles of the generalist were threatened by the pace of specialization, the difficulties of keeping up to date (and buying expensive equipment), and the decline of their local hospitals. The latter had once offered an opportunity to bridge the divide and resist the take-over of swathes of their professional activity by rival practitioners in the community (medical officers of health, community nurses and midwives).

Since the middle of the nineteenth century the voluntary hospitals had been expanding their outpatient departments, for these were their shop windows. The BMA represented GPs in opposing this expansion because of the effect it had on their earnings, but they expanded nonetheless. By 1939, six million attended them every year, in spite of complaints about inadequate waiting facilities and perfunctory and inconsiderate treatment. In contrast, the hospitals run by local authorities had poor or non-existent outpatient departments and less reason to build up large ones.

Control of referrals came to be central. GPs were vexed by the volume of self-referrals to out-patients departments and dispensaries during the second half of the nineteenth century.[61] Because treatment was free of charge, this undermined their practice. That medical referral should be the basis of admission gained acceptance from the 1890s and added status and security to GPs' livelihoods, unlike in the

USA.[52] As we saw in the previous chapter: *'The physician and surgeon retained the hospital, but the general practitioner retained the patient.'*[62]

Metropolitan boroughs led the way towards novel forms of primary care delivery, e.g. the Peckham Centre, Bermondsey, Finsbury. They combined curative and preventive work along lines promoted in the Dawson Report and offered the potential to win back professional territory but many GPs feared health centres would take them away from families.

The lack of cover for wives and children in the 1920s and 1930s prompted the development of the Public Medical Services - the usual services for subscribers to a central fund.[63] The BMA moved towards reform pre-war but ideological differences between devotees of socialized, voluntary or private medicine coupled with financial stringencies impeded these. Professional horizons remained rooted in a sickness service. A municipality-based system centred on the ministry of health was abruptly terminated by the NHS.

A more favourable balance was achieved with community nurses despite fears that competition would bring down fees. *'...our district nurses were taking away a great deal of the doctor's practice and in consequence they found it hard to live.'*[64] The first half of the twentieth century saw diminished community involvement of the GP. There was a collective wringing of hands and a failure to respond to this diminishing role partly because NHI had secured a role for GP in state-funded primary health care.

All the while, medical science was extending the clinical areas in which the GP needed to be knowledgeable. In 1926, the Lancet feared the GP might disappear under the weight of growing specialisms. Increasing demands and expectations were not being matched by resources and organization.[65]

Conclusion

If the doctor moved from the margins to the mainstream of social life from 1850 to 1900,[66] the medical profession underwent its most meteoric development between 1900 and 1950. This generation had witnessed continuing improvements in life expectancy, although to these the rapid strides of medical science were only indirectly related.

Gladstonian Liberalism with its doctrine of limited government intervention and balanced budgets was supplanted. Following victory in the election of 1906, a renewed Liberal party had espoused a costly programme of ambitious social reform. The compromises required to reconcile Victorian commercial priorities with Edwardian welfarism were exemplified by British GPs' reluctant participation in NHI. Lloyd George later aptly commented that *'No scheme was ever more needed or less wanted.'*[67]

In many respects, NHI was more revolutionary than the formation of the NHS. NHI was a necessary interim stage in the evolution of the right of citizens to health care. Within the Liberal government's political philosophy, health was still subsidiary to welfare and labour productivity linked to wealth creation. However, under NHI, individuals had at least a conditional right to health care dependent on their function in society.

NHI stabilized the financial lot of GPs and helped secure improvements in the quantity and quality of care. Paradoxically, NHI payments insulated some doctors from the need to effect clinical, technological or organisational change. In many respects, general practice on the eve of the NHS - especially in Holt - would have been entirely familiar to my Victorian forebears.

Traditional person-centred medicine had derived its authority as much from social as from clinical skills. These 'arts', always vigorously defended,[68] were henceforth combined in the exercise of scientific medicine and a resurgent professionalism. *'These country doctors knew their patients, their personal and family histories, their idiosyncracies, their weaknesses and their strengths. They were in return trusted, respected and revered.'*[18]

My Great Uncle Harry is perhaps the forebear for whom I feel the greatest affinity. He died two years before I was born but I have heard testimony from many who knew him. Early on, he lived in the shadow of his more charismatic older brother, Jack. He was a dull conversationalist by comparison. Yet he seems to have exemplified the virtues that all patients want from their doctors. He was exceptionally able and highly regarded as a diagnostician. He knew the worth (and the worthlessness) of his nostrums. He was conscientious, kind and reliable, seeming always to place the needs of family, friends and patients before his own. Wedded to his work, he never married. Apparently, according to a schoolfriend, he always feared *'passing on a tendency to instability.'* From a distance, a less unstable man can hardly be imagined.

Chapter Six – The birth of the NHS
(1925-1955)

'We are all here on earth to help others;
what on earth the others are here for I don't know.'
W.H.Auden

The sixth generation

Without a family of his own, Harry and Jack moved swiftly to take over their father's responsibilities in the aftermath of Joseph's tragic death. Many family members required support but his newly bereaved sister Dorothy proved unexpectedly resilient. My great grandmother is perhaps the foremost heroine of this story. Her particular misfortunes - her mother's early incarceration, her father's recent suicide, the early loss of brother Jack and now her devoted husband - could have broken a less capable individual.

Figure 6.1 John and Geoffrey, 1916

Her first move was to let Shrublands and move back into Hill House while arranging for her children's education. John, then aged 9, went straight to Gresham's in 1912. The following year Geoffrey, then aged 8, started at Epsom which offered scholarships for doctors' orphans (figure 6.1). The girls boarded at Howell's in Denbighshire, similarly supported by bursaries. Dorothy then took a small house on the Cromer Road, while Harry continued at Hill House with Amy. The Great War found a number of army officers billeted in the house. Harry 'did his bit', being commissioned briefly as a Lieutenant in the Norfolk Volunteer Regiment.

Of Joseph's sons, my grandfather Geoffrey had more tangible success at Epsom, finishing as head of the school with a classics scholarship to Clare College, Cambridge. He too distinguished himself on the cricket field - as a crafty bowler. He used to tell of how *'I blotted my copybook in my final year.'* When the Headmaster, the Rev Canon A.C. Powell, told him of his intention to make him Head Boy, he celebrated by noisily lobbing a number of light bulbs into the quad from an upper floor physics lab window. For this, on speech day a year later, he was denied the Headmaster's Prize - traditionally awarded to the Head Boy.

Both Geoffrey and John went into medicine and both were to become consultants after some years in general practice. In 1921 Dorothy moved to 79, Hamilton Road, a modest end-of-terrace house in Golders Green, London. This enabled the boys to attend medical school, and their sister, Margery, to go to Bedford College and qualify as a teacher.

John Gillam
John qualified MRCS, LRCP from St Thomas's in 1925. He upgraded to FRCS after an early house job at the Norfolk and Norwich Hospital, before joining his future father-in-law's practice in Chesterfield as an assistant. He too married his boss's daughter. In 1931, with his new wife, Sallie Pooler, he joined a practice in Haverfordwest, Pembrokeshire. There he was to be appointed as a consultant surgeon with the establishment of the NHS in 1947.

John's career evolved from several years of part-time surgery, undertaken while working in general practice. His reputation locally was well established and no further training was deemed necessary. (Today, GPs require extensive training and approval to so much as lance a boil.) As his son Pat recalled: *'John was a general surgeon, making himself efficient at all the usual emergencies and the cold cases that a general surgeon was expected to attend to in the first 30 years of his working life. Nowadays surgeons tend to specialise early. John, in his early days, was undertaking operations from thyroids to prostates, from gall bladders to kidneys, and had a good deal of trauma to deal with as there were no orthopaedic surgeons within 30 miles.'*

He was to be warmly remembered in an obituary in the BMJ, written by a colleague who acted as his anaesthetist: *'He was a skilful, slow and careful surgeon with an amazing gift for recalling cases, which made his diagnostic skill quite extraordinary. He read widely and was always aware of the latest thinking and techniques. His contribution to clinical debate was invaluable, and for many years the Pembrokeshire Medical Society flourished, with meetings on Sunday mornings well attended by staff and general practitioners from the area.*

John's formal manner hid a warmth and geniality in which it was a pleasure to share. He worked tirelessly for his patients and always seemed to be around to deal with difficulties. He arrived in the hospital every morning including Sundays, and retired home only when he was satisfied that no more could be done that day, subordinating all other claims on his time. He was constantly trying to improve hospital services in Pembrokeshire and seeking developments that would ensure an enlarged and viable hospital. He was for many years chairman of the medical staff committee, as well as serving on several other committees.'[1]

John never forgot that he had been a general practitioner and retained a deep appreciation of their problems. A GP colleague added: *'John Gillam's wisdom and experience were such that his advice was sought on a wide range of matters besides general surgery. Domiciliary visits were memorable occasions both as an opportunity to learn from his gentle and thorough bedside examination, which would coax the most confused clinical picture into clarity, and because his years in combined surgical and general practice left him with an understanding of the difficulties and circumstances of general practice that made his advice all the more relevant and practical. For me his domiciliary visits gave added pleasure because my patients mostly belonged to families that had been on his National Health Insurance panel and his prodigious memory would yield an apposite story that would sometimes illuminate the immediate problem but would always enhance my knowledge of the family. He was a shrewd, perceptive observer of colleagues as well as patients, and he relished people's idiosyncrasies but his judgments were never unkind and his harshest reproach was a sorrowful gaze over the top of his glasses.'[2]*

John settled in Pembrokeshire, living first in Haverfordwest. In 1950 he acquired a magnificent house that he had long coveted on the clifftop at Druidstone Haven. It overlooks the long, curving beach and was the scene of many of my family's holidays. (Today his grandson runs it as a well-known hotel.)

Pat recalled many examples of his father's commitment: *'Andy Morrison was a US seaman who fell from the mast to the deck of his ship, breaking nearly every bone in his body. John was on duty and spent many hours that night putting him together. Morrison supplied us with the National Geographic Magazine for many years, and wrote every Christmas for years after that.'*

In the fifties, Haverfordwest Hospital was threatened with downsizing because the administrators of the South Wales Hospitals found they had spare capacity due to the success of new antibiotics in curing tuberculosis. The closing of unprofitable mines and steel works, too, reduced the number of accidents in mining and heavy industry. From the oil refineries and power stations at Milford Haven, alternative hospitals, such as Carmarthen (40 miles) or Morriston (60 miles), were too far away. John fought hard to persuade the Cardiff-based administrators that, especially for serious injuries, these travel times were dangerous.

In the end, a tragic accident occurred on the Haven Bridge which was being built at that time. Two contracted labourers sustained serious injuries when a crane broke in the section they were working on. This tipped up and sent them sliding into the metalwork. The ambulance failed to get these two to Morriston in time to save their lives. Thus in 1985 did Pembrokeshire acquire its new hospital.

Geoffrey Gillam

Geoffrey's medical school career at University College Hospital (UCH) was exceptional. He qualified MB,BS (London) in 1928, winning the Liston Gold Medal (footnote 1) for Surgery, the University's most prestigious prize. The previous year he had taken the Conjoint Exams so was already MRCS, LRCP. More significantly, he had become engaged to Mary Frances Oldaker Davies, a fellow student at University College. Her father William was a merchant seaman turned business entrepreneur. My grandmother was to prove as redoubtable as her future mother-in-law.

With the exception of Ernest's supposed sexual indiscretions (see chapter 4), these pages reveal disappointingly little of their subjects' love lives. Geoffrey was dashing and formed an unfortunate attachment to his future sister-in-law, Elizabeth. Weeks before his own marriage, they eloped to the west country in his two-seater. Further scandal was averted through the intervention of other family who hauled them back to their respective partners. He was perhaps not entirely reformed. My father once remarked, with an uncharacteristic want of decorum, that *'Various distraught memsahibs pursued him back from India but, as far as we ever knew, there were no FitzGillams distributed around the Subcontinent.'*

Geoffrey stayed at UCH as house physician to the Senior Consultant, Sir Thomas Lewis (footnote 2), before moving to Norfolk as house surgeon to Jasper Blaxland at the Norfolk & Norwich Hospital. Looking then for a country practice, it was natural to consider joining his uncle Harry. However, Mary was uncertain that their business acumen would bode well; Harry was famously relaxed about sending out bills. Instead they moved to Bungay, Suffolk where they were to stay for there for seven years. Geoffrey became a junior partner to Dr Leo Cane, an excellent doctor with a distinguished naval record earnt in the First World War.

After five years at 17, Trinity Street, a small terraced house, they were able to move across the street to Trinity House. This rather grander property was owned by the Duke of Norfolk and better befitted my grandmother's social aspirations. They set about modernizing it at the cost of a rent increase of £5 for every £100 spent. Two bathrooms were installed and a central heating system; a garage was built and a tennis court laid down. Such was the cost of living at the time that they could employ a cook, two housemaids (with a day uniform and one for the evening), and a gardener, for under £100/year.

Footnote 1. Robert Liston (1794-1847) was a pioneering Scottish surgeon reputed for his skills in the pre-anaesthetic era. He was famously reputed to have amputated a limb in 28 seconds. Gordon described the scene thus: *'He was six foot two, and operated in a bottle-green coat with wellington boots. He sprung across the blood-stained boards upon his swooning… patient like a duelist, calling, 'Time me gentlemen, time me!' to students craning with pocket watches from the iron-railinged galleries. Everyone swore that the first flash of his knife was followed so swiftly by the rasp of saw on bone that sight and sound seemed simultaneous. To free both hands, he would clasp the bloody knife between his teeth.'*[3] He does not record what happened to the patient.

These were rewarding, active years of hard work - visits three nights a week was the norm - but Geoffrey was dogged by duodenal ulcers. In part driven by ill-health, he decided upon a career change. He returned to UCH to gain further qualifications with a view to hospital consultancy as a physician.

Did Geoffrey feel wasted in a rural backwater? This seems unlikely for his immediate family background was in country practice. Leaving Bungay was a wrench but, after a heart-warming send-off with the public presentation of a silver salver (figure 6.2) inscribed with regrets for their short stay in the town, and various other initialled personal objects (still in my possession), they were off: to 10, Hodford Road, Golders Green.

Figure 6.2 Salver with Liston gold medal.

For a consultant post, his basic qualifications were initially inadequate. Within a year he was to gain Membership of the Royal College of Physicians and, by examination, an MD. For a man in his thirties, after seven years' work in the country, this was no mean achievement.

However, his career was to be put on hold by the Second World War. Relocating to Hemel Hempsted, he determined to join the Royal Army Medical Corps (RAMC). After initial setbacks, a medical friend was prepared to overlook his health record and he was commissioned. According to his eldest son, he had 'a whale of a time'. He always claimed he was most at risk while stationed at Benenden School when doodlebugs flew over nightly, but he did see Normandy a few weeks after 'D Day'. His longest stretch of overseas service was in India, after the end of the war in Europe (figure 6.3). Here he was mostly involved in closing down redundant hospitals. For a while in Poona, later at Jubbulpore, he saw places and met people whose paths he would never otherwise have crossed.

One most unexpected encounter was with a Skrimshire relation. Captain J.F.P. Skrimshire, a second cousin and grandson of Frederic (see chapter 4) now also in the RAMC, turned up as a junior officer to 270072 Lt Col G G Gillam, in the same

Footnote 2. Sir Thomas Lewis (1881-1945) was an eminent cardiologist still spoken of in reverential terms by my teachers at UCH in the 70s. His research at UCH focussed particularly on disorders of heart rhythm. Lewis suffered an early myocardial infarction at the age of 45. Among the first to realize that smoking damaged the blood vessels, he promptly gave up his 70 cigarettes-a-day habit. Sadly, this did not prevent his early demise - from heart disease - aged only 63.

mess. Their thoughts turned to Norfolk. Come demobilisation, it was time to pick up the threads of his career.

Figure 6.3 GGG in India.

The twins, John and Peter, were born in Bungay in 1930, and Anthony, in Hemel Hempsted in 1939 (figure 6.4). Geoffrey and Mary took back a house in Holt (Shrublands) in 1944. In his heart Geoffrey never left Norfolk. All three children were to go to Gresham's and the move inoculated them with a life-long love of the county.

The Norfolk and Norwich Hospital would have been his first choice, but there were no imminent vacancies. In the event, his job hunt took him to Birmingham, as a consultant physician to Selly Oak Hospital. Shrublands was sold and Ravenswood, 52 Augustus Road, Edgbaston, became their home. A fine house with neo-Jacobean features standing in two acres of garden (chosen as suitable for the family dog, James), for seventeen years it made an excellent family base.

Geoffrey had developed an interest in cardiology working with Paul Wood (footnote 3) at the National Heart Hospital, before the war. At Selly Oak, he was responsible for the creation of two new consultant posts and for its coronary unit. As a colleague, Bob Nagle, commented: *'He laid foundations on which his successors were proud to build.'* The lack of cardiological equipment at the hospital did not stop him from keeping abreast of developments and mastering many new techniques. He was Chairman of the Medical Staff Committees at both

Footnote 3. Paul Wood (1907-1962) was a popular family friend. He was the first modern interventional cardiologist and his *Diseases of the Heart and Circulation* achieved biblical status. He was Australian and famously brash. These were the early days of antihypertensive therapy and much reliance was placed on low-sodium diets. Presenting a patient to students one day, Wood asked him to say how he managed his diet. The man went into great detail about how he made his entire family cut out salt. When going to a restaurant he would make a fuss, ask for the manager and insist that all house delicacies be served salt-free. After the patient left, Wood asked the students what they had learned. They gave various answers such as that the diet worked, or that it needed perseverance. *'All wrong'*, he declared, *'patients likely to stick to a low-salt diet are overly compulsive, meticulous, arrogant, and often insufferable'*. He too smoked heavily; he too died of a heart attack.

Selly Oak and Solihull and, at one time, President of the West Midlands Physicians Association. He was elected to Fellowship of the Royal College of Physicians in 1967.

He was remembered later *'as tall, urbane, slightly detached...but behind a bland exterior he had an active enquiring mind...calling him into consultation was rather like calling in the Recording Angel; that which had lain hidden was made apparent. As a clinical physician, I doubt if I have ever worked with a better. He seemed a very even-tempered man, but he was not tolerant of the bogus or pretentious, and in (his) quiet questioning way he was apt to take apart those who showed these qualities...it was impossible to leave him behind in conversation. He always understood and was apt to end up two or three moves ahead'* (Nagle, personal communication).

Figure 6.4 With Peter, Anthony and John

These memories were paralleled by some in Munk's Roll (footnote 4): *'He was an excellent colleague and his great interest in those worked with him evoked in turn an unlimited devotion from all his associates...It is a mystery how, after all this, he found time for his many cultural pursuits, including music, poetry and a special interest in Shakespeare, as well as fishing and bird-watching. Unfortunately, the last year of his life was dogged by ill-health and after his official retirement he was only back for a short while in his Holt home, his beloved Norfolk, before death claimed him.'*[4]

In other words, he was in most ways carved from the same stone as his father, uncle and grandfather: upright of bearing, conscientious and compassionate. Yet many photos betray a wistful world-weariness about the eyes. My memories are of a kindly, silver haired man with a sardonic smile who smelt faintly of pipe smoke. A model grandfather, he was always kind and, for someone otherwise reserved, surprisingly playful. He taught me to fly fish on the Hill House lawn where previously he had tickled me to choking point. He put my brother and I through cricket school at Edgbaston and was generously enthusiastic about any minor achievements of my own on the rugby or cricket field.

Footnote 4. Munk's Roll is a series of published works containing biographical entries of all past fellows and licentiates of the Royal College of Physicians. It was initially the work of the College's Harveian Librarian, William Munk. The first volume (published in 1861) contains details dating back to the foundation of the College in 1518; subsequent volumes (available online) take us up to the present day.

He must have had a raffish side for he wore a monocle and drove a black Armstrong-Siddeley. My grandparents were sociable and both big spirits drinkers in the Madmen manner of the times. Sadly, he died relatively young from pancreatic cancer in 1970 (figure 6.5). In those days, sufferers were frequently subjected to a Whipple's procedure - wholesale clear-out of many abdominal

Figure 6.5 On the Jolly boat, 1967

organs. He retired early for Christmas. I picture him pale, emaciated, carving the turkey. He died six weeks later.

His brother John, another smoker, lived on till the age of 78 when lung cancer claimed him. Both brothers illustrated a different meaning of the term, general practitioner. They were men who began their careers in the community before moving into hospital practice. As GPs, they had honed more specialised skills; as consultants, they remained generalists who never forgot their roots. The absence of such generalism among their counterparts is one reason for inefficiency in the NHS today.

#   #   #

The creation of the NHS

There is a tendency to assume that the National Health Service Act of 1946 was the culmination of a single clear idea, realized in a glorious post-war dawn. The reality was messier: the NHS Act was a *'composite of multiple and parallel motives and notions.'*[5]

Across Europe following the First World War, the need for reconstruction favoured state intervention. Newly formed central health departments, often guided by medical experts, engaged in the delivery of health care. The Dawson Report of 1920 highlighted the need for better coordination between general practice (primary), hospitals (secondary) and specialist centres (tertiary care).[6] This period saw a rapid expansion of clinics and dispensaries, particularly for infants and children. The 1929 Local Government Act permitted local boroughs to increase their investment in health provision. Poor Law hospitals were transferred to municipal authorities and developed as general hospitals.

In other words, the inter-war years were more than a blank backdrop to later reforms. Nevertheless, there was growing consensus in the years leading up to the Second World War that existing services were inadequate and unsustainable. The outbreak of war necessitated the creation of an Emergency Medical Service (EMS) for the wounded. The EMS is credited with establishing an embryonic health service and facilitating nationalization. The War itself reinforced support for expansion of the state's social and economic responsibilities.

By 1941, some 21 million people were provided care under the National Insurance Act and two-thirds of GPs were participating in the panel system. Many people remained uncovered. The Ministry of Health was formulating a post-war policy by which services would be available to the whole population. William Beveridge (1879-1963) laid the foundations for the new service in his eponymous report the following year.[7] He provided a blueprint for post-war welfare reform while the landslide Labour victory of 1946 allowed for its realization.

The key political figure popularly credited with steering negotiations to a successful conclusion was Nye Bevan (1897-1960). From Tredegar in the South Welsh Valleys, he started work in coal mines aged 13 years. He witnessed his father and other family members die from poverty-related conditions. He also experienced first-hand the merits of a small 'Medical Aid Society'. He rose from union activist to be minister of health in Clement Atlee's reformist Labour government (figure 6.6).

Figure 6.6 'Nye Bevan

The NHS Act 1946 finally provided a family doctor to the entire population. The new service was tax-funded, accessible to all and free at the point of delivery. Nationalization of existing voluntary and municipal hospitals was effected and Lloyd George's insurance scheme extended to all. The Bill originally emphasised that health centres were to be a central feature. At public cost, premises would be equipped and staffed for medical and dental services, health promotion, local health authority clinics and sometimes for specialist outpatient sessions. However, this programme was aborted before it even started.

New regional structures were set up with medical representation at all levels. The establishment of the NHS involved inevitable compromises leaving certain tensions unresolved, e.g. between local government control and national government's responsibility, between public accountability and professional participation. Notably, the price for Bevan of hospital consultants' accepting salaried contracts was continued private practice; GPs remained outside the service altogether as independent contractors. The final outcome was a victory for paternalistic rationalists and medical technocrats - for the values of efficiency and equity rather than responsiveness.[8]

Medicine politicized

Honigsbaum has highlighted the importance of doctors as key decision-makers.[9] Certainly, civil servants could not match the influence of the BMA in the creation of the NHS. That said, an important constraint on the BMA was its inability to speak for a unified profession. It represented non-elite GPs and faced a more powerful interest group, the consultants represented by Royal Colleges.

Panel doctors had long recognized the need to organize a professional association focussed on their needs; hence the formation of the Medical Practitioners Union (MPU) which affiliated to the Trades Union Congress in 1937. From the late 30s, the MPU worked with the Socialist Medical Association (SMA) to formulate a transition from the panel system to a more comprehensive health service. Key elements were to be health centres, salaried teams, state-provided equipment and support staff. Both were opposed to vested interests like the BMA.

The BMA represented three quarters of all doctors by 1948. Unsurprisingly, the BMA privileged remuneration over other concerns.[10] The SMA was therefore dissatisfied with the final settlement and its lack of democratic accountability. More idealistic GPs viewed the BMA as the petty bourgeois - representing the traditional entrepreneur interested only in raising capitation rates, predictably anti-government and anti-NHS. These antagonisms have reverberated ever since.

Like everyone else, Britain's GPs were weary after six years of war. The younger ones had been called up while those who had stayed behind had done their own work and that of their colleagues as well. They felt that doctors who had been in the services had enjoyed an interesting time while those who had served were resentful that their practices had disintegrated. They returned to a vastly different world, an atmosphere of demoralisation and disillusion, with poorer relationships within the profession than ever before.

Money, status and recruitment go hand in hand. GP pay was based on the recommendations of the Spens Committee, appointed in 1945.[11] Spens believed that the GPs' average income was too low, in the light of the length of training, the arduousness of life compared with other professions, the greater danger to health, and the skills required. Spens thought that, before the war, many doctors had been deterred from becoming specialists by the certainty of many lean years. The NHS would remove this deterrent and, if GPs were not well paid also, recruitment would suffer. Only less able young doctors would enter this branch of medicine, to the detriment of the profession and the public. Spens recommended a payment level above the pre-war average and wished to see a system enabling good and energetic doctors to achieve substantial earnings.[11]

The Spens report determined pay on the basis of capitation, i.e. GPs' income depended on the number of their patients. Their independence thus assured, GPs would be taxed as though they were self-employed (though, unlike most people in small businesses, they could not set their own fees). With a few exceptions, such as payment for a medical certificate for private purposes, no money would pass between patient and doctor. This system provided no financial incentive to improve services, but nor was there any incentive to over-treat patients.

Relations between the BMA and Bevan were embittered by his unwillingness to raise capitation rates as recommended in the final Spens report of 1946. BMA rhetoric was increasingly militant with GPs' views of the impending changes generally hostile. Bevan had persuaded consultants into the service in part by merit awards - 'stuffing their mouths with gold' in his famous phrase. It was a tactic he decided to employ again. Finally, Bevan offered concessions that minimized the importance of salaries and resistance crumbled with 8000 doctors changing sides between February and May, 1948.[12]

GPs, fearing that they might be no more than officials in a state service, had argued successfully for a contract for services rather than a contract of service. As a result, they remained independent practitioners, self-employed and organising their own professional lives.

The public were encouraged to sign on with those doctors willing to enter the scheme, leaving others with the choice of joining as well or losing their practices. Within a month 90 per cent of the population had signed up with a GP. Twenty thousand GPs joined the scheme as they saw private practice disappearing before their eyes.[13] The NHS Act made it illegal to sell 'goodwill'. Instead, a fund was established that compensated GPs when they retired, but it was not inflation-linked. The GPs' contract for a 24-hour service, the nature of the complaints procedures and even the patients' NHS cards were virtually unchanged.

Overall, medical practitioners proved more influential in the creation of National Health Insurance a generation earlier because NHI was more congruent with private practitioners' interests. By 1948, the war had moved citizens' interests centre stage with the extension of a welfare state. Amended NHS legislation retained capitation fees as the basis for GP remuneration although a salaried component was to assume greater importance during reforms of the 60s and 90s.

Mirroring GPs' principal inclinations, the new service was individualistic and curative rather than social and preventive.

Early years, early challenges
Rose-tinted historiography in support of Beveridge's vision coupled with critical coverage of the role played in transition by Bevan and the British Medical Association have tended to obscure shortcomings in the new National Health Service.[14]

The NHS swiftly ran into difficulties at a time of austerity. Costs were expected to peak in the face of new demands, then fall as these were met. Unsurprisingly, both demands and costs continued to rise. There was a desperate need for investment in plant. The quality of care was variable, particularly in inner cities. In 1952, prescription charges were introduced (at the rate of one shilling a prescription). These did not reverse the rising national drug bill but did trigger Bevan's resignation.

The idea of the NHS as a fundamental turning point reflects more substantial changes affecting the secondary sector where hospitals were effectively nationalised. Social changes that pre-dated the NHS (notably, the egalitarianism of the war years) or post-dated it (such as more recent major therapeutic breakthroughs) are also conflated with 1948. In reality, general medical care had been reorganised but not transformed.

For general practitioners, the NHS represented an elaboration of the system of National Health Insurance under which a capitation system also operated. Many of the detailed regulations of the NHI scheme were simply transferred into the NHS. These were compiled in that industrial artefact of hallowed memory, the 'Red Book'. The major change was to extend health care, free at the point of delivery, from insured working-class males to the whole population. However, there were limited economic incentives to provide good patient care; lists were kept long and costs low. The standards and social ethos of care were largely a continuation of the old panel system.[15]

Workloads rose with the incorporation of more women and children onto patient lists and the expanded take-up of free health services.[16] Patients, uncertain of their rights, came with questions. There appeared to be a rise in the workload. Much untreated illness was brought to light, particularly in women who had suffered for years from chronic conditions such as prolapse.

Doctors had feared a loss of independence and the growth of bureaucracy. Many GPs adjusted in ways redolent of 1911 and the club or 'sixpennny doctors' with fast throughput where prior conditions were similar. The alacrity with which doctors jettisoned their private patients after the NHS was revealing. Meeting their superior expectations was no longer economic. *'I didn't mind wasting my time with these patients before the (National Health) Service started, but they're not worth it anymore.'*[17]

Paperwork changed; bills were no longer necessary but there were forms for eye tests, sickness, milk and coal. Under NHI, GPs had received medical record envelopes in which they had to keep a note of consultations *'in such a form as the Minister determined'* (see chapter 5). Wisely, ministers never defined how this should be. Now the entire registered population had an NHS envelope which transferred from one GP to another when they moved. It came to contain not only the GP's notes but also hospital letters, so potentially everyone now had a single medical record from birth to death.

The medical profession had not anticipated the scale and speed of change in social character, having envisaged it as merely an extension of NHI to the working class. GPs liked not having to send bills and enjoyed more egalitarian relationships though patients were apparently more assertive. Incorporating better-educated patients who expected more time and attention could be problematic but a two-tier service did not materialize.

GPs remained the backbone of country cottage hospitals and small voluntary hospitals for services like anaesthesia and geriatrics but, as independent contractors with fewer hospital appointments, they became more cut off from hospitals.

The tide of health reforms left GP morale at a low ebb. Some considered the future of general practice itself to be in jeopardy.[18] GPs were unimpressed by the financial compensation for the goodwill of practices and the initial remuneration settlement, only 20% above the 1939 level. The Danckwerts award (see below) was to raise it to 100% above the 1939 level only in 1952.

Working conditions
In 1948 little information about general practice was available. By 1952 more was known: there were 17,204 GPs in England and Wales providing unrestricted services, plus 1,689 permanent assistants and another 309 trainees.[19] The number was increasing only slowly. A little over half were in partnership. In rural or semi-urban areas a third of GPs were single-handed, a third in partnerships of two, and a third in larger partnerships. The main surgery would be in a small town or other convenient focal point. In urban areas most of the doctors were single-handed, practising from their own homes. Even in partnerships, the GPs might see little of one other. The arrangement was largely financial, though it was easier to cover the doctors' time off.

The distribution of GPs was uneven. An autonomous body, the Medical Practices Committee, established a system that defined areas as over-doctored, under-doctored or intermediate, and barred over-doctored areas to new entrants.[20] The largest lists were found in the industrial Midlands, the northeast coast, south Yorkshire and Lancashire. Half the population lived in under-doctored areas where the average list size exceeded 2,500 and which were designated as in need of more GPs. Here it was possible for any doctor to set up practice, putting up a name plate and encouraging patients to register.

Before the NHS began a few GPs had made an excellent living but many were poorly paid and some had to employ debt collectors. The NHS gave them security and a higher average income. Because they were paid by a flat capitation fee, those in the industrial areas who had large lists of 4,000 became more affluent but had difficulty serving their patients properly. Previously wealthy GPs in rural or rich suburban residential areas with many private patients, but with small lists, were far worse off.[21]

New entrants to general practice were supplicants; they would be expected to work long hours, reach equality of pay with their seniors in possibly seven years, accept the hierarchical system of the practice, generally behave themselves and probably do most of the practice obstetrics.[22]

With the advent of the NHS, perceptions of a desirable lifestyle evolved. Some of their successors viewed the 'old school' critically - for their total absorption in work, unlimited hours, instant availability, moral and financial support to some patients. This change was both the cause and effect of several factors: the growth in partnerships, purpose-built premises, ancillary staff, appointment systems, fewer surgeries, more stable public funding and rising status. All contributed to the growth of a private space and reduction in priority attached to public duties rather than personal satisfaction.

Clinical changes
Central to their increased workload, GPs noted an increase in their treatment of 'women's complaints' and childhood illnesses. Maternity services were safer with the advent of Obstetric Lists of GPs approved to undertake deliveries, wider access to consultants and hospital pathology services. Patients came for free treatment and prescriptions, e.g. for Epsom salts, that they could have purchased over the counter but the capitation system gave GPs little incentive to spend more on their patients.

One of the first quantitative accounts of the work of a GP was presented by John Fry practicing in Beckenham.[23] He analysed attendances in 1951 by age and sex, noting the reasons for the consultation (table 6.1). Respiratory infections, digestive diseases, neuroses, skin disorders and cardiovascular problems headed the list. The GP dealt with minor ill-health and those major diseases that did not require admission to hospital. Three-quarters of his patients came to see him during the year.

Table 6.1   A year in John Fry's practice, 1952: diseases detailed[23]

Disease	No in practice	Sex ratio (M:F)	No per 1000
Hypertension	58	16:42	12.9
Coronary artery disease	29	22:7	7
Valvular heart disease	18	11:7	4
Peptic ulcers	55	45:10	12.3
Neoplasms	31	19:12	6.9
Epilepsy	16	8:8	3.5
Tuberculosis	40	21:19	8.8
Diabetes mellitus	10	7:3	2.3
Neurological	18	8:10	4.0
Disc lesions	30	18:12	6.7
Pneumonias	66	37:29	12.5
Chronic bronchitis	44	24:20	10
Rheumatoid/osteoarthritis	14	5:9	3.1
Pernicious anaemia	9	5:4	2.0

Philip Hopkins studied the impact of general practice on the hospital service in the early 1950s. He presented data for a practice of roughly 1500 patients with a consultation rate of 3.3 per year. In three years the practice had referred 860 patients on a total of 1,225 occasions. Of the referrals, 54 per cent were for treatment, often already defined by the GP. Because direct access to laboratories and X-rays was denied by the local hospital, many were referred solely for a test. Often referrals were to exclude serious illness before a label of 'psychoneurosis' was attached. Only in 183 cases was it for a consultant's opinion on diagnosis or further management.[24]

The NHS established GP referral as almost invariable practice, imposing at least a partial barrier for patients seeking hospital care. The decision to go to hospital was transferred from patient to GP, reducing patient freedom and increasing the cost-effectiveness of the system. The 'gatekeeper system' institutionalised the separation of primary and secondary care. Family doctors defended it because they had continuing responsibility for individual patients, consultants because it protected them from cases that might be trivial or outside their field of interest, and government because it saved money to have a filter system.[25]

Relationships between GPs and specialists altered over time. Previously, specialists had made their money from private practice and many patients came on referral. Once the NHS was established there was no shortage of NHS patients and few consultants made a substantial income from private practice. All were at least partly salaried and most ceased to have any financial reason to be grateful to GPs.

Growing discontent

The Spens Committee left the adjustment of post-war remuneration to others. GPs had therefore entered the service paid on a provisional basis with the promise of a review. They rapidly became dissatisfied with their earnings and a grossly inadequate betterment factor to bring GP pay up to 1948 levels.[26] The review that had been promised did not materialise. Two years after the NHS began, the annual conference of Local Medical Committees (which represent all GPs in an area) instructed the General Medical Services Committee (GMSC) of the BMA to make preparations for the ending of contracts.[27] The dispute continued until 1951 when it was agreed to go to arbitration. GPs grumbled but there was little constructive discussion about how matters could be improved.

> *'Something has gone wrong in general practice today. We treat the same people and similar complaints, and many of us have been doing the job for many a long year, and it is puzzling to say what has happened to bring about the change, for change there is. The doctor is irritable with the patients and they are noticing it and commenting on it. The patients are more aggravating and the doctor is noticing it. GPs had been promised more help, an easier life and no bad debts. He had got much more work, in some cases less income as private practice slumped, no bad debts, no help at all, a lot of personal frustration, had lost his soul when he lost the right to sell his practice, and felt that he no longer ran his practice - it was run for him.'*[28]

There was concern that practice would evolve into *'a sort of glorified hospital out-patient department where intimate knowledge of the patient, continuity of care and the idea of the doctor as guide, philosopher and friend are sacrificed to a hurried impersonal machine.'*[29] As before and since, the mythical virtues of a golden age were contrasted with scenarios for the present day. The reality was more prosaic and more complicated. The editor of the Lancet took up the GPs' cause:

> *'Admittedly general practice in this country was deteriorating long before the NHS was introduced, and its further deterioration is due rather to a heavier load than to any legislative alterations in the Act. But on balance the effects of the Act on such practice have so far been for the worse and there is little evidence that its problems are being squarely faced. Of the two possible policies, the first is to say general practice is so often unsatisfactory that the correct course is to compensate for its defects - to develop hospital and specialist services in such a way that the short-comings of GPs become relatively unimportant. This, we cannot help thinking, is the policy that is, consciously or unconsciously, being followed. The alternative is to make a big positive effort to raise the level and prestige of general practice. This can still be done.'*[30]

GPs as a body politic have often appeared repellently self-preoccupied but the state of their morale is captured in these *cris-de-coeur*. It was about to get worse.

The Collings Report

In 1948 the Nuffield Provincial Hospitals Trust funded Dr Joseph Collings, who had trained in New Zealand as a GP, to look at general practice.[31] Collings surveyed 55 English practices, all outside London. His report, published in the Lancet, highlighted wide and unacceptable variation in standards.

'There are no real standards for general practice. What the doctor does and how he does it, depends almost wholly on his own conscience.'[17] In city practices the conditions were so bad that he neither saw effective practice nor believed it was possible. He described surgeries without examination couches, where records lay loose round the room or in boxes, consulting rooms with a chair for the doctor but not for the patient, and couches where boxes and bottles had rested so long that they adhered to the surface. Symptoms clearly demanding examination or referral were often passed over. Snap diagnosis and outdated medical knowledge were commonplace. Anything approaching a general or complete examination was out of the question under the prevailing conditions. In rural practice the surgeries were more pleasant, although often lacking basic equipment.

General practice was poorest in proximity to large hospital centres and improved in scope and quality as one moved away. The worst practice was found where the need was greatest, in areas of dense population. The country doctor apparently spent more time with his patients and knew them better. Urban-residential practice fell between the two; conditions for the patients were better than in the industrial surgeries for *'the patient with more cultivated taste expects attention to the niceties.'*[17] Some city premises required condemnation in the public interest.

Taken as a whole, the report (of just 30 pages) was a damning indictment. Collings wrote that there were no objective standards for practice and no recognised criteria by which standards might be established. The reputation of general practice, Collings said, had been maintained through identification with an ideal picture that would no longer stand up to examination.

Yet Collings remained an enthusiast for general practice. Instead of building up hospital services, he felt the aim should be to see how they could be reduced. That meant team-working among doctors, nurses, social workers and technicians in good premises, which might be based on group practice units perhaps serving 15,000-25,000 people. The widening schism between hospital and general practice, the lack of local authority interest and the failure of administrative co-ordination, in his view, did nothing to help.

Collings' three further articles in 1953 were largely ignored.[32-34] In them he argued for group practice, rather than health centres. Group practice was evolutionary and was the only way to breathe life back into the finest elements of traditional general practice. Collings laid out a detailed and costed plan both at practice and at national level. He discussed the staffing, the architectural design of premises and the management and personality issues that arose in groups. He considered the financial inducements required and the financial advantage to government: the better general practice became, the less the burden on expensive hospitals.

Collings entered the demonology of general practice, but stirred others into activity. Charles Hill, Secretary of the BMA, advised the Council that Collings had to be 'answered'. Stephen Hadfield, an assistant secretary at the BMA, visited four or five practices chosen at random each week over the following year.[35] His report was more balanced and statistically based. 92 per cent of GPs were providing adequate quality of care or something better. Three out of four paid reasonable attention to record keeping. Seven per cent of both young and old GPs needed to revise the methods of diagnosis they used. In 10 per cent of surgeries the accommodation was dismal, bare, inhospitable and dirty.

Relations with the hospitals were good and probably better than before the NHS, when voluntary hospitals kept outpatients to maintain high attendance records. With public health services the position had deteriorated. GPs valued district nurses but reported little co-operation from health visitors and complained bitterly about them as a waste of nursing manpower. Hadfield believed that GPs, hospital consultants and public health doctors had to work more closely with one another. They were treading different paths while the NHS was crying out for unified administration.

Another problem that faced GPs was their 24-hour commitment. They were contracted to provide a round-the-clock service. As independent practitioners, they had to find cover for holidays and leisure time. The first deputising service made its appearance in 1956 as a private venture of two South African doctors working in London. Against the initial opposition of the BMA, and with no support from government, Solomons and Bane launched an emergency call service, providing duty doctors in cars with two-way radio contact to a central base. GPs, at least in the capital, now had a new way of covering their practices to give themselves time off duty.[36]

Every profession, said the BMJ, has its quota of unsatisfactory practitioners; that a few should be outstandingly bad was only to be expected. The remedy was in better selection of students. Unsatisfactory relations with other parts of the service also impeded the work of the GP and the NHS' tripartite structure was a root cause of this. Finally, the rapid advances in medical science over the previous three decades were creating additional stresses.[37]

The Danckwerts Award
Mr Justice Danckwerts had been commissioned to examine GPs' pay. His report
of March 1952 proved to be a portent of change. Taking account of inflation since
1939 and increases in the incomes of other professions, he recommended that the
central pool divided among the country's GPs should be increased to £51 million, a
rise of roughly 25 per cent.[38] The government had never expected an award of this
size but it certainly benefited general practice. Within three months there was
agreement on raising the flat capitation rate to increase recruitment, an initial
practice allowance to make it easier for new doctors to enter practice, and financial
encouragement to form partnerships and group practices.

The maximum number of patients a single-handed doctor could have was reduced
from 4,000 to 3,500, which also became the maximum average per principal for a
partnership.[39] The profession was broadly satisfied with the outcome and the award
rapidly had the desired effect. GPs received a considerable sum in back-pay; some
spent it on modernising their premises. The following year there was a net increase
of 806 doctors and 1,118 new doctors joined partnerships. Longstanding assistants
often became partners. The number who were single-handed fell by 312.[40] It was a
powerful demonstration of the effect of financial incentives on general practice.
The profession agreed that £100,000 each year should be top-sliced to provide
interest-free loans to group practices wishing to provide new or substantially better
premises. This loan scheme was so popular that some applications could not be
approved. In 1954, 36 applications were accepted totalling £159,000.

Appointments systems, tried experimentally in a few places, had been shown to
reduce the number of visits requested. A more even distribution of doctors was
emerging as a result of the work of the Medical Practices Committee. There was a
steady decrease in the number of patients living in under-doctored areas, from 21
million in 1952 to 9 million in 1956. Although the arrangements went some way to
encourage group practice, it remained difficult for a small practice to find the funds
to pay an additional doctor. There were comparatively few vacancies and two-fifths
of them attracted over 40 applicants each. The easiest place to enter practice was
the north of England, where list sizes were biggest.[40] Health centre development,
which might have provided new posts, was minimal. The concept was unpopular
with GPs, rents were high and it took a long time to design and build health centres
partly because of the need for many parties to agree plans.

The Danckwerts award illuminated the path ahead but it did not solve all problems.
Variation of practice standards remained a consequence of independent practitioner
status. While the energetic could improve their practices substantially, not all GPs
bothered - and their patients suffered. Enoch Powell observed that whether the
practitioner was good, bad (up to the point of incurring a disciplinary stoppage) or
indifferent, he got the same payment for the same list.[41] Inside general practice he
could increase his earnings only by increasing the size of his list. The doctor was

not primarily dependent on ability or reputation to increase his list. The doctor's willingness to prescribe a placebo or to complete the desired certificate, might be as effective as skilled and conscientious care.

The GP's situation combined private enterprise and state service without the characteristic advantages of either. He could not reap the rewards of building up a practice, and the better he did his work the worse off he was. Money spent on premises, equipment and staff did not increase his income, for the cost came from an income that would be undiminished if he did nothing. If he restricted his list to the number that could be treated properly, he merely ended with a smaller income than less able or less scrupulous fellows. Powell believed that the essence of the private enterprise system, competition for gain, had been gouged out of family doctoring, leaving an empty shell.[41]

A Royal College at last

Meanwhile, another longstanding struggle was reaching its climax. The proposal for a college of general practitioners was presented once more to the BMA General Practice Review Committee in October 1951. As usual, it encountered strong opposition from the Royal Colleges of Physicians, of Surgeons and of Obstetricians and Gynaecologists. They would have supported a joint faculty of general practice within their own structures, but not a separate institution which risked weakening their influence.

In November 1952 the College of General Practitioners was finally formed in secret when the memorandum of articles of association was signed by a steering committee. The College ethos was, from the start, to lead from the front. It encouraged high standards of service, teaching and research. After six months there were 2,000 members.[42,43] Within four years it had developed 22 regional faculties. Although membership increased steadily, only a minority joined; in 1957 the membership was a little over 4,000. College influence was largely restricted to its adherents and no responsibility was taken for 'weaker brethren.'[12] Unlike the older colleges, membership as yet played little part in professional advancement. The General Medical Services Committee of the BMA had wider responsibilities and was in a position to influence all GPs, as it did in 1954 when Local Medical Committees were asked to inspect practice premises.[44]

Central to the College vision was that family medicine had its own skills and knowledge base that were as important as anything the hospital services might bestow upon it. The work of men such as Keith Hodgkin, a GP, and Michael Balint, a psychoanalyst, was central to this. Balint, at case conferences at the Tavistock Clinic (see chapter 7), cast new light on the nature of the consultation and was an important figure in the establishment of general practice as a discipline in its own right.[45] He argued for a different type of education and research. He regarded the relationship of the GP and the consultant as a perpetuation of the pupil-teacher relationship.[46]

One of the College's first initiatives was to see what medical students were taught about general practice. Although medical students from a number of schools visited GPs, only Manchester and Edinburgh had teaching units in the medical school.[47] It was the beginning of a struggle to attain recognition of general practice as a subject entitled to a place in the overcrowded student curriculum.[42]

The College epidemic observation unit in Surrey was established to plot infectious disease in the community. The Birmingham research unit, led by Crombie and Pinsent, undertook national morbidity surveys. Between May 1955 and April 1956 careful records of a year's consultations were kept by 106 practices, involving 400,000 patients and 1.5 million contacts.[48] These practices provided a clear description of their clinical work. The study showed who was consulting GPs for what, and what was being referred to hospital. National consultation rates for cancer, neurosis, circulatory and respiratory disease, and arthritis and rheumatism were provided for the first time and the surveys improved knowledge of the incidence and prevalence of most forms of disease.

The College was granted its Royal Charter in 1972. Its lasting impact on education and training standards has been enormous. Nowadays membership via examination is an absolute prerequisite for entering the profession. The College journal exemplifies the extent to which the academic foundations of general practice have been transformed. Latterly, the College has also raised its political profile as an effective advocate for the discipline.

Conclusion

The advent of the new national service afforded generalists such as my grandfather and his brother unforeseen opportunities to develop their careers. Nevertheless, jobbing GPs felt that they were held in little respect. Matters were not improved by the evidence of Lord Moran, President of the RCP, to the Royal Commission on Doctors' and Dentists' Pay in 1958.

> *The Chairman: 'It has been put to us by a good many people that the two branches of the profession, general practitioners and consultants, are not senior or junior to one another, but they are level. Do you agree with that?'*
>
> *Lord Moran: 'I say emphatically No. Could anything be more absurd? I was Dean at St Mary's Hospital Medical School for 25 years, and all the people of outstanding merit, with few exceptions, aimed to get on the staff. It was a ladder off which they fell. How can you say that the people who fall*

off the ladder are the same as those who do not? . . . I do not think you will find a single Dean of any medical school who will give contrary evidence.'

The Chairman: 'I think you are the first person who has suggested to us that general practitioners are a somewhat inferior branch.'[49]

Moran's infamous dictum reflected the low status of general practice at the time - *'diagnostically destitute and therapeutically sterile'* - especially among teachers in medical school. He later attempted a retraction, stressing that he only wished to secure material rewards for those who spent long years of training as specialists, waiting in comparative penury.[50] Family doctors never forgave him.[51]

GPs' fortunes continued to fluctuate and varied geographically. From the 1920s onward, rapid advances in medical science had *'imposed stresses and strains on all types of practice.'[52]* It was particularly hard to sustain both performance and income in poorer areas. In suburban or rural areas where mixed social practice could be created, higher standards were achieved.

Overall, the early years of the NHS had seen remuneration stagnate and morale (ever a commodity that general practitioners could talk down) decline. My grandfather and his brother both looked back on their earlier career moves with relief and satisfaction. On the other hand, these reforms had brought fewer changes than GPs might have feared. Therapeutic advances were all the while extending the range of conditions that family doctors could manage effectively. The stage was set for another upturn.

Chapter Seven – High Water
(1955-1985)

'Education is simply the soul of a society
as it passes from one generation to another.'
G.K.Chesterton

The seventh generation

The careers of eleven doctors to succeed the first William Skrimshire, apothecary and surgeon of Wisbech, have thus far been outlined. In rather different ways, John's son, Pat, and Geoffrey's son, Peter (my father), were next to maintain the generalist tradition. Their boyhoods were coloured by the excitements, though not the depradations, of war. They qualified into a National Health Service that over its early decades was both popular and organisationally stable. As their careers reached their conclusion, its popularity and stability were being called into question. The post-war optimism that floated the welfare state had long evaporated.

Peter Gillam

My father went to Gresham's, inevitably, where his collection of prizes rivalled his uncle Harry's and he followed two Skrimshires as Captain of the School. He went on to St Catharine's, Cambridge with a scholarship before following his father to University College Hospital.

In 1953 he married Anne O'Brien Bell, a nurse at UCH. Her father, Louis, was a GP and the first Roman Catholic to be accepted by Trinity College, Dublin to read medicine. Sadly, he died young from tuberculosis contracted while working in the slums of Birmingham (see Appendix). (One anecdote of my mother's recalls Harry Skrimshire's generous approach to his patients. At a time when poverty made payment of doctors' bills difficult to many, Louis told his wife, Greta, that *'if I don't treat patients, regardless of payment, they won't come back when they really need me.'*)

Two house jobs at UCH preceded Peter's national service at Oswestry - perhaps the nearest he approached to a GP's work. He returned to the Hammersmith Hospital in London before going back to UCH as senior registrar to Max (later Lord) Rosenheim (footnote 1), a contemporary of Geoffrey's. Though seldom home before his children's bedtimes, he was a fond and affectionate father (figure 7.1). He would drop us off at school on the way to work. Bizarrely, he drove a red, Meschersmitt 'bubble car' barely longer than he was tall (6' 4'').

Footnote 1. My father would expatiate at length on the merits of Max Rosenheim (1908-72) of whom he was a protégé. Of German Jewish extraction, Max was professor of medicine at UCH, went on to become President of the RCP and ended his days as Baron Rosenheim of Camden.

Figure 6.1 Peter with the author, 1956

In the late sixties, he published (with Brian Pritchard) two seminal papers on the treatment of hypertension using the first beta-blocker, propranolol.[1,2] They were to be among the most frequently cited articles published between 1945 and 1989. With an illustrious CV, he was expected to apply for London teaching hospital jobs but he was a country boy at heart. He always hoped that a consultant post might come up in Norwich and take him back to his beloved Norfolk. That was not to be, but the choice of Salisbury proved in many ways felicitous.

The early loss of her father cast a long shadow over Anne's life and her schooling through the years of the second war was much disrupted. A naturally extrovert, bubbly personality, she had suffered a first psychotic breakdown at the age of 18. Peter knew of this but, like his great grandfather before him, he was undeterred. Following the birth of their fourth child, she suffered a further hypomanic episode and thereafter relapsed every four or five years. Manic depression, or bipolar disorder as it is now termed, can take a surprisingly predictable course. Oftentimes, Peter would reflect on the strange symmetry and wonder if, like Lizzy, his Anne would end her days in an asylum.

Peter was scrupulously committed in his care of Anne down 52 years of married life together but they struggled to come to terms with her illness. He could not bear to see her locked up and largely looked after her himself. The result was that she never adjusted to a more formalised regime of care. The GMC discourages doctors from treating family members with good reason.[3]

He took refuge in his work. James Marigold, a consultant colleague, described him thus: *'Peter's capacity for hard work was legendary. He was always in the infirmary before his colleagues in the morning and left after them at night, often to make a domiciliary visit on the way home. He never failed to see his patients on Saturdays and Sundays as well, if necessary. He would ring his patients and carers up in the evenings if there was some test result which he knew was concerning them. He would go to see them at home, both as a friend and a doctor. As he had himself written, remembering his long line of ancestors, what kept them going was their commitment to working beyond the call of duty.*

Less tangible was his astonishingly positive effect on all who worked in the hospital. Life with Peter was full of laughter and great fun. He was prone to gently mocking whoever and whatever was under discussion. Yet he was self-deprecating and free of pomposity. He participated in, and usually led vigorously, all sporting activities and the hospital pantomime and was invariably first on, and last to leave, the dance floor. He was the first port of call for patients, staff and colleagues needing advice and help, being blessed with a disarming grin, coupled with ease of approach and profound wisdom. Once you had contact with him you were hooked by his distinguished appearance, wit, kindness and abundant good nature. He was always ready to listen and help, however frenetically busy he was.'

If not a GP, Peter was certainly a generalist. Highly trained in chest medicine and cardiology, he turned his hand to all forms of acute medicine. With the burgeoning number of medical specialisms, each with their own training regimes, the 'general physician' was fast becoming extinct. His successor described the shock of taking on his outpatient clinics. *'I was expected to manage heart and chest disease but found myself looking after cancers and conditions I was quite untrained for. I don't know how Peter kept so up to date.'*

There is growing recognition that the NHS is weaker today for the lack of such generalists.[4] Most users of the service are older people. Many of them have several chronic conditions. The ability to manage 'multi-morbidity' patients without cross-referral to costly colleagues is bound to increase efficiency and lower costs, as well as improving patients' experience.

Peter set up the first Coronary Care Unit, a Lymphoma and Leukaemia Clinic, and was very much part of the Day Diagnostic Unit at Salisbury Hospital. Day care is a central part of the NHS now, but 30 years ago it was revolutionary. He served as Chairman of the Hospital Medical Advisory Committee, and on numerous other working parties. He was Regional Advisor to the Royal College of Physicians and was prominent in medical education. As clinical tutor from 1973 to 1978, he helped to establish the new medical school in Southampton.

His academic inclinations found later expression as editor of the monthly Salisbury Medical Bulletin. He contributed a regular ethical column and these writings reveal a wise, practical and only sometimes tendentious sensibility. They provided another outlet for occasionally unorthodox views. A cultured man, he developed a late liking for Bob Dylan and was of the view that Dolly Parton should better have been an opera singer.

Perhaps his proudest achievement was the establishment of the Salisbury Hospice (figure 7.2). He was chairman of the Hospice Trust from 1981 to 1997, and the day centre is named after him. His belief that *"there was no point in joining a committee if you couldn't chair it"* perhaps concealed more autocratic tendencies. He was, after all, 'officer class.'

Politically liberal, he might better be described as a one nation Tory. He was a strong believer in the NHS. As he liked to point out, where other than in his outpatients would he see landed aristocrats wait alongside farm labourers. That said, he saw private patients (among whom was Anthony Eden) in his private rooms in the Cathedral close. He defended this with an uncharacteristic lack of conviction in terms of needing to meet the local expectations of the senior physician. At this time, Secretary of State Barbara Castle, was trying without success to banish private patients from NHS beds.

A commemorative *festschrift* was arranged by his colleagues nine months after his death, followed by a memorial service held in the Cathedral. *'He was the pillar of Figure*

7.2 Opening the hospice, 1990   *medicine in Salisbury, both intellectually and physically - always the epitome of the distinguished physician - tall, and resplendently topped with white hair.'* His father's son.

The last word should fall to John, his twin brother and closest friend. *'Success did not spoil him. He remained the best of companions, most frequently in outdoor activities. Sailing in the creeks at Blakeney (rather bossy at the helm, it should be said), fishing for trout on the Bure or in Wiltshire's chalk streams, bird watching on the marshes at Salthouse, and sharing many a glass, often over a tightly fought game of croquet or bowls on the Hill House lawn.'* I can also picture him thus.

Pat Gillam
Following his father John Gillam (see chapter 6), Pat developed his career in Pembrokeshire. As a family doctor based in Solva, he too left his community better provided for on his retirement than when he started.

He followed his cousins, John and Peter, to Gresham's but chose, like his father and grandfather before him, St Thomas's Hospital for medical training. A stalwart of the hospital water polo team, he also found time to court a school friend of his sister, one Rosemary Collins. She was a frequent summer holiday visitor to the bungalow at Druidstone; so, as her mother-in-law said, 'most suitable.'

He undertook national service in the Navy and was stationed in Malta. Three daughters were followed by a son. He assisted in various practices before settling on a practice near home in Pembrokeshire. At Solva, he and Rosemary converted the Old Church School into a splendid house, with an annexe for his surgery. He ran the practice single-handed, with only reciprocal covering arrangements with other doctors nearby, and undertook his own dispensing. In his last years, he oversaw the building of a medical centre in the village.

Pat's knowledge of the Welsh language was minimal, but his deep identity for their way of life endeared him to his patients. With Rosemary, he developed 40 acres of hill across the bay for a flock of 50 sheep (Dorset Poll, Jacob and Welsh Black), with stabling for their carriage driving horses and Shetland ponies. His Maltese-built sailing boat was immediately recognizable in the bay, so too was he a familiar sight in the country lanes on his chestnut cob (figure 7.3).

Figure 7.3. Pat with Ceri.

His mode of practice, even then, was increasingly unusual - on call round the clock for 365 days of the year. I undertook occasional locums for him and experienced this first-hand (footnote 2). He reminded me of no-one more than the subject of John Berger's acclaimed meditation on humanity, society and the value of healing. *A Fortunate Man* blends text with Jean Mohr's photographs in a series of sociological and philosophical reflections on the doctor's role, the roots of cultural and intellectual deprivation and the motivations that drive medical practice.[5]

A Fortunate Man is a memorial not just to an exceptional individual, Dr John Sassall, but to a way of practising medicine that has now disappeared. In today's culture of working-time directives and the commercialisation of disease it is near impossible to sustain. The book's case studies convey the extraordinary depth of Sassall's commitment to his patients. They also show how powerful an influence the landscape exerts on the community and its stories. *'Sometimes a landscape seems to be less a setting for the life of its inhabitants than a curtain behind which their struggles, achievements and accidents take place.'* Within that landscape, as to Sassall, the community in Solva looked to Pat Gillam as a 'clerk of records'; the

Footnote 2. Being on-call 24/7 was demanding but satisfying. I remember vigils, touch and go, at the bedsides of the seriously ill, with seemingly interminable waits for the ambulance from Haverfordwest. All GPs worry about 'becoming deskilled'. I certainly needed to resurrect old skills. One hardy sheep farmer appeared having all but severed the last third of his index finger. ("Caught it in a saw, didn't I.") He refused hospital. ("Too busy, Boyo.") Surgery was never a strong suit but I somehow cobbled the pieces of his finger together, assuming later gangrene inevitable. The following year he appeared in surgery gesticulating with his heavily scarred, rather rigid but complete digit. ("Look see, you done good, Boyo - but granted not as good as Dr Pat.")

figure to whom they could tell their stories. *'He keeps the records so that, from time to time, they can consult them themselves.'*

Pat's last years were clouded by dementia but, long after the names of people and places had dissolved, he might be seen ambling along the same lanes on the same elderly chestnut cob. Local people knew gently to point his horse in the direction home.

\#   \#   \#

Patterns of illness

This generation witnessed the culmination of an epidemiological transformation as well as a revolution in the means of managing it. The infant mortality rate fell from 36 deaths per 1000 births in the 1950s to less than eight in the 1990s. In the early 1930s, over 400 women died of pregnancy-related causes for every 100,000 births. (Similar maternal mortality ratios are found in low income countries today.) By the 1990s, this figure had dropped to less than 10 deaths per 100,000 births.

More striking still was the shift away from acute infectious diseases to the degenerative diseases associated with ageing of the population. Henceforth, the GP's work consisted in long-term care of chronic diseases like diabetes, in health promotion and screening. Social and economic advances were largely responsible for increasing longevity but a therapeutic revolution played its part.

The remedies available to my grandfather had been extremely limited. The thirty years from 1950 produced an explosion of therapies: e.g. vaccines, steroids, antibiotics, drugs for mental illness, cancer, heart and lung disease. A veritable new Golden Age of Physic and Big Pharma. Despite setbacks such as the thalidomide disaster, 'breakthroughs' seemed a daily media occurrence. Prescribing costs duly escalated.

The modern GP needed to absorb an enormous amount of new and constantly changing knowledge. Between 1959 and 1974, the number of blood tests and x-rays ordered by GPs in England and Wales rose seven-fold as hospitals opened access to these investigations. Between 1953 and 1993, outpatient attendances rose from 47 million a year to 64 million. The shift of care into the community was also associated with a degree of specialisation in general practice. Within partnerships, individual GPs might develop special interests in particular diseases: hypertensions, asthma, diabetes, etc. The sheer volume of new knowledge represented a threat to the generalist.

Reversing the decline

The notorious Collings Report had drawn attention to the poverty of many premises and the variable quality of care provided (see chapter six).[6] By the early

1960s, general practice was in crisis as economic realities failed to match professional aspirations. Three factors helped to restructure general practice. First, there was another change in the way family doctors were paid. This provided a financial incentive to improvement in ways both the profession and government desired. Secondly, innovative GPs began to describe a vision of practice as it might be and sell the vision successfully to their colleagues. Articles began to appear describing better systems of practice organisation, record keeping, appointment systems and the work of nurses.[7] Thirdly, professional organisations began to work behind the scenes to improve facilities, such as GP access to diagnostic services. The BMA was already involved. A quiet partnership between government, the BMA and the Royal College of General Practitioners (RCGP) moulded the most important ideas into a new policy.[8] Donald Irvine, an Ashington GP later Chairman of Council of the RCGP, later listed its six elements[9] (table 7.1).

Table 7.1   *Requirements for renewing general practice (after Irvine[9])*
- Encourage group practice.
- Rehouse GPs in properly equipped, purpose-built premises.
- Help individual GPs develop a viable organisation.
- Give GPs access to hospital-based diagnostic services.
- Introduce nurses and other professionals to form primary health care teams.
- Provide better postgraduate education.

Improved premises and more staff, in the wake of the Danckwerts award, inevitably meant higher costs. GPs were paid from a 'global sum' divided among them. Practice expenses were reimbursed, but reimbursed unselectively, so that those who spent less than average got back too much and the rest too little. Doctors paying little attention to their facilities were financially better off than those trying to provide a good service. The alternative was for family doctors to design, fund and build premises for themselves.

The Family Doctor Charter
In 1961 the Central Health Services Committee set up a special sub-committee under Annis Gillie to advise on the future field work of the general practitioner. The Gillie Report of 1963 described general practice as a 'cottage industry' and made recommendations that were agreed with the BMA leadership.[10] A working party chaired by Sir Bruce Fraser, a wily one-time treasury official and now Permanent Secretary at the Ministry of Health, set about thrashing out the details of implementation.

Following a now familiar pattern, negotiations were disrupted by a bout of professional militancy over unpalatable recommendations from the pay review body. The perspicacious minister, Kenneth Robinson, intervened to avert the threat of mass resignation and broker agreement with the profession's representatives. They too were adroitly led by James Cameron, new chairman of the BMA's

General Medical Services Committee. The resulting Family Doctor Charter was translated into a new contract in 1966. It introduced major changes to remuneration that were to have lasting effects on practice organisation and structure (table 7.2).[11]

A new dispensation
Kenneth Robinson dropped his insistence on a salaried service option, the profession its desire for item-of-service payment, and an atmosphere of trust developed.[12] Overall pay was increased while the proportion of capitation-based income fell relative to basic practice allowances and fees for services such as immunisation. Each doctor was reimbursed for 70% of the wage costs of up to two nursing and/or ancillary staff.

Table 7.2   Aims of the 1965 Family Doctor Charter[11]
  - Increasing recruitment, reducing maximum list sizes to 2,000
  - Undergraduate education orientated towards practice, and good postgraduate education
  - Improved premises and equipment, and an independent corporation to provide funds
  - Adequate supporting staff
  - Direct reimbursement of staff and premises expenditure
  - Incentives for skills and experience
  - Pay to reflect workload, skills and responsibility
  - Reasonable working hours; freedom from unending responsibility to provide services personally
  - Proper pay for work done outside the normal working day
  - A worthwhile, effective and satisfying career with clinical freedom in a personal family doctor service

An independent finance corporation to make loans for the purchase, erection and improvement of premises was set up. There would henceforth be direct repayment of the costs of providing premises, a notional rent reflecting their quality. The central pool was modified so that it covered only general medical services.[13] A basic practice allowance was introduced, with larger allowances for practice in groups, in unattractive areas, after vocational training and for seniority. There was also to be a small fee for every immunisation given and cervical smear carried out. GPs' income became the sum of many fees and allowances, each a reward for work done or an incentive to improve the practice. Paperwork inevitably burgeoned.

The proportion of doctors in single-handed practice declined by three quarters to 12% over the next 25 years as the primary care workforce diversified. The proportion of female practitioners doubled over the same period to 25%. The advent of practice nurses further changed the face of primary care as labour was re-divided. The large-scale expansion of purpose-built health centres and owner-occupied premises supported the growing primary health care team in their evolving roles. Only 28 health centres were built in the first years of the NHS; in the decade following the Charter over 700 new health centres appeared.[14]

The average duration of a consultation was only five minutes and many doctors felt that further advance in general practice would occur only if patients were given more time. Where was this time to come from?[15] Reception staff allowed for structured appointment systems and more efficient allocation of practitioner time according to clinical need. The average number of patients per principal declined from 2282 in 1966 to 1812 in 1991.[16]

Home visits, with all the travelling involved, were regarded as clinically unproductive. Increasingly, GPs reduced visiting, cutting out routine calls to elderly patients whose condition seldom changed, and to sick children whose parents could bring them to the surgery for an immediate appointment. More delegation to ancillary staff freed time for longer consultations. Geoffrey Marsh, a GP in the northeast of England, found that his new practice nurse could successfully relieve the GPs of part of their workload.[17]

There was rapid growth of deputising services in urban areas where the density of the population made them economic. Doctors without access to a deputising service were generally disparaging, but when a service opened most freed themselves of night work for at least some of the week.[18]

These developments gradually altered the doctor's working day. The proportion of patients visited at home halved over the same period, just as the annual number of consultations per patient rose from three to five per patient. The increasing size and complexity of practices was one reason why more practitioner time was spent on activities other than patient care - administration, meetings and training.

Not all the products of the Fraser Working Party were advanced. For example, progress on a comprehensive scheme for universal vocational training of new entrants was delayed by the shortage of doctors. Another commission[19] and further legislation were required before plans evolved by the RCGP were fully implemented in 1982 (see below).

Beyond these changes, the Charter facilitated a subtler ideological shift. The newly instituted College helped to hasten the development of academic departments and the promotion of higher clinical and training standards. The Charter provided an indispensable material base from which to attain these standards.[20]

The premises premise
It is hard to deliver modern, comprehensive primary care from cramped, inadequate accommodation. The health centre had long been considered the solution to this dilemma - paid for, designed and built by local authorities for their own nursing

staff, and for GPs who might rent accommodation. In the first decade of the NHS barely a dozen had opened. Why had they been so unpopular?[21] It was a good idea to have local health authority staff working alongside the GPs, but communication was often minimal, and sometimes there were even separate entrances. GPs lacked confidence in local authorities, with whom they were often at cross-purposes. They might not be consulted before a new health centre was planned. Often the last building to be erected on an estate, the new residents were already on the lists of neighbouring GPs. There might not, after all, be a living to be made.

Until 1966 general practice was under-capitalised, mainly because GPs had to pay for any improvements to their premises themselves, although interest-free loans had been part of the Danckwerts settlement. The GPs' charter introduced direct payments for rent and rates and encouraged the trend towards group practice and the employment of additional staff, which in turn demanded better premises.

There was therefore an upsurge of interest in health centres, for the high rentals were now no longer a charge against personal income. The way the services were delivered was changing; secretaries and receptionists, nurses, health visitors and midwives were increasingly part of group practice teams and needed space. Trainee GP assistants might be employed. Postgraduate education required library space, and if a practice replaced the medical record envelope (which dated back to Lloyd George) with A4 records the space needed for files trebled. No sooner were new surgeries opened than they were found to be cramped.

A group practices loan scheme (subsequently operated by the General Practice Finance Corporation) made it easier to raise the money, and the system of reimbursing 'notional rent' or a 'cost rent' made the option practicable. Self-help became the most common way to improve premises and the cumulative effect on standards was enormous. Only in the inner cities, where there might be planning problems and the cost of land and building was often too much for the practice to bear, did the scheme fail.

In the mid-1960s John Fry estimated that 60 per cent of GP premises had been built before 1900.[22] Health centres were large, costly and slow to build. Yet their popularity increased and construction began to accelerate. By the early 1970s 100 or so were opening each year. By 1974 15 per cent of GPs were working from them, the numbers rising about 2.5 per cent per year.[23] The economic downturn that followed the oil crisis of 1973 (itself the product of the Yom Kippur War) cut the money available for building. Capital spending was limited and priority was given to deprived areas. Barbara Castle's attack on private practice alarmed GPs who thought that if they moved to a health centre they would lose autonomy. The popularity of health centres waned once more.

The advent of the primary health care team

Danckwerts and the Charter together provided a major stimulus to practice expansion. There was a slow but steady increase in the number of doctors working in partnerships and in the closer proximity of group practice. By the end of 1963 every practice had its own health visitor attached. They began their own child welfare and antenatal clinics. In the same year attachment of district nurses to local practices began, followed shortly by midwives. Previously, each nurse or health visitor had served a small geographical area; now her population became that of the GP's practice.[24] Almost unnoticed, there had been a major development of the domiciliary 'primary health care team' (PHCT). Naturally, GPs claimed its leadership.[19]

As the decade progressed, PHCTs increased in number and size. A typical team might comprise four or five GPs, two health visitors, two district nurses, one midwife, one bath attendant and two relief nurses. The incorporation of nurses was most rapid in rural areas. Here, for geographical reasons, the territory of community nurses and GPs usually coincided. In the cities progress was slower for there was a criss-cross pattern of practices. Although city streets had been allocated to individual nurses, in each there might be 30 to 40 GPs with a few patients. Senior nurses often opposed attachment schemes, preferring to care for a population defined by geography rather than by GP registration. They feared the loss of control of community nurses who developed loyalties to the GPs and their patients.[25] Following the Charter, the number of practice nurses employed by the GPs themselves steadily increased.[26]

A broader remit

In the light of various College reports and the work of pioneers, the remit of the PHCT expanded beyond the treatment of minor illness to complex chronic disease management and prevention. The most influential GP of his generation, Julian Tudor Hart, coined the phrase *'anticipatory health care'*. Working in Glyncorrwg, a mining village in South Wales, he began to screen patients between 20 and 64 years of age for risk factors for coronary heart disease and stroke - smoking, cholesterol levels, obesity, diabetes, airways obstruction and alcohol problems. His aim was to move back from end-stage disease to its origins, improve the health of the whole practice by identifying treatable problems at an early, often pre-symptomatic stage, and to look for them systematically, building up a profile of patient information to track progress.[27]

In 1952, Sir George Pickering had demonstrated that blood pressure was continuously distributed in populations. The view that hypertension was not, after all, a discrete condition was resisted by the medical establishment (led by Lord Platt). The epidemiologist Geoffrey Rose later elegantly re-framed the Platt-Pickering controversy by contrasting high risk and public health approaches to disease prevention.[28] In theory, GPs with practice lists covering 97% of the population were uniquely positioned to solve Rose's 'prevention paradox' (footnote 3). By taking responsibility for whole practice populations, GPs could play a major role in improving health by reducing the prevalence of disease risk factors (figure 7.5).

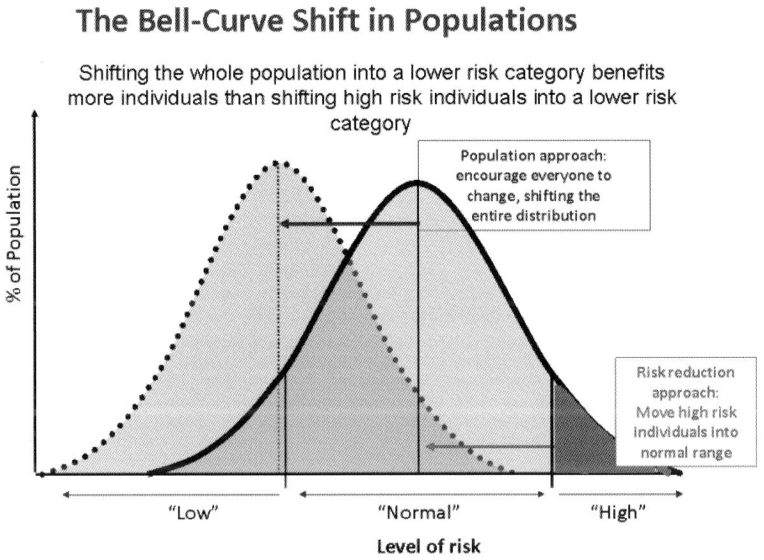

The Bell-Curve Shift in Populations

Shifting the whole population into a lower risk category benefits more individuals than shifting high risk individuals into a lower risk category

Population approach: encourage everyone to change, shifting the entire distribution

Risk reduction approach: Move high risk individuals into normal range

"Low"   "Normal"   "High"

Level of risk

% of Population

Figure 7.5 Prevention paradox[28]

Diagnostic services such as electrocardiography and endoscopic examination became more readily available to GPs, without the need to refer first to a specialist.[29] General practice was entering a phase of revolutionary improvement.[30] Younger doctors were predominantly entering groups rather than smaller practices. Postgraduate centres were increasingly accessible throughout the country. Better organised doctors questioned the need for much home visiting; patients could be attended more quickly and more thoroughly at the surgery. Flexible appointment systems and better surgery organisation made same-day attendances easier. Patients more often had transport. Doctors and their receptionists attempted to reduce what they saw as unnecessary home visits, the numbers falling by at least a third.[31]

Technophile GPs had begun to find ways of linking their practices to large, distant 'mainframe' computers. They enthusiastically explored the problems to which a computer might be a solution. The costs were so high that GPs could not fund systems personally and general introduction was not possible but the main applications, including registers, appointment and immunisation scheduling, prescribing and recording the nature of conditions seen in the practice were soon apparent.

Footnote 3. Rose first described the 'prevention paradox' in 1981. Accordingly, the majority of cases of a disease come from a population at low or moderate risk of that disease, and only a minority of cases come from those at high risk. This seeming contradiction is because the number of people at high risk is small. For example, most alcohol problems are not found among dependent drinkers but among the rest of us. Greater societal gain will be obtained by achieving a small reduction in average alcohol consumption across the whole population than by trying to reduce problems among a small number of dependent drinkers.

Turning point

The 1966 Family Doctor Charter has to be viewed in the social, political and technical context of its time but can any relevant lessons be drawn after fifty years? This was a suite of top-down, clearly targeted and well-financed innovations - no place for pilot projects or energy sapping policy research. The money went on basic building blocks - staff, training, premises - rather than mystical quick fixes. It was the fruit of careful planning over years and painstaking negotiation in which the profession's leaders played a decisive role. The timely stewardship of wise politicians was vital. Policy makers at that time faced exactly the challenge that they face today: how to incentivize collaborative integration between practices, between primary and secondary care, and between health and social care.

The idea of the NHS as the fundamental turning point remains prevalent because the new service symbolized - then as now - an equitable welfare state in times of austerity. However, for general practice more significant discontinuities arguably attended the Charter.[32] Of course, its importance can be exaggerated for many of the developments described above were being led from within the profession. Nevertheless, at a time when the discipline is once more under threat, the Family Doctor Charter remains an iconic event in the late history of general practice. A settlement of comparable significance is long overdue.

For most doctors in practice at the time, benefits were immediately noticeable. Morrell wrote that *'it was a great pleasure and privilege to work in general practice during the decade following the Charter.'*[33] However, Ann Cartwright's landmark surveys of practitioners identified some misgivings with post-Charter practice. In particular, the patient's continuing and exclusive relationship with 'their' doctor was inevitably eroded in an age of large multi-disciplinary teams and timed appointments.[34]

The changes came too late for some reluctant emigrants. My uncle John O'Brien Bell, later President of the Canadian Medical Association, recalled: *"Many doctors were demoralised and angry. Leaving the country gave them hope, something the BMA did not provide. They found that job satisfaction in countries like Canada and Australia and never returned"* (personal communication).

Silent minorities

Reflecting changes in the population at large, the NHS workforce was changing too. The post-war years saw an influx of people from Commonwealth countries to staff new public services. The NHS needed doctors, nurses, porters and cleaners. Ironically, the first major expansion took place under the ministry of Enoch Powell.

It is hard to exaggerate the beneficial contribution of immigrant doctors. The majority had trained on the Indian sub-continent. They faced institutional and more overt racism, as evidenced in the columns of the BMJ. Letters decrying their training, language skills or standards of practice were a frequent feature.[35]

As many as two thirds of these doctors were unable to pursue their chosen specialist careers and ended up in less popular 'cinderella specialties' (e.g. psychiatry, geriatrics) - or general practice. They tended to find work where indigenous graduates feared to tread: in deprived inner cities. Their practices served poor populations with high levels of health need that had arrived from different parts of South Asia. It was not simply that white graduates did not want these jobs. They could not have done them anyway for they might be required to glide between three or four languages.

Aneez Esmael has drawn parallels with other indentured labourers recruited from the colonies to support imperial projects.[35] They were tied into the NHS but unable to fulfil their training aspirations or return home. This may be a stretch but the nineteenth century history of the Indian Medical Service (IMS) helps explain why so many Indian doctors still work in the UK.

The IMS was open only to Europeans until 1855. Colonial education policy was ever a battleground between the 'Orientalists' who maintained that indigenous culture should remain intact and 'Anglicists' who argued that it should be replaced by western culture transmitted through the English language. Suffice to say that the Anglicists prevailed. Indigenous courses for the training of Indian doctors were abolished. New medical colleges were modelled along western pedagogic lines. They served the needs of the IMS and GMC rather better than the needs of the rural majority of India's population.[36] At the time of independence further education in Britain was thus the aspiration of the ambitious in many different professions, including medicine.

The NHS has continued to drain doctors from other needier countries. Overseas doctors even today make up nearly a third of the medical workforce (though these same minorities make up just 8% of the population). Their lot has improved but institutional racism has continued to be reflected in discriminatory selection, assessment and disciplinary procedures.[37]

A comprehensive account of the contribution of immigrant doctors remains to be written. It will include testimony from their patients and peers (like myself) whose lives have been enriched through their work. It should incorporate the perspectives of their descendants who have entered the profession in disproportionately large numbers. They will provide medical dynasties going forward of rather greater interest than my own.

Vocational training at last

Over the 30 years following the establishment of the NHS, the number of consultants doubled while the number of GPs increased by only 20 per cent. A temporary reduction in medical school intake was affecting the numbers qualifying and the corrective expansion of medical schools would take six or seven years to work its way through. Many doctors were approaching retirement. A rise in the numbers of the young and old was increasing the number of patients for whom more work was necessary.

In 1942, the Spens Report on GPs' remuneration had suggested that 10 per cent of GPs should be selected, because of their success in practice and suitability, to take on a trainee.[38] The scheme was later developed to provide vocational training, though that was not its original purpose.[39] In 1950 a committee, chaired by Sir Henry Cohen, reported that the status and prestige of the GP should be the equal of colleagues in any and every specialty, and that no higher ability, industry or zeal was required for the adequate pursuit of any of them. Cohen considered that, as general practice was a special branch of medicine requiring supervised training, there should be three years' preparation: one in practice (any principal having the right to train a new entrant) and two in supervised hospital posts. GPs should continue their education and reading throughout their professional life.[40] In 1957 the General Medical Services Committee of the BMA circulated guidance to achieve greater uniformity in trainer selection and to eliminate abuses.

When young doctors entered general practice, they soon discovered that the spectrum of medical problems they encountered was not that they had seen in hospital. Ideally, much of the GP's education should take place within general practice itself.[41] Care in general practice had to reflect the way human beings behaved and related to each other, and the society in which they lived. The work of Michael Balint (see below) was suggesting dimensions of clinical practice quite unlike anything taught or learned at medical school.[42]

John Horder, later President of the RCGP, made the introduction of effective vocational training his long-term objective. In the College journal he wrote:

> *'Specialists expect to remain under part-time training until they are from 33 to 40 years old. Is it surprising that some of them have feelings of superiority - and some of us feelings of inferiority - when our own training is so much shorter?'*[43]

Vocational training had been popular in the early years of the NHS and in 1957 there were more than 400 trainees. Then entry to general practice became less competitive and rapid partnership became the rule: security and better pay were easily obtainable. The young doctor could immediately become a principal, though ill-prepared for general practice. Few became vocational trainees; many early schemes had a bad name, the number participating was decreasing and those who did might be used as cheap labour without a systematic programme of education.[44]

A national system of vocational training by selected and trained teachers was crucial, but only in a few places, for example Inverness and Wessex, had there been attempts to construct a proper training programme.[39] The RCGP asked for two years' postgraduate education in supervised general practice and three years in hospital posts.[45] The BMJ thought this idealistic and doubted whether it would be wise to make vocational training compulsory; offering GPs good working conditions was more important and the urgent need was for more pairs of hands.[46]

By 1968, trainee entries had fallen to 150 per year. Horder gave evidence to the Royal Commission on Medical Education. The College said that personal and family doctoring could survive only if it had as rigorous a training as did the specialties. In its report, the Royal Commission treated general practice like other branches of medicine. It recommended that vocational training should be compulsory and last three years.[19] This was a major coup for the RCGP, transforming over time its power and influence.

Most trainees took a newly introduced examination for membership of the College and trainees formed their own organisations and groups. The College consistently argued that mandatory vocational training was required, and this was finally accepted by the BMA in 1974. It was one thing to campaign for vocational training; quite another to define it. This task was undertaken by a small group of doctors at the College. Their report, *The Future General Practitioner: Learning and Teaching*, showed the relationship of general practice not only with clinical science but also with such basic sciences as physiology, pathology, epidemiology, psychology, sociology and with the theory and practice of educational methods.[8] The content of training included the study of health and disease, human development, human behaviour, medicine and society, practice management and organisation. Trainers were now selected for their ability to teach, their facilities and other qualities.

The RCGP also wished to see academic departments of general practice based in every medical school to ensure that students were presented with a balanced picture of health and disease. The first Professor of General Practice, Richard Stott, was appointed in Edinburgh in 1963. England only slowly followed suit and it was another 20 years before the absence in a medical school of a department of general practice was regarded as backward.[47] (In the best Moranian tradition, Cambridge forbore to appoint its first professor of primary care till 2005.)

The RCGP celebrated its 20th anniversary in 1972 and could claim substantial success for its policies. The 'College model' of general practice was widely accepted. Research units had been established in Birmingham and Dundee. Its advocacy of university departments of general practice ensured that, though few had yet been established, most medical students saw patients on practice attachments in their homes as well as in hospital.

Continuing professional development and self-audit were also evolving.[45] In 1974 family planning services, provided previously by local health authorities, became part of general medical services. Family doctors wished to provide them, and women wanted the choice. Many clinic staff thought GPs were inadequately equipped for the work, but courses were established, fees were agreed and doctors duly trained. Since then, continuing education has been steadily decentralised: from teaching hospital to district hospital, from peer group to practice, from team to desktop.

General practice now attracted its share of the best medical students. Vocational training that had existed on a voluntary basis for many years became mandatory in 1982. I remember the mad dash among some colleagues to enter practice before this deadline. Young doctors entered a three-year course, one year in general practice with a suitably experienced trainer and two years in appropriate hospital posts. Training schemes were popular because they provided stability in one area, good posts and a passport to general practice if that later seemed the best option.

Research in the community

The notion that no meaningful practice-based research preceded the College's establishment is fallacious. Enquiring general practitioners had always contributed to the advance of medical knowledge. There can be no more notable example than Edward Jenner (1749-1823) working in rural Gloucestershire. The story of his particular contribution - the development of a vaccine against smallpox from cow pox and how he subsequently demonstrated its protective effects - is well known. Jenner and colleagues formed the Gloucestershire Medical Society or 'Fleece Medical Society', so called because it met in the parlour of the Fleece Inn, Rodborough. Members dined together and read papers on medical subjects. Similar societies provided my forebears with access to the latest learning.

Most GPs kept up to date by reading the BMJ or The Practitioner. Unusual cases might be presented to colleagues at a local medical society and written up in transactions but results reached restricted audiences. The habit of sending off case reports to the BMJ or Lancet (as Joseph did) became more common in the second part of the nineteenth century. Astonishingly, over a quarter of British GPs had published work. Around a third of GPs at that time had medical doctorates (MDs)[48] as compared with less than 2% today. They were more likely to publish than other GPs, often based on their dissertations.

As described in chapter 4, the nineteenth century saw laboratory medicine achieve pre-eminence in teaching hospitals. However, many like James Mackenzie argued vigorously against purely lab-based research. A GP in Burnley for 25 years, he championed community-based tracing of disease from its earliest stages.[49] His own work detailed different irregularities of the pulse (arrhythmias) and their management.[50] Like Jenner before him, he eventually succumbed to the blandishments of a specialist career in London (footnote 4).

The third of a triumvirate of iconic GP-researchers, William Pickles, believed the country practitioner occupied a *'strategic pinnacle'* from which to investigate infectious disease. Practising for over 50 years in Wensleydale, his *Epidemiology in Country Practice* contained pioneering work on the incubation periods of common infectious diseases.[51] He aimed to stimulate colleagues to keep their own records of epidemic disease. Pickles was to become the RCGP's first president.

The establishment of university departments, as promoted by the College, was to transform the discipline's academic base. The first focus of research was the description of service activity. John Fry and Keith Hodgkin, continued their pioneering analyses of general practice and of the difference between hospital work and their own (table 7.3).[52] They demonstrated that GPs manage 90 per cent of their patients alone and require hospital specialist help for only 10 per cent.[53] Roughly 18 per cent of Fry's patients were referred each year, 3.7 per cent for an outpatient consultation and 3.8 per cent for admission; the rest were for a test or X-ray. GPs had long known that psychiatric illness was common in general practice. It has always been one of the most frequent causes for consultation and GPs deal unaided with the vast bulk of such cases.[54] One implication was that improvement of mental health services needed not a proliferation of specialist agencies but a strengthening of the family doctor's therapeutic role.

Academic departments of general practice tended to be based within departments of epidemiology or public health. Positively, this allowed for the infusion of other perspectives such as sociology or health economics. Negatively, general practice was often seen as a facility for developing hospital research rather than developing new analytic perspectives. Accelerated change was only to follow the 1994 Culyer inquiry into research and development in the NHS.[55] This noted the need to develop infrastructure and programme-based funding for research in primary care. General practice was fast becoming established as a distinct discipline with its own evidence base, rigorous training programmes and holistic philosophy of care.

Footnote 4. Ironically, Mackenzie himself suffered from an irregular heart beat, atrial fibrillation. By 1907, he was experiencing frequent episodes of angina about which he consulted Thomas Lewis. His symptoms worsened down the years before another heart attack killed him around 4am in the morning of 26 January 1925. Before his death Mackenzie had asked that his friend John Parkinson perform his autopsy. This confirmed his extensive coronary heart disease.

Table 7.3.   Comparison of morbidity per 1000 incidents (Hodgkin[52])

Hospital inpatients	Disease	General practice
300	New growths	4
12	Disseminated sclerosis	12
30	Cerebrovascular disorders	2
5	Malignant hypertension	0.5
15	Benign hypertension	6
15	Coronary heart disease	2
40	Rheumatic heart disease	1
0	Upper respiratory infection	250
45	Pneumonia and bronchitis	20
90	Peptic ulcer	30
15	Regional ileitis and ulcerative colitis	0
75	Acute appendicitis	1
65	Hernia	2
25	Acute intestinal obstruction	0.5
25	Gall bladder	0.5
25	Neuroses	140
2	Psychoses	1

The 'hidden' consultation

The psychodynamics of the consultation were to become a major preoccupation of GPs from the 1950s onwards. Michael Balint (1896-1970) was a Hungarian psychoanalyst who spent most of his adult life in England. He was a proponent of the Object Relations school, heavily influenced by Sigmund Freud, which maintains that infant's relationship with the mother primarily determines the formation of personality in adult life. In particular, the need for attachment is regarded as the bedrock of the development of the self and a sense of identity.

His classic work, *The Doctor, his Patient and the Illness*, arose out of a series of seminars conducted with general practitioners at the Tavistock Clinic in London in the 1950s.[56] The book documents case reports presented to illuminate aspects of the doctor-patient relationship. Of central interest were those patients who presented repeatedly to GPs with psychological or physical complaints but whose investigation findings were often normal and who were difficult to treat satisfactorily. Balint concluded that *'some of the people, who for some reason or other, find it difficult to cope with the problems of their lives resort to becoming ill.'* His focus in group discussions was those underlying reasons, the 'hidden agenda'.

Balint introduced the idea of the doctor as 'drug': how a doctor's actions influence a patient responses to illness and treatment.[56] Some patients were harder to help because GPs had to rely on the standard medical model (*'elimination by physical examination'*) and learnt from hospital consultants (*'perpetuation of the teacher-*

pupil relationship'). In many cases where a patient passed through the hands of several specialists, each looking only at one aspect of a problem, a diffusion of responsibility seemed to arise, even for important decisions (*'collusion of anonymity'*). Balint went on to discuss ways in which GPs could help such patients, including through psychotherapy.

With his wife Enid, a fellow psychoanalyst, Balint set up groups for GPs to explore the psychodynamics of doctor-patient relationships. Instead of repeating futile investigations of increasing complexity and cost, and then telling these people there was nothing wrong with them, Balint sought to unravel the causes of anxiety and unhappiness. He promoted remedial education aiming at insight, rather than tablets for suppressing symptoms. 'Balint groups' were widely established for GPs to discuss aspects of their work with patients for which they had previously felt ill equipped. At its height, the Balint movement had something of the aura of a quasi-religious cult. In recent years the place of Balint groups, and psychoanalysis as a whole, on the training of GPs has declined.

Balint spawned an explosion of enquiries into the dynamics of the consultation.[57] The advent of timed appointments made them a necessary focus of training and research. The most durable framework has been that of Roger Neighbour.[58] His 'five checkpoints' are still widely used to structure the teaching of consultation skills (footnote 5).

Balint's book remains as relevant today when many patients still come to their GPs with recurring complaints that have no obvious physical cause ('medically unexplained symptoms'). It offers alternative approaches when the conventional medical model is found wanting. Whether they are any more effective and how best to tackle deep seated psychological issues continues to be debated.

Sociological insights
Building on the classic work of Émile Durkheim (1858-1917), contemporary sociologists were exploring the norms and values that determine the behaviour of patients and their doctors. The structural-functionalism of Talcott Parsons placed

Footnote 5. Neighbour suggested structuring the consultation around five questions[58]: 1. Connecting: have we got rapport? 2. Summarising: can I demonstrate to the patient that I've sufficiently understood why she's come, for example that the patient's ideas, concerns and expectations have been explored and acknowledged adequately. 3. Handing over: has the patient accepted the management plan we have agreed? 4. Safety netting: What if...?, predictions and contingency plans.5. Housekeeping: Am I in good condition for the next patient? These questions reflect the preoccupations of their time - with a medicalized but less psychoanalytical form of 'patient-centredness' and the need for 'shared decision-making'.[59] Yet they affirm that general practice is - as it always has been - the art of managing prognostic uncertainty. The traditional business of history-taking, examination and investigation is buried in step 2. This reflects the extent to which decision-making in general practice often involves almost instantaneous pattern-recognition rather than hypotheco-deductive reasoning.

medicine firmly on the mainstream theorists' map. He viewed illness as a form of 'sanctioned deviance'. The 'sick role' implies customary rights (e.g. exemption from normal roles) and obligations (e.g. seeking help). In various ways, he saw the medical profession policing and legitimating this disturbance of social functioning.[60]

The work of Cartwright, Jefferys and others drew attention to how much advice-seeking and self-medicating is done before seeking medical help.[61] Less than 20% of symptomatic people consult and more than half take non-prescribed medicines.[62] For most people visiting the doctor is still a rare way of managing illness. Zola identified the different 'triggers' to help-seeking of which 'sanctioning' (the advice or insistence of someone else) was as significant as the impact of symptoms on activities or relationship.[63]

Analyses of the doctors' role yielded shocking insights into taken-for-granted medical behaviours but these changed (almost) all domains of medical practice. Paternalism and more egregious insensitivities around the use of language in face-to-face encounters are (mostly) things of the past. General practice led the way in the use of video-cameras and simulated patients as an integral part of training and examinations.

Observational studies showed how the organisation of the hospital ward can influence patients' symptoms and recovery. The classic studies of Erving Goffman drew attention to dangers of institutionalization among American mental patients and fuelled the rise of the anti-psychiatrists.[64] Systemic analyses of health care have been used to re-design care in the name of efficiency. Broader sociological analyses exposed the nature of vested (often medical) interests and the nature of change (or the lack of it) in different health care systems.

The most important work illuminated understanding of the social origins of disease. In classic studies, for example, George Brown explored contextual associations with depression - income, education, life experience and loss, housing, employment - and how such factors interacted.[65] These too changed medical awareness, though not necessarily prescribing practices.

Finally, medical anthropologists began to examine how different cultural groups explain the causes of ill-health and act on their beliefs.[66] Patients and their doctors use different 'explanatory models' to interpret and pattern symptoms.[67] Lay theories of illness causation still need to be understood, as the 'Antivaxx' movement has graphically demonstrated. Transcultural psychiatry has been the field to benefit most prominently. Comparative and ethnographic studies exploring higher levels of mental illness in minority ethnic groups have helped practitioners to widen their appreciation of normal behaviour and reduce the impact of social labelling.[68]

GPs form a distinctive sub-group with their own sub-culture within the medical profession and the manner of their sub-socialization remains largely uncharted. Surprisingly, the influence of sociologists on medical training has receded in recent years. This retreat may owe much to ongoing 'medical imperialism'.[69] To earn acceptance, sociological research was required to adhere to the canons of scientific empiricism. In that respect, the recent steady growth of qualitative research in the field of general practice is encouraging.

Iconoclasis

Ironically, these years of plenty for general practice coincided with a period of intellectual foment and growing self-doubt. This found expression in well-documented challenges to the traditional view of the role of medicine in the conquest of disease and the pursuit of health.

'Complete freedom from disease and from struggle is almost incompatible with the process of living, ' René Dubos asserted in his classic essay on ecology and health.[70] All the accomplishments of science and technology, he argued, will not bring the utopian dream of universal well-being, because they ignore the dynamic process of adaptation to a constantly changing environment that every living organism must face. Much of what was then an original critique is now - as we grapple with microbial drug resistance and complex disease aetiologies, let alone the impact of climate change - mainstream thinking.

The view of medicine and its role in society that had hitherto been inculcated at medical school was curiously naive and self-satisfied. Scientific medicine, it was claimed, had rescued mankind from most of the terrible diseases and suffering that had afflicted people in past centuries. It was only a matter of time, and sufficient resources, before all the ills of mankind would be banished in the same way by medical progress. The nerve centre of this great operation was the teaching hospital, of which one's own was, in some curious way, even more worthy than the rest.[71] As well as a scientific role, there was also a caring role for these great hospital institutions. To their open arms would come all who needed help, and the hospital would provide it. When considering future careers, it was made evident to students that to be a consultant in a teaching hospital was to join a medical elite which, in a society soon to come, would be able to do all things for all men. If that was not possible, there were always the provincial hospitals. Finally, there was general practice where those unable to make the grade would at least be able to earn a living, even if the work was rather unimportant.

Dubos exploded the popular myth that it was medicine that had conquered the plagues of mankind. He offered an alternative view of the role of the doctor in relation both to her patients and society. Two very different views of the role of the doctor have existed since the earliest history of medicine. On the one hand, doctors have actively intervened in the process of disease. In the Greco-Roman world this activism was associated with a school of medicine that took Aesculapias as their symbolic spiritual father. On the other hand, associated with the name of Hippocrates, an alternative school felt that the most important function of medicine was to discover and teach the natural laws which ensure a healthy mind in a healthy body. There was much that medicine could do, but much more that it could not do. This latter view was personified by Hygeia, the serene and benevolent goddess who once watched over the health of Athens.

As Dubos pointed out, *'In one form or another these two complementary aspects of medicine have always existed simultaneously in all civilisations.'* Certainly, both aspects are necessary, but his book redressed a balance that my medical training had distorted. The omnipotence of the hospital gods was being called into question.

Another influential assault on those professional delusions of self-importance came from a different source. Working from the Department of Social Medicine in Birmingham, Thomas McKeown (1911-88) employed his epidemiological skills to show that medical interventions have scarcely affected mortality. He first demonstrated that dramatic increases in the British population could only be accounted for by a reduction in death rates, especially in childhood. He estimated that 80 to 90% of the total reduction in death rates from the beginning of the eighteenth century to the present day had been caused by a reduction in those deaths due to infection - especially tuberculosis, chest infections and water or food-borne diarrhoeal disease.[72]

Most strikingly, with the exception of vaccination against smallpox (which was associated with nearly 2% of the decline in the death rate from 1848 to 1971), immunisation and antimicrobial therapy had an insignificant effect on mortality from infectious diseases until well into the twentieth century. Most of the reduction in mortality from TB, bronchitis, pneumonia, influenza, whooping cough, food-borne and water-borne diseases had already occurred before effective immunisation and treatment became available. McKeown placed particular emphasis on raised nutritional standards as a consequence of rising living standards (see chapter 4).

In other words, neither the reduction in epidemic infectious disease, nor major changes in the age structure of the population have been significantly related to health care, including even immunisation. As we have seen, McKeown's thesis was to be modified in the face of later evidence for the benefits of public health measures.[73] His core message was nevertheless a source of dismay to the medical profession, though not one the health care-consuming public appears to have heeded.

The most potent critique of the *'health industrial complex'* was penned by a Catholic priest, Ivan Illich.[74] His story is redolent of the Fall of Man. Illich described three levels of iatrogenesis. *Clinical iatrogenesis* is the injury done to patients by ineffective, toxic, and unsafe treatments. Nearly 10% of patients suffer harm while hospitalised. Yet only recently had doctors begun to take patient safety seriously.

Social iatrogenesis results from the medicalisation of life. More and more of life's problems are seen as amenable to medical intervention. Pharmaceutical companies develop expensive treatments for non-diseases. Health care consumes an ever-growing proportion of the budget. In 1975 the United States spent $95 billion on health care, 8.4% of its gross national product. Thirty years later that figure had risen to $3000 billion, 17% of GNP. Could this be sensible?[75]

Most insidious for Illich was *cultural iatrogenesis*, the destruction of traditional ways of dealing with and making sense of death, pain, and sickness. *'A society's image of death,'* argued Illich, *'reveals the level of independence of its people, their personal relatedness, self-reliance, and aliveness.'* For Illich ours is a morbid society, where *'through the medicalisation of death, health care has become a monolithic world religion…Society, acting through the medical system, decides when and after what indignities and mutilations he [the patient] shall die…Health, or the autonomous power to cope, has been expropriated down to the last breath.'*

His proposed solutions were decidedly vague. They included handing back to lay people responsibility for their health, and limiting the power of doctors, insurance companies and pharmaceutical firms. While it spawned many others, Illich's was the most widely read polemic of its kind. His erudition disarmed those who would brush his Marxist rhetoric aside and his messages are broadly as pertinent nearly half a century on.

These critiques seldom found their way into medical school syllabuses but they affected many of my generation profoundly. They certainly altered my way of thinking and set me on a path towards general practice and public health.

Medicalisation

Perhaps the most enduring product of these various assaults was a wider understanding of 'medicalisation': the process by which problems are defined and treated as medical conditions under the authority of health professions. This has long been a key concept for sociologists and social historians. For Foucault, starting in the eighteenth century the maintenance of health turned medicine into a force for social control. His concept of 'governmentality' linked the state and medical practitioners together in creating a set of practices that operated on people's bodies.[76]

Later scholarship would suggest that Foucault exaggerated the biopolitical power of both parties.[77] GPs, after all, have often in these pages offered resistance to state control. In the second half of the twentieth century, the promotion of health became an important political goal in post-industrial society. GPs were only too aware of how lifestyle messaging fuelled health anxieties and the rise of the 'worried well.' They remain understandably wary of such social responsibilities.

Conclusion

Entering the last quarter of the twentieth century, medicine appeared on the surface to be all-conquering. This had been dramatically symbolised in the first heart transplant conducted by Christian Barnard in 1967. My father's generation enthusiastically adopted the advances - from computerised diagnosis to experimental keyhole surgery - that were transforming medical practice. Genetic technologies promised the stuff of science fiction. New antihypertensives (such as Peter had trialled), antidiabetic and ulcer-healing drugs were helping to move more care into the community.

By the 1980s, general practice was a self-confident discipline with a burgeoning research base and enviable training standards able to attract those from the highest rungs of Moran's infamous career ladder.[78] For many, these years are a high watermark.

Yet all was not well. Health is the capacity to cope with the existential realities of death, pain, and sickness. Modern medicine had gone far in its mission to eradicate these experiences but was falling prey to its own successes.[79] General practice was struggling to deal with burdens of dis-ease for which it was ill-equipped. Technology can often help but, in so doing, it can turn people into consumers or objects - destroying their very capacity for health. The commodification of health care was to preoccupy the next and final generation.

Chapter Eight – Markets and recession
(1985-2020)

'It is more important to know what sort of person has a disease
than to know what sort of disease a person has.'
Hippocrates

The eighth generation

I awoke with fright. A child was crying somewhere down the ward. A kindly nurse emerged from the gloom smelling vaguely of antiseptic and placed a reassuring hand on my brow. I went back to sleep. I was five years old, in hospital for a second time with nephrotic syndrome (footnote 1). I became used at that time to daily steroid injections and regular blood tests. Those experiences may have left me with a lifelong abhorrence of hospitals. How they affected other life choices, I cannot say.

Following a gap year spent travelling in Africa where I was first exposed to real poverty, I followed my father to St Catharine's College, Cambridge. Perhaps surprisingly, I never felt pressured to pursue a medical career and was blissfully unaware of the ghosts looking down on me. To begin with, I struggled with the bawdy college culture and disappointed expectations. If I knew little else, I knew how to drink having been expelled from school for an alcohol-related infraction. So low did I sink that, coming out of a lecture one day, I sought help from the Samaritans. An unlikely voice answered the phone: *"No point talking to me, luv – I'm Doris, the cleaner."* *"But I could be suicidal, about to jump off St Mary's!'*, I wailed. *"O, don't do that love"*, she warmly intoned. *"Go away and have a cup of tea - phone back later."* I didn't need to.

Derided by my tutors who felt such pursuits a 'complete waste of time', I undertook a tripos in sociology and political sciences. I owe an early interest in social medicine to the study of Marx, Durkheim, Weber and the coming man - later apostle of Tony Blair's third way - Anthony Giddens (footnote 2). There too I first read Julian Tudor Hart's lucid enunciation of his 'inverse care law': the principle that the availability of good medical or social care tends to vary inversely with the needs of the population served.[1] As true today as it was in 1971.

In those days before the establishment of a clinical school in Cambridge, most students went down to London to complete their training. My first interview was at

Footnote 1. Nephrotic syndrome is the result of kidney malfunction. Retention of fluid resulted in my blowing up like a Michelin man. Mine was due to 'minimal change glomerulonephritis', probably triggered by a viral infection. I was miraculously 'cured' by the steroids which were at that stage an experimental therapy. I only afterwards discovered that most such glomerulonephritis resolves spontaneously. An early insight into medicine's inclination to claim more credit than it is truly due.

Guy's. The opening question took me by surprise. *"Gillam? Have you ever had any relatives pass through here?" "No, sir"*, I responded. Interest drained away from my interrogators' faces leaving only grey dullness. Halfway through the interview, a Dickensian ancient in tails tottered in to wind up the grandfather clock. I related the experience to my father afterwards. He didn't seem unduly surprised. *"I suppose you told him about your great great grandfather who walked the wards at Guy's in the 1860s."* And I thought he was joking.

During clinical studies at University College Hospital my first career interest was in psychiatry, fomented by the psychoanalyst, Professor Heinz Wolf. With no knowledge as yet of my inheritance, I was also beginning to think about a career in the community. The rituals and hierarchies of hospital life felt alien.

Most doctors, at one time or another, inadvertently kill people. One week into my first house job, I was injecting dye into a 67 year old man as part of a kidney investigation (ancient history as this would now be undertaken ultrasonically) when he began gasping for breath. Responding to the tell-tale signs of anaphylactic shock, I was horrified to see him fall back unconscious onto the bed. We were unable to resuscitate him. My consultant placed a reassuring hand on my shoulder, condolences were offered (to me, at least). The professional cocoon closed supportively around me. The experience still haunts me.

I applied for a place on the GP 'vocational training scheme' at Northwick Park Hospital, site of the new Clinical Research Centre (footnote 3). Such schemes by then included two years in various specialties and a year as an apprentice in general practice. I began working on a deprived housing estate in Wembley at the Chalkhill Health Centre in 1982. My GP trainer, John Salinsky, was a major influence inclining me to work in deprived inner cities. A highly intelligent man with strong literary leanings, Salinsky was a powerful exponent of the work of Michael Balint (see chapter 7).

Having acquired a basketful of postgraduate qualifications, I fulfilled a long-held ambition to work overseas. I spent the next couple of years working for the Save The Children Fund (SCF) in Dhankuta, eastern Nepal, running a mother-child health project. My responsibilities were for planning, administration, teaching and

Footnotes 2. Anthony Giddens went on to be the most prominent British sociologist of his generation. He is known for his theory of structuration and his holistic view of modern societies. In *The Third Way* (1998), Giddens supplied a broad range of policy proposals aimed at the progressive centre-left in British politics. He sought to get beyond both market fundamentalism and traditional top-down socialism. He was for a time the 'go to' wonk for the New Labour governments of Tony Blair.

3. Northwick Park Hospital was the site of the new Clinical Research Centre. This flagship was especially resourced to enable the Medical Research Council to retain its place as an international leader. It was a costly failure and signalled the declining impact of clinical science.[2]

medical support to a busy clinic with an attached in-patient unit for severely malnourished children. This was the base for several field programmes, e.g. training community health workers (in nine weeks to do most of what doctors gained training over six years), supporting government health posts and working in schools.

Personal undertakings included the development of guidelines for the management of malnourished children in all SCF's units and the establishment of a programme training traditional healers (Dhamis and Jhankris).[3] For all my clinical experience, I found myself lacking in two relevant areas - epidemiology and (with 40 staff to oversee) management.

Figure 8.1 The author, Dhankuta, 1986

Even now, I can conjure up exquisite personal memories - sights, smells and sounds - from those two short years. The work was sometimes harrowing but, in many respects, this was the most fulfilling experience of my career (figure 8.1). The hill tribespeople were extraordinarily resilient. Men would walk for days on fractured limbs to obtain help, although expectations of the state's health services were not high. I remember assisting the local doctor with an obstructed labour. The baby had appeared arm-first and lodged for many hours low down in her mother's vagina. We finally dislodged the shrivelled and floppy little creature. An assistant tossed the lifeless body onto rags in the corner - after all, it was another girl - as we attempted to resuscitate her mother. Only later did I detect twitching movements and occasional respirations, the first signs of life. Astonishingly, both mother and baby survived.

Infant, child and maternal mortality were among the highest in the world. Families of ten or more lived around the smoking fire in one-roomed huts and traditional practices included coating the newborn's umbilicus with buffalo dung. In the monsoon season, when the rains washed sewage into water supplies and dysentery struck, parents would appear from many miles away clutching emaciated babies and children. How much did our emergency nutritional rehab unit achieve? Did these children survive a crisis only to return to their villages and die later? I set up a study to find out. Reassuringly, their mortality rates at two years were only slightly higher than those of controls from their own family or village.[4]

I returned to live with my partner of over 30 years. I had met Anne in my first month at work. Both her parents were GPs in a deprived area of Liverpool. She is a woman of exceptional abilities and went on to become a distinguished haematologist. Together we raised three daughters. All marriages face particular strains when both parties are heavily committed to their work. 'Men are from Mars, Women are from Venus. Doctors are from Krypton' (footnote 4). We nevertheless retain an enduring bond.

I spent the next year in a combined post - working on another deprived housing estate and in the academic department of general practice at St Mary's under Professor Brian Jarman. There I tasted for the first time the vicarious thrill of high-profile publication - a paper on ethnic variations in attendance in general practice.[5]

Working in a low income country changed me irreparably. I could never again ignore the structural determinants of inequality or the minor contribution of health services alongside material influences on health. Looking back, I suppose I experienced something akin to William the Older's impotence in the face of overwhelming odds. I had already decided to re-train in epidemiology and public health.

Poacher turns gamekeeper

Four years later I accepted a consultant post in the Bedfordshire, little knowing that I would retain working links in Luton for over 20 years. My responsibilities were for the development of primary care across a large rural county with centres of urban deprivation. There was plenty of scope here for observing the inverse care law in action. I demonstrated, for example, that certain preventive services were more likely to be available in the wealthiest, healthiest wards of the county.[6]

These were days of unrest among GPs in the wake of Margaret Thatcher's reforms. A major concern was the introduction of fundholding (see below) which proved divisive and inequitable. I was responsible for devising a locality-based alternative model that involved all practices in an area. Fairer yes, but still cumbersome and bureaucratic.

Footnote 4. This aphorism is attributed to Greg Skipper of the Alabama Physician Health Program.[7] None other than William Osler once remarked: *'What about the wife and babies if you have them? Leave them! Heavy are the responsibilities to yourself, to the profession and to the public.'*[8] Medical divorce rates are no higher than for other occupational groups but many medical marriages are unhappy. Partners share understanding and conversation but are often tired and overloaded. Characteristically, doctors are reluctant to seek help. Articles on medical marriage trot out a predictable sequence of 'do's and don'ts'. Sadly, we didn't. Medical schools now enrol more women than men. Half of them marry other doctors.[8] In time, over half of all doctors with be married to other doctors - a major change from Osler's time and a significant one.

These experiences tempted me next to a position working for the King's Fund, an independent charity that seeks to improve the health of Londoners. I had already spent three years evaluating a King's Fund project on community-oriented primary care (COPC). Pioneered in rural South Africa, COPC used epidemiological principles to help primary health care teams in the assessment of their populations' needs, together with the design and evaluation of appropriate interventions to meet them. I developed training materials and supported practices involved in the national pilot programme. An evaluation formed the basis for an MD (research degree). However, the COPC model offered little in the UK context - despite enthusiastic converts.[9] With characteristic acerbity (and accuracy), Julian Tudor Hart whom I had recruited onto the steering group described COPC as *a lead aeroplane.*

As well as giving grants and providing leadership development, the King's Fund is the leading health 'think tank'. Shortly before the Blair ascendancy in 1997, I was appointed to be Director of Primary Care, responsible for a programme of policy research and development. I managed a small core team with a larger number of grant-funded staff. The programme's outputs were pitched at disciplines with an interest in the variable quality of primary care provision in London. I became heavily involved in charting the impact of primary care policy under new Labour, and the development of Primary Care Trusts (see below).

The Department of Health (DoH) funded research into the impact of new policy but was seldom interested in awaiting its findings. Pleas for evidence-based policy making generally overlook the imperatives of a five-year election cycle. Politicians want the answers they want - and now.[10]

Frequent encounters with ministers were one of the dubious delights of this job. Personal Medical Services pilots (PMS) were a flagship policy development. We launched our research at a conference in central London to which we invited the Minister of Health. His acceptance was a gratifying coup. Frank Dobson had been appointed rather for his 'old Labour' street-cred than his fleetness of intellect (footnote 5). Halfway through the first plenary I caught sight of a scrap of paper passing from Dobson to his minder: *'What's PMS?'* it said.

Another quirk of this job was regular contact with the Prince of Wales who was the Fund's president. HRH had established a Foundation for Integrated Medicine. This was really a front through which assorted toadies could promote complementary

Footnote 5. Frank Dobson (1940-2019) was a popular and successful health secretary under Tony Blair. He set up two institutions that became central to the way it functions: the National Institute for Clinical Excellence (NICE, now the National Institute for Health and Care Excellence), and the Commission for Health Improvement (now the Care Quality Commission). Unusually, Dobson interviewed all NICE's non-executive director candidates himself. When one asked him if the new body was going to work, he replied, *"Probably not, but we're going to give it a fucking good try."*

and alternative medicine. I had no problem with people who wanted to pay for expensive placebos or simply for extra time to be heard - indeed, I had trained in acupuncture myself after witnessing its benefits first-hand in Chengdu - but there was little evidence to justify the provision of 'CAMS' (complementary and allied medicines) on the NHS. I was not the ally He wanted, though I did rather enjoy an afternoon at Highgrove listening to a royal drone on the benefits of osteopathy for his cattle.

The influence of 'think tanks' ebbs and flows according to the political complexion of the governing administration. The left-of-centre King's Fund was pleased to see a New Labour government but sometimes reluctant to criticize it. Under prime minister Blair, there was a sharp rightward shift, effectively shoring up the market-oriented reforms inaugurated under Thatcher. There are few genuinely original policy ideas under the sun but plenty of pundits happy to re-cycle old ones. I hankered after a return to the front-line - the imminence of teaching and clinical practice.

Turns poacher again
In 2003, I returned to Cambridge as a teacher. My main responsibilities at the Institute of Public Health were for the development and delivery of public health education within the medical school. Students are generally attracted by the 'high tech' specialisms and the stuff of Holby City, especially at Cambridge. Firing up youthful enthusiasm for *'the science and art of preventing disease, prolonging life and promoting health through the organized efforts of society'*[11] is always a challenge but it was one I relished. Early on I conducted a survey of my counterparts across the land. It revealed just how neglected teaching was in relation to research - ever the case in academic departments. I subsequently set up and ran a national network for Public Health Educators in Medical Schools (PHEMS). We did much to strengthen undergraduate public health education.[12]

Simultaneously, I expanded my clinical work at the Lea Vale Medical Group in Luton. This large primary health care team served an inner city population from a purpose-built health centre. We opened a second branch surgery on a poorly served estate. A first wave fundholder turned total purchasing pilot, the practice joined the third wave of Personal Medical Services (see below). I developed the practice as a training base and took responsibility for a succession of GP registrars. I was an increasingly rusty but reflective, reasonably evidence-based but sometimes disgruntled practitioner.

Luton, once voted 'The Crappest Town in Britain', suited me well. Designated a 'port town' (airPort), it hosted successive waves of new arrivals: Iranians in the '70s, Iraqis in the '80's, Ruandans and Zimbabweans in the '90s, eastern Europeans in the noughties and beyond. The different South Asian populations were well established. Scots and Irish had come to work in the car industry before the war. I loved this diversity; I once counted over 32 different nationalities on my personal list. But my patients' lives were often difficult, their stories sometimes unbearably poignant. I was also blessed with colleagues that reflected this diversity. Many of the first generation Asian doctors were single-handers, courteous and kindly, rusty too but seldom taking holidays. They frequently worked on into their 70s. Like my predecessors, they often died in harness, in part because they were literally irreplaceable.

General practice was my career anchor but I always relished multiple roles - like my predecessors. They kept me sane(r) in the face of the relentlessness of clinical practice. At one time I held six contracts including a Visiting Chair at the University of Bedfordshire. I most miss training. New, untarnished recruits were always a source of learning and the best defence against any luddite tendencies.

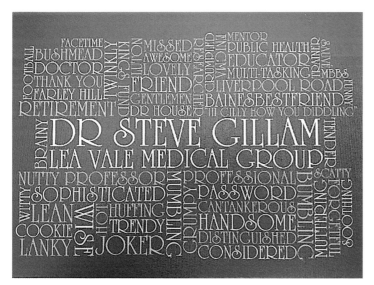

On leaving the Lea Vale Medical Group, I was presented with a rather more ambiguous leaving gift than my grandfather (figure 8.2). Staff had been asked to list words they associated with me. I know I was sometimes cantankerous and crumpled; I hope I was sometimes compassionate and kind. I had many of the flaws of my ancestors and fewer of their virtues. My

Figure 8.2 Leaving gift, Lea Vale.

CV is nothing if not testimony to reliability and stolid completer-finishing skills. Always an essential for authors.

Fenwick's descendant?

I had long nurtured an interest in research and began publishing as a trainee in general practice.[13] Much early work was at the interface between public health and primary care: on health promotion, screening, audit, ethnic and child health. The unifying purpose of this work was to help primary care organisations, including general practices, more effectively address inequalities in health. Later research examined the impact of pay-for performance in primary care, more specifically the effects on practice and public health of the Quality & Outcomes Framework (see below).

I wrote hundreds of articles and a dozen books but was incurably dilettante and wondered occasionally whether any of this huffing and puffing changed national policy or practice. Evidence is only ever one of the influences on policy development. I had reasons to believe that some of my team's policy research at the King's Fund influenced the evolution of personal medical services, the development of primary care trusts and the genealogy of practice-based commissioning. We were consulted by ministers on PMS and the teams negotiating new GP contracts. I acted for a period as an adviser to the NHS Alliance and the National Institute for Health & Care Excellence. Ever mindful of the law of unintended policy consequences, the end results were not always those I had anticipated or wanted.

Now post-retirement, I continue hands-on working as a GP in Norfolk, appraise colleagues and undertake occasional inspections for the Care Quality Commission.[14] I am now familiar with many of the hamlets, villages, highways and by-ways upon which George Skrimshire rode out in weather fair and foul. I continue to write.

#   #   #

The 'primary care led' NHS
The first major reorganisation of the NHS had been undertaken in 1974 in an attempt both to curb and to rationalize resource expenditure. A layer of bureaucracy was stripped away but, by general agreement, neither efficiency nor accountability were improved. The Griffiths reforms of 1987 introduced professional management in place of the older style of consensual administration as the NHS came under continuing critical scrutiny. The Family Practitioner Committees which monitored GP practices (descendants of the insurance committees set up in 1911) were given a more intrusive role overseeing their performance. The 'new managerialism' was supposed to address 'institutional stagnation'. This presaged far-reaching change.[15]

Before 1948, GPs had been central to health services, a position they lost with the explosive growth of specialist medicine. The 1990s were to see a return of their power that few would have predicted. Although spending had increased in real terms by a third in the previous ten years, the NHS's fifth decade began with another financial crisis. Regular reports of clinical disasters, bed closures and nursing crises were attributed to money shortages. The existing system had several advantages, including easy movement of patients between hospitals and good cost control. However, as we have seen, there were few incentives for efficiency.

Conservative think-tanks suggested that the days of a fully funded health service were numbered.[16] In January 1988, the Chancellor Nigel Lawson told Prime Minister Thatcher that he would be reluctant to allow a further significant increase in NHS funding unless the service was reformed, and he could be sure that monies would be well spent.[17]

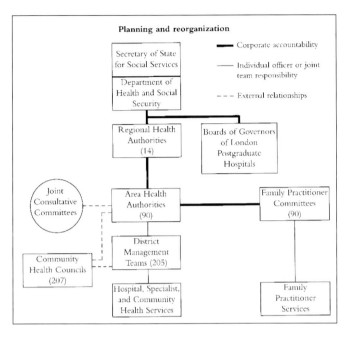

Figure 8.3 The NHS in England in 1974

The following year Kenneth Clarke, the new health secretary, embarked on a major review focused on the delivery of care, rather than the source of funding. Clarke had been involved in the 1974 NHS reorganisation and he viewed Keith Joseph's adoption of consensus management as a disaster (figure 8.3). Its abolition was his starting point. He rapidly persuaded the Treasury to allocate an additional £1.8bn to health.[18]

The *Working for Patients* white paper, published in January 1989 accepted many of the NHS's founding principles.[19] To the surprise of the Left that had predicted a move towards health insurance, this included funding arrangements. The NHS would continue to be paid for centrally from taxation, the simplest and cheapest way of raising money. It would remain largely free at the point of usage but productivity would be improved by introducing an 'internal market'. The purchasing function would be separated from the provision of services (figure 8.4). Health authorities would concentrate on the assessment of needs and contracting for services provided by hospitals and community units. GPs were to hold the purse strings for secondary health care.[18]

Hospitals were to become self-governing, freed - like schools - from centralised control. Good performance would be rewarded, for money would follow the patients. It was clear, although not stated, that once contracts were in place any limitation of services for financial reasons would be laid at the door of the purchaser, and no longer at that of the hospital. It was a model well suited to elective surgery, but less appropriate for elderly people and for psychiatric services. Markets have winners and losers; would the poor, deprived and disabled be at risk? Just as the USA was considering European health care systems, the UK was moving in the opposite direction. Much of my own research and writing explored the impact of these and subsequent reforms on general practice.

The rise and fall of 'Fundholding'

Hospital contracts were thus henceforth placed in two ways: with fundholding practices for their patients and with district authorities for the remainder. The central idea of fundholding was that GPs could act as informed purchasers with the

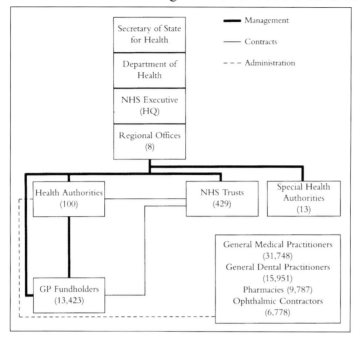

introduction of their own practice budgets. If GPs controlled the flow of money, good hospitals would flourish while bad ones would dwindle away. Fundholders were allocated money on the basis of their historic expenditure and could use it for practice staff, prescription medicines and hospital services such as laboratory tests, outpatient appointment care and elective surgery. Procedures could be purchased from the private sector as well as the NHS. Hospitals could increase

Figure 8.4 The NHS in England in 1997

their revenue at the margin by serving fundholders' patients and had an incentive to provide the care GPs wanted.

Many in the hospital service believed that GPs would prove incapable of handling money and that fundholding was at odds with the role of district health authorities trying to ensure equitable service delivery across a larger population. That there would be GP volunteers was never in doubt. Their prime motivation was the improvement of patient care. They were articulate and were not going to be pushed around by the Department or their professional colleagues.

Glennerster recorded the reactions of fundholders: *"As I sat down and I realised what we were about to do, I thought this is a revolution happening here. No consultant has ever talked to me about what I might think of his service, or any of the general problems we might have in twenty years of professional life."*[20]

By April 1991, there were 720 GP fundholders in 306 practices.[21] Budgets averaged £1.3 million. Few in prominent positions risked participation. It took consultants a year to recognise the extent to which fundholding moved power to family doctors. GPs noted that Christmas cards, traditionally sent from GP to consultant, began to flow in the opposite direction.[22] Then consultants too added their voice to the opposition.

The services covered were expanded to include district nursing and health visiting, dietetics and chiropody. By 1994, 6 per cent of the total NHS budget, equivalent to £1.8 billion, was being spent by fundholders.[18] However, inner cities where the population was mobile and the workloads high were slow to adopt fundholding.[23]

William Waldegrave memorably described fundholders as the 'grit in the oyster' (footnote 6). Fundholders faced patronizing hostility from the local health authority purchaser which was burdened with ultimate responsibility for maintaining the viability of the district hospital. The local providers had to veil their own misgivings behind a veil of sycophantic compliance for they needed their business. In fact, fundholders tended to shift patients to other hospitals only as a last resort.

Fundholders were nonetheless energetic negotiators on behalf of their patients. They established new counselling, physiotherapy and consultant outpatient clinics in their practices. In theory, patients were seen sooner in practice-run consultant clinics, the costs were lower because hospital overheads were not incurred, and GP-specialist contact was possible. Hospital management was afraid to lose the referrals that outreach clinics could generate and they rapidly increased in number.[241] However, consultants in particular argued that outreach clinics were a poor use of scarce resources, did not provide adequate facilities for investigation, and undermined teaching and the role of the district general hospital. My own research lent support to the latter view.[25]

A thousand flowers bloom

Though voluntary, the take-up of fundholding was spectacular, covering nearly two thirds of the English population by 1998. But what was the impact of this revolutionary upheaval? The academic verdict was mixed. Some evaluations suggested that fundholders cut elective admission rates and waiting times. They helped drive improvements to local services in the community.[26] Combining financial and clinical decision making, fundholding harnessed the enthusiasm of GPs eager to develop their practices. Access to elective health care was faster for patients of fundholders as compared with non-fundholders.[27] Although there were modest successes with fundholding, most initiatives focussed on small-scale new services, and many GPs lacked the skills and desire to take a population-based approach to planning.[28] Critics of fundholding argued that the system generated inherent conflicts of interest, involved high transaction costs and fragmented the profession.[27] Mounting evidence of a 'two-tier' service (inevitable if fundholding was having any beneficial effects at all) was regarded as unfair.

Footnote 6. William Waldegrave was an old Etonian aristo and notable 'wet' who served as Secretary of State for Health from 1990-2. I cannot find a reference to this but suppose that, for most of his listeners, gritty oysters were one of life's rarities.

After 1994 as a response to these equity concerns, ministers decided to encourage a variety of schemes.[29] New kinds of primary care organisation were emerging: fundholding practices, multi-funds, total purchasing projects, GP-led commissioning groups and out-of-hours co-operatives. They broke down the traditional isolation between practices and increased co-operation.

The rapid growth of fundholding had left the GMSC in a quandary. The BMA was bound to represent the interests of all its members - fundholder and non-fundholder alike. An increasing number of GP fundholders believed that they could not trust their professional leaders to act on their behalf. In the timely tradition of previous medical dissenters, a new National Association of Fundholders was established. As a result, the GMSC ultimately found itself arguing against the new Labour government in favour of fundholding, with *The Times* in support.[30] Most GPs were now fundholders, and were determined to keep their own budgets, irrespective of the political party in power. Once elected, the new Labour government promised equity between fundholders and commissioning groups. Fundholding in its purest guise was now doomed.

The genealogy of primary care commissioning
General practice has always been, in a sense, the victim of its own successes. The same self-confidence with which early fund-holders assumed responsibility for addressing the wider service's inefficiencies looks oddly hubristic in retrospect. Surprisingly, given the absence of evidence to support this strand of policy, all subsequent governments have remained committed to GPs as 'commissioners' of care (footnote 7).

Fundholding was abolished under the new Labour government of 1997. It was replaced by a sequence of more or less ineffective organisations of varying size, structure and budgetary prowess (figure 8.5).[31] The idea was to develop a model with the benefits of fundholding but without the disadvantages. Despite financial inducements and without the 'grit' of competition, GPs were slow to get involved. Those who had honed their management skills as fundholders became frustrated and disillusioned. Those who had not were never interested anyway.

Under the Health and Social Care Act 2012, power and responsibility for commissioning was devolved to GPs in Clinical Commissioning Groups (CCGs) in order to shift decision making as close as possible to individual patients.[32] The NHS Commissioning Board became the interface between the government and healthcare spending. It set budgets for CCGs, providing clear national standards,

Footnote 7. The term 'commissioning' emerged from the creation of an NHS 'quasi-market' as part of the Conservative reforms of 1990. The commissioner's role is to secure, rather than directly provide, services that meet the needs of the populations for whose health they are responsible. Four main steps make up the commissioning 'cycle': assessment of need, priority setting, contracting for services, and reviewing their delivery.

and holding them accountable for some £60 billion. CCGs took shape in the face of severe financial stringencies, tasked to help deliver the government's 'efficiency targets' (savings).

GP fundholding
I
Total purchasing
I
Locality purchasing
I
Primary care groups
I
Primary care trusts
I
Clinical commissioning groups

Figure 8.5 Genealogy

Different forms of primary care led commissioning have given rise to a canon of research literature, with sometimes inconsistent messages. In summary, there is little substantive research evidence to demonstrate that any commissioning approach has made a significant impact on secondary care services.[33] The consequences of the ill-fated Health & Social Care Act have been particularly lamentable. Given that the main policy objective of commissioning is to shape health systems around the needs of patients and, in particular, to shift funding from hospitals into the community, this is a disappointment.

Nevertheless, administrations of all hues have continued their search for the holy grail: a market model that is more efficient. Governments and their ministers, despite pledges to the contrary, immersed themselves in needless structural reorganisation - or 'redisorganisation' as it has been waggishly termed.[34] Faith is currently reposed in Primary Care Networks, the latest administrative creation tasked with delivering general practice from all its afflictions.[35] I am not holding my breath.

Inner city practice
General practice in inner cities, and London in particular, has always been of varying quality.[36] Most of the social problems associated with material deprivation are concentrated in run down city centres. These are the sites of higher morbidity and mortality. Without reasonable accommodation it was hard to develop teams. The combination of high land values, unsavoury locations and planning problems made it difficult to find new sites in the right place. Recruiting young doctors of high quality was a perennial problem. The archetypal inner-city doctor was older, had trained overseas and worked single-handedly. Few had purpose-built premises or staff attached to the practice. Young doctors seldom wished to enter such practices, and when single-handed vacancies became available energetic young GPs often lost out to those with more experience. 'Better' doctors went to greener pastures.

Donald Acheson's report of 1981 was the first of several analyses of problematic care in London and made no less than 115 recommendations.[37] The catalogue of defects identified was reminiscent of Collings' findings thirty years earlier (see chapter 7). Among those providing evidence was my old boss, Brian

Jarman, at St Mary's Hospital Medical School. He had developed a measure of the social characteristics that in London GPs' opinion most increased their workload or the pressure on their services. His index used eight census variables and correlated with other indices that attempted to measure deprivation or the levels of illness in different areas (table 8.1). The index was controversial but subsequently accepted by the BMA. The 'Jarman score' was used by the DHSS as part of the payment system, to compensate inner city doctors for the additional work in deprived areas.[38]

Table 8.1   Indicators of deprivation in the Jarman index[38]
- Pensioners living alone
- Children under five
- One-parent families
- Unskilled breadwinners
- Unemployed
- Overcrowding
- Mobile population
- Ethnic minorities

Numerous policies have since aimed to improve conditions where needs are greatest. Lasting attempts properly to link workload to income have been desultory. Inner city practice remains of poorer quality, less well staffed and rewarded. The glaring persistence of an inverse care law in general practice is the profession's greatest indictment.

Computerization
By the early 1980s, a few GPs were beginning to install practice-based microcomputers, smaller, more powerful, faster and cheaper though lacking in tailor-made software.[39] Initially, the main benefits to practices lay in their newfound ability to aggregate information and review clinical activities before making changes. From then on computerisation proceeded apace.[40] Systems were installed in increasing numbers and many software companies entered the market. It is no coincidence that the success was achieved mainly by small and responsive suppliers often run by former general practitioners. By 1995, 90 per cent of practices were computerised and systems were regularly used for prescribing, call and recall, and medical audit. They were by now also essential to financial security.

The term 'clinical audit' was first associated with the American guru of quality improvement, Avedis Donabedian.[41] It involves measuring performance against predefined criteria and implementing changes until pre-set standards are achieved. When doctors first began to examine how well they were treating their patients with diseases like hypertension, they were frequently dismayed to observe a 'rule of thirds' (a third of patients with the disease not identified, a third uncontrolled, a third treated adequately).[42] Hardly reassuring. Financial incentives and improved software have transformed this picture. Computers have routinised ever more searching and sophisticated analyses of clinical activity, particularly in the field of prescribing.

Other new technologies were beginning to find their way into the community. For many years certain laboratory tests had been performed near the patient. Tests had become simpler; boiling urine in test tubes had been replaced by more convenient dip-stick tests for sugar, protein, ketones and blood. Such tests could improve the speed and accuracy of clinical decisions and the quality of chronic disease monitoring. Some tests could be used by patients, as tests for pregnancy, blood sugar and cholesterol measurement were available over the counter. Technological advance made small desk-top analysers affordable in general practice for a wider range of investigations.

Prescribing
Since the earliest years of the health service there had been concern over the large and growing sums spent on medicines (see chapter 6). Following another balance of payments crisis and a devaluation of the pound, economies were necessary and prescription charges had been re-introduced in 1968. The number of prescriptions fell in the short-term, people increasingly bought common household remedies across the counter, and GPs prescribed larger quantities. Exempt groups were established, including some with chronic diseases such as diabetes, the young, the old and people on Supplementary Benefit. More than half the prescriptions issued were for these categories, reducing substantially the benefit to the exchequer.

Different companies marketed the same drug under different names for different costs. Less expensive but effective, 'generic' alternatives often existed. The trend to more prescriptions at increased cost soon continued once more. The Hinchcliffe Committee found no evidence of widespread extravagance but believed that expensive preparations should give way to cheaper alternatives.[43] Doctors henceforth needed to justify prescribing a branded product rather than its generic equivalent. The days of unfettered 'clinical freedom' were drawing to a close.[44]

Some GPs had introduced practice formularies and audited their prescription costs. In the view of the Department of Health and Social Security (DHSS), safe and effective prescribing was often economical prescribing as well. In November 1984, with little warning, Norman Fowler, the Secretary of State, announced that certain groups of medicines would no longer be available for prescription on the NHS.[45] The groups had been carefully chosen and were generally those for minor and self-limiting ailments including tonics, antacids, mild pain relievers, cold cures and laxatives.

The cost of prescribing continued to increase because of the increasing rates of long-term illness, for example high blood pressure and asthma, and the encouragement of 'case-finding'. The rising numbers of elderly people, many of whom were on several different forms of treatment, augmented the increase. Because prescribing patterns and costs varied widely, GPs had long been sent information about their prescribing. In 1988 a better system was introduced, Prescribing Analyses and Cost (PACT). It compared each doctor's costs, broke down prescriptions into six major therapeutic groups, such as the cardiovascular drugs, and showed the percentage of items prescribed generically rather than by a brand name.

Later, indicative drug budgets were produced, showing how much each practice would be likely to spend. The Audit Commission calculated that about a fifth of the total GP prescribing budget was being wasted on over-prescribing, drugs of limited value or expensive ones where cheaper ones were equally effective.[46]

Concerns about over-prescription dated back to the beginning of the century. During the 60's, loose controls helped fuel dependence on benzodiazepines and other tranquilizers ('mother's little helpers'[47]). More than half the adult population regularly take prescription drugs. 60% of people over 60 have a long-term condition. While this reflects positive pharmacological advances, drug companies have also sought to create new markets in advance of any evidence of benefits, for example in the treatment of 'pre-diabetes'. 72 million prescriptions for antidepressants were given out in 2018, compared with 36 million in 2008. Doctors would like to believe this massive rise is due to better detection of mental illness rather than over-readiness to prescribe when little else is available. Much could be done to reduce our apparent dependence on prescription drugs. A significant amount of GP time is now spent trying to limit so-called 'polypharmacy' and wean people off unnecessary medications.

GPs down the ages have inclined to therapeutic nihilism - relying on placebos and sceptical of the benefits of supposedly scientific remedies. The use of placebos raises ethical concerns, for introducing dishonesty into the doctor-patient relationship. It was once assumed that this deception was necessary for placebos to have any effect. Fascinatingly, there is now evidence that they can work even when the patient is aware that the treatment is a placebo.[48]

Repurposing general practice
By now, GPs were being given financial incentives to improve standards. Primary health care teams grew larger and were increasingly well housed. The number of GPs in England rose by 10 per cent between 1985 and 1995, by which date nearly a third were women. Average list sizes fell. Nearly half of all GPs were in partnerships of four or more. The distribution of general

practitioners, evened out by the Medical Practices Committee, was reasonably uniform but doctors who had qualified outside the UK were found predominantly in the old industrial areas where single-handed practice remained more common.

As ever, clinical practice revolved around the care of acute illness and the management of chronic disease. Patients' problems changed only slowly. Seventy-eight per cent of people were consulting their GP at least once a year. As ever, the commonest reasons were respiratory diseases (31%), nervous system disorders (17%) and musculo-skeletal problems such as arthritis (17%). Patients expected longer consultations. More consulted for preventive health care, immunisation, contraception, screening and advice than for any other single disease grouping (33%).[49] The most notable trend, mirrored in increasing rates of anxiety and depression in the community at large, was the rising burden of mental ill health.

One potential of the British primary health care system had always been under-exploited; GPs were too busy dealing with illness to worry much about prevention.[50] Health promotion was the subject of a series of special reports published by the Royal College of General Practitioners.[51] Much research examined the effectiveness of practice-based interventions to reduce cardiovascular disease risk factors.[52-4] They nevertheless provided the basis for repeated reviews of the GPs' contract encouraging disease prevention throughout the 80s.

In November 1987 another White Paper, *Promoting better health*[55], presented the profession with a package that left room for negotiation only at the margins. Financial incentives were to encourage specific services such as immunisation, cervical cytology, comprehensive care for elderly people, postgraduate education and practice in the inner cities. Whereas the changes of 1965 had altered the structure of practice, these focussed on the processes of care. Some such as annual health checks for all people over 75 were not based on firm scientific evidence of benefit. These changes were thus both more intrusive and more contentious.

It was perfectly legal for the Secretary of State to decide the terms on which family doctors worked, but in law there had to be a clear attempt to negotiate alterations. As always, the profession were inclined to the status quo. The deal was hard for the profession's leaders to accept and it was unusual for government to lay down so precisely what doctors should do in clinical terms.

GPs believed their contract could not be altered without agreement and angrily rejected the package. They were wrong; Kenneth Clarke implemented it anyway. The louche, jazz-loving, cigar-toting attack dog was later to morph into national treasure as 'remoaning' father of the House of Commons. It is hard to imagine the loathing he inspired among doctors back then.

In 1966, the profession's negotiators had held a strong hand. General practice had been deteriorating and was widely regarded as second rate. Morale was low. GPs were leaving practice. Health minister Kenneth Robinson was the son of a GP and Labour regarded the NHS as its political baby. By 1990, GPs were well motivated and worked in premises provided largely at the public's expense. They had no difficulty in recruiting colleagues. Public attitudes to organised industrial action had changed under Thatcher and following the miners' strike of 1984. GPs faced a strong government determined on consumer-orientated reforms and their negotiators held but modest hands.[56]

For all the resentment, the 1990 contract did not represent a fundamental break with the past. Its outcome was not always as envisaged. Health promotion activity tended to be segregated in special clinics, rather than being incorporated into routine consultations. Neither the GMSC nor the Department of Health (DoH) had understood just how effective these financial incentives would prove. GPs appointed many more nurses, increased their minor surgery, organised their practices better, installed more computers, and achieved higher rates of immunisation and cervical cancer screening.[57] First the front runners and then other GPs improved the quality of their service.[58]

Practice nurses, to their surprise, were also beneficiaries. With their workloads rising, GPs found the assistance of nurses keen to develop their careers highly congenial. They were popular with patients.[59] They were recruited in their thousands at great cost to a bemused Treasury that had to pick up the bill. From fewer than 2,000 whole-time equivalents in 1984, the number of practice nurses rose to more than 9,000 in 1994. As their numbers grew, the range of their work increased. Nurses took over health promotion and were subsequently involved in traditionally medical areas such as the care of chronic disease, the management of diabetes, asthma and high blood pressure.[60]

The concept of the 'nurse-practitioner' became a semantic battleground.[61] Broadly, there were two directions for practice nurses. One was to continue to do more of what they were already doing: managing chronic disease with additional training. Alternatively, they might become a first point of contact, assessing patients (making a diagnosis), determining the treatment of acute illnesses, prescribing, and becoming a member of a medical team with a defined role and accountability within that team.[62] They did both, becoming team members with newly defined roles and accountability.

Shifting boundaries

Problems in health systems as complex as the NHS frequently occur at structural boundaries. Patients and their doctors have always faced difficulties at the interface between general practice and the hospital service. There might be long waits for outpatient appointments and delays for hospital reports to arrive in surgery. From this period, it became a policy axiom that the boundary or locus of care, where possible, be shifted into the community.[63]

General practitioners and community nurses were encouraged to develop new skills and practice-based facilities. Hospital-at-home schemes sought to avoid hospital admission and facilitate early discharge. Shared care schemes were developed for chronic disease management, paediatrics, mental health and maternity care. Often, however, schemes such as the encouragement of minor surgery in general practice had little effect on the demand for hospital care, because they encouraged patients to come for treatment who otherwise might not have done so.

Although GPs were still opposed to the 1990 contract, many saw in it opportunities for improving the quality of their service, despite increasing workloads.[64] Typical of the innovators was Geoffrey Marsh in Stockton-on-Tees. His practice covered both deprived and more salubrious areas.[65] His group deployed health visitors almost entirely in poorer wards where the health gains to be made with immunisation and child health care were greatest. He was among the first to train experienced practice nurses to manage minor illness.[66]

The development of new drugs and point of care technologies furthered the shifting of boundaries. In no area was this more dramatic than diabetology. The obesity epidemic was exploding the number of sufferers from diabetes. This provided a huge boon for the pharmaceutical industry but was overwhelming diabetic out-patients departments. Consultants gratefully relinquished the routine monitoring of diabetes. They had no choice.

The Social Care conundrum

The most important interface was that between health and local authority services. When patients were discharged there was frequently difficulty in obtaining continuity of medical and nursing care, and delay before patients from hospital could be transferred to residential care.

The question of how to fund long term care of the elderly and the disabled has long confounded politicians across the developed world. While health care in England has been 'free at the point of delivery' since 1948, social care has been subject to means tested charges. Calls for free personal care (as in Scotland) have never garnered support from the English exchequer. A series of commissions had agreed that the current system was confusing, unfair and unsustainable.[67] Many people's last years are blighted by fear of penury. David Cameron's Coalition government asked Andrew Dilnot, an Oxford economist, to come up with new proposals.

The root problem remains the artificial demarcation between two forms of care. For some, the very phrase 'social care' demeans older people by detaching the source and solution of their suffering from disease and frailty. The arguments against continuing to separate personal and nursing care remain strong.[68] The privatisation of long-term care has been accompanied by fragmentation of service provision and inefficiencies.

Dilnot's commission recommended that people should contribute a standard amount - between £7000 and £10000 per year - towards their living costs, such as food and accommodation, in residential care.[69] Eligibility criteria for service entitlement were to be set on a standardised, national basis to improve consistency and fairness. As a result, more people would have received significant help and no one would have lost more than 30% of their total assets. All this would have been costly for the state - an extra £3.6 billion pounds annually by 2025 - but a mere fraction of what has been wasted since. Needless to say, politicians kicked this and subsequent similar proposals into the long grass.[70]

Yet there is widespread public acceptance of the principle of taking responsibility for costs up to a point past which the state pays. Contingent risks need to be pooled in a universal manner so reducing the threat of financial devastation for many older people. This type of social insurance policy, with a significant 'excess' which people will need to cover themselves, may yet provide a model for the future funding of the NHS.[71] At the time of writing, another government review is underway.

Salaried service
The imposition of the 1990 contract and the increasing bureaucratic burdens of their new commissioning role sapped morale in general practice. Fewer doctors sought vocational training and GPs increasingly rebelled against their round-the-clock responsibilities. They felt that the public - consumers accustomed to 24-hour services from many organisations - wanted primary health care to be available on the same basis. Some GPs were prepared to consider radical revision of their contract, even salaried service, to control workloads.

Since 1948 all GPs had worked under a single contract for services, nationally negotiated and set out in the 'Red Book' (see chapter 7). The traditional contract, highly structured, was not necessarily suited to meeting the needs of all communities and made short term employment impossible.

Following another review, a more flexible framework was proposed.[72] The white paper *Choice and opportunity*, published late in 1996, heralded the deregulation of general practice by allowing experimentation with different forms of contract.[73] This would allow new organisations to provide primary care and represented a major threat to traditional general practice.[74]

The NHS (Primary Care) Act 1997 was passed shortly before Labour came to power and allowed health authorities to commission primary care services in new ways. A new style contract for so-called 'Personal Medical Services' (PMS) with a group or practice, instead of with individual GPs, was for a defined package of services. Contracts were local, rather than national, and linked firmly to measures of quality. Services could be tailored to the needs of specific groups, such as the unemployed. Flexible contracts were more adaptable to the complex needs of inner cities and allowed for experimentation with alternative systems and mixes of skill. In particular, under PMS salaried employment became possible for the first time.[75]

In 2003, the Health and Social Care (Community Health and Standards) Act allowed Primary Care Trusts to commission 'anyone capable of securing the delivery of those services.' Firms such as Boots, and some groupings of general practitioners took advantage of the opportunity. PMS contracts became a mainstream option before any evaluation was completed. GPs seemed willing to trade income for better conditions, freedom from out of hours working, from administrative responsibilities and an ability to work part time. Being an employee appealed to doctors early in their career, those approaching retirement and especially to women.[76] There was a progressive shift towards PMS with salaried GPs working alongside 'independent contractor' GPs.

Partnership remains the gold standard in the view of the BMA but over the last 20 years the number of salaried doctors has steadily increased. By 2005, 40% of GPs worked under PMS contracts. Salaried practice often suits young doctors unwilling to commit to the responsibilities of partnership. However, they earn less - perhaps two thirds of a full partner's income - and were sometimes exploited in other ways. Their lot could be compared to that of pre-NHS assistants.

The Alterative Provider Medical Services Contract (APMS) allowed primary care trusts to contract services from groups outside the NHS, including commercial and voluntary organisations. By 2008 some 100 practices were being run by alternative providers and it was GP-led companies that had been most successful in bidding for these contracts. Some supported this initiative as encouraging innovation; others saw it as an aggressive commercial take-over of general practice. These developments led some commentators to fear for the wholesale privatization of general practice.[77]

Performance-related pay

Another far-reaching change was the radical extension into general practice of performance-related pay. Paradoxically, this was driven by the confluence of two competing forces. Academics propounding the virtues of EBM (Evidence Based Medicine) tended to oppose ideologically right-wing economic policy, a field largely devoid of evidence. For managers keen to ensure the best bangs for their bucks, any evidence for cost effectiveness had a seductive allure.

The UK Quality and Outcomes Framework (QOF), introduced as part of another new contract in 2004, was the most comprehensive national primary care pay-for-performance (P4P) scheme in the world.[78] The QOF comprised a number of elements including financial incentives and information technology (computerized prompts and decision support) to achieve evidence-based quality targets. The QOF was designed to improve the quality of chronic disease management by rewarding practices for delivering interventions linked to improved health outcomes for heart disease, diabetes and other major scourges. The money to implement the scheme raised annual pay for general practitioners by over 30%, to more than £100,000. The inducements were substantial and its impact was immediate. Most income was still determined by capitation, but the QOF now provided a about a quarter.

Technical care for chronic conditions improved as most practices hit most targets. The gap between high and low achieving practices diminished thereby reducing inequalities in care. Doctors reported improved data recording and team-working, and nurses enhanced their specialist skills. However, these advances came at unexpected costs. 20% of indicators referred directly to drugs, and many others required pharmaceutical interventions for the targets to be met. The QOF therefore contributed to polypharmacy and rising treatment costs. Prescription rates for antidepressants, statins and other drugs have continued to rise.[79]

Economic research suggests that while financial incentives promote simple repetitive tasks, they can be counterproductive for tasks requiring more complex mental processes.[80] Financial incentives may encourage delivery of care that follows a simple algorithm, but algorithms are hard to apply meaningfully in the real world of individuals with a variety of symptoms, diagnoses and expectations, in their particular social context.

These practical concerns chimed with the experience of many clinicians (like myself) that a reductionist approach to managing markers of chronic disease could conflict with the humanitarian values of general practice. Health professionals need to place biomedical algorithms in the context of the individual patient's concerns and life experience.[81] Research suggested that the person-centredness of consultations and continuity had been negatively affected.[82,83]

Bunker calculated that better health care has contributed about half of the 7.5 years increase in life expectancy observed over the second half of the 20th century.[84] Sadly, there is no good evidence that the QOF improved the population's health. Against a background of so many interacting determinants, there was never likely to be.[85] With burgeoning evidence that its benefits to patients were at best modest,[86] policy makers eventually reduced the proportion of general practice income commanded by QOF. This did not diminish the ethical imperative to practice in the light of best evidence.

Access, access

Workloads in general practice continued to rise. Between 1995 and 2008, the annual number of patient consultations more than doubled, from 171 million to more than 350 million. The average patient consulted 6.7 times last year, up from 3.9 times in 1995, with the biggest increases taking place amongst those aged over 70 years.[87]

Gaining swift access to the doctor had long been difficult. In 1948, patients turned up and waited. In some practices, they still do (footnote 8). In the 1960s appointment systems were introduced. Later governments promoted a series of wheezes designed to 'relieve pressure on hospitals' while assuaging the public's supposed desire for limitless primary care. Did any of them work?

NHS Direct, a nurse-led telephone helpline, was established in 1998. New primary care outlets, accessible after hours and at weekends, were established in city centres. Neither of these innovations yielded significant reduction in the use of A&E departments or ambulance services longer term.[88]

The most comprehensive attempt to manage demand was the Advanced Access initiative, originating in the US and launched here in 2001. This comprised various strategies to support same day appointments including telephone triage, bookings to support same day appointments including telephone triage, booked telephone appointments, e-mail consultations, advice on self-management (leaflets, websites), delegation to minor illness nurses and health care assistants. Appointment slots were held for 'urgent problems', the delay for a routine consultation lengthened and surgery phone lines were blocked each morning as patients fought to get through.

Footnote 8. Aldborough is a village of 590 inhabitants some seven miles from Holt. With the surrounding villages, it is served by a single-handed practice. Some of my great great grandfather's night-time rides would be to hamlets at the western edge of the practice's catchment area. I sometimes cover Dr Mark when he needs holidays or other relief. It is to step back into another era. Patients await their turn at morning surgery and rare are the calls or visits that are unmerited. His patients know not to overwhelm him. In return, they value personal care from someone they know and trust.

Notwithstanding early enthusiasm, Advanced Access had little impact on access, patient or staff satisfaction.[89] Telephone triage in-hours and out-of-hours may have reduced the numbers of immediate face to face contacts and visits by GPs, but the evidence was inconclusive.[90,91] Workloads tended to be redistributed rather than significantly reduced.[92]

The NHS Plan of 2004 set a target that one should be able to see a health professional within 24 hours and a GP within 48 hours. Recalcitrant practices were threatened with financial sanctions but target-setting alone proved toothless.

Fundamentally, this was a zero-sum game. From where would additional staff come from but the locum pools already propping up general practice elsewhere? The public rarely understood the trade-offs involved. Hastening access tended to reduce the availability of named doctors and fragment care.[93]

All practices nowadays employ a range of strategies for managing demand: telephone triage, online consultations, delegation to minor illness nurses or health care assistants. These techniques have had little effect on the satisfaction of staff or patients as improving access simply increased demand. The Covid-19 pandemic has accelerated the move to virtual consulting with longer term consequences that are as yet unclear.

Continuity of care
For generations of practitioners, trained in the humanist skills of consulting, the defining characteristic of the care they provide is relational continuity. While this view of their trade may sound increasingly anachronistic, population health goals remain less motivating.

Traditionally, GPs had undertaken home visits and emergency night calls. Continuity of care ('from womb to tomb') had long been a core value. With the introduction of deputising services and GP cooperatives in the 1960s, up to 90% of GPs had devolved out-of-hours care though they remained legally responsible for it. The 2004 contract afforded GPs the right to transfer this responsibility to an 'accredited organised provider of out-of-hours services'.

Few GPs wished to do much out-of-hours work, and there was an increasing trend among GPs to part-time working, reducing continuity of care even within working hours. The service now provided by a variety of independent organisations, linked neither to hospitals nor to general practice, was increasingly patchy.

Doctors have always known that staying active characterizes their heathier patients. Yet evidence for the myriad benefits of exercise has only recently begun to be quantified. In part, this is because exercise is harder to measure than blood pressure, cholesterol or other risk factors. Similarly, the importance of continuity of carer has been overlooked because it is hard to measure and research.

GPs and their patients alike have always understood the advantages of personal knowledge of one another. Much unnecessary investigation can be avoided on the basis of that knowledge. For patients, particularly older people, value the reassurance of seeing someone they recognize and trust on the basis of past experience. Staff shortages, part-time working, multiple access points, diversification of roles and responsibilities all make it increasingly difficult to see a doctor of choice.

Early work examined theoretical aspects of continuity and ways of measuring it. 'Longitudinal continuity' (care over time) is usefully distinguished from 'personal continuity' (an ongoing therapeutic relationship). After all, seeing the same doctor does not guarantee patient satisfaction and all doctors have their 'heartsink' patients. Both forms are distinguished from 'informational continuity', provided by an electronic record accessible to different staff.[94]

Nowadays, satisfactory care may be given by trusted members of a working team but continuity has now been associated with increased patient satisfaction, increased take-up of health promotion, greater adherence to medical advice and decreased use of hospital services. Recent systematic reviews have even linked increased continuity of care by doctors to lower mortality rates.[95,96]

Most practices have long abandoned personal lists whereby patients saw the doctor with whom they were registered. Symbolically, the notion of the practice itself has changed - away from personalities and towards teams or buildings. No longer 'Dr Ward and partners', we became the Lea Vale Medical Group. The government attempted to make the allocation of named GPs to patients a contractual obligation but, as a purely administrative procedure, this had little impact. Continuity, as traditionally understood, is largely a thing of the past.

Regulation
Regulation in health care occurs on many different levels. In 1997, there was no national policy covering all aspects of safety and quality of health care provision. The new Labour government concluded that the quality of care provided by the NHS had been 'variable' and that the service had been slow to respond to 'serious lapses in quality', most notably at the Bristol Royal Infirmary (footnote 9).

The Commission for Healthcare Improvement (CHI) was established in 1999 to offer guidance to NHS providers on clinical governance. This was superseded by the Care Quality Commission (CQC) in 2009, set up to regulate and inspect the quality and safety of all providers of health care and adult social care services. Registration requirements cover areas such as the management and training of staff, the state of premises and provision of information. The CQC has a wide range of enforcement powers, including closure if essential standards are not met.

In 2013, the CQC began its programme of GP surgery inspections starting with a list of practices already considered by CCGs to be among the worst. Not surprisingly a significant number fell short, sometimes because of hygiene and cleanliness, sometimes because of staffing problems. The CQC uncovered a catalogue of failings at more than 300 practices. The horror stories included maggots on the floor of consulting rooms, patients given out-of-date medicines or injections, and nurses not trained in basic first aid.[97] However, fears of a latter-day Collings report were unrealised. Indeed, most practices comfortably cleared the hurdle (footnote 10). Nowadays, the CQC inspection is accepted as a necessary, if tiresome, evil.[14]

With 1.7 million employees and an annual budget of £140 billion, the NHS is one of the largest organisations in the world. The regulatory structures which aim to ensure that patients receive high-quality care are increasingly complex. Despite these structures, adverse events have continued to occur. Government-led investigations such as the Mid-Staffs Inquiry and Shipman Inquiry have sadly served to remind us that organisational failings and the actions of individuals can place patients at risk. Professional accountability has thus been increased in very many ways.

Individual doctors are required by law to apply for licences to practice from our professional regulator, the General Medical Council (GMC). Created *'to protect, promote, and maintain the health and safety of the public by ensuring proper standards in the practice of medicine'*, the GMC struggled to adapt to a new environment where greater levels of public accountability were required. Publicised failures of the medical profession stoked public perceptions of a closed clique impervious to criticism in defence of its own interests. The right to self-regulation was further challenged by the Shipman affair (footnote 11).

As set out in the Medical Act of 1983, the GMC's main role is to keep a register of qualified doctors and erase from the register those who are deemed unfit to practice.

Footnotes 9. The Bristol Royal Infirmary was the setting for a scandalous failure of medical care and oversight in the early 90s. 34 babies died after after cardiac surgery. An anaesthetist, Stephen Bolsin, finally blew the whistle on a unit which had performed poorly for years. Ian Kennedy's inquiry exposed minimal leadership, an 'old boy's culture' among doctors, lax approaches to safety, secrecy about doctors' performance and a lack of monitoring. Cardio-thoracic surgeons have since been leading efforts to publish more data on the performance of doctors and hospitals.

10. 5% (327) of practices have been ranked as outstanding, 90% (6196) as good, 4% (264) required improvement and 1% (86) were inadequate.[98] Tautologically, the high proportion of practices doing well is sometimes used as evidence for the benefits of regulation. Reassuring yes but, if anything, it strengthens the sense that many visits are an unwarranted waste of time.

Its remit includes responsibility for setting standards in medical education and professional conduct, and for revalidation. The GMC's governing council is now lay dominated.

Revalidation is the process by which all licensed doctors are required to demonstrate on a five yearly basis that they are fit to practice. It was started in 2013 and aims to give patients confidence that their doctor's professional knowledge is up to date. Doctors are assessed using their annual appraisals and supporting portfolios. The latter include the results of surveys of both their patients and their colleagues. In other words, their professional practice is under closer scrutiny than ever before.

These changes have been met with grudging acceptance. The GMC's judgements are widely regarded as having swung too far out of sympathy with the medical profession. The decision to prosecute and debar Hadiza Bawa-Garba - later reversed - was a lightning conductor in this regard (footnote 12). The sense of disempowerment has been amplified with the emergence of other overseers like the CQC.

The waning workforce

Over the years the work of the GP had changed significantly. With an accent on health promotion and the management of chronic diseases, payment systems were partly based on ensuring that patients were reviewed and targets met. As a result, much effort went into regular reviews. Practice nurses increasingly took on responsibility for care of diabetes, asthma and chronic obstructive pulmonary disease. GPs inevitably spent more time on administrative and financial matters.

A GP workforce crisis was emerging. Not enough GPs were being trained, more worked part-time, and more existing GPs planned to retire early. A cap on the permitted size of a 'pension fund' was a factor; when this was reached some doctors thought the tax implications of continuing to work in a stressful job made it not worthwhile. The percentage of women GPs rose from 31% to 42%. Men worked

Footnotes 11. Harold Frederick Shipman (1946-2004), a GP in Hyde, was the most prolific serial killer in history. His total victim count is estimated to have been about 250, 80% of whom were elderly women. Much medical regulation was tightened as a result of the Shipman Inquiry. The processes of death certification and prescribing were modified. Whether any of these changes would ever 'prevent another Shipman' is widely doubted among doctors. Perhaps surprisingly, he is the only British doctor ever to have been found guilty of murdering his patients. I had the dubious pleasure of appearing on Newsnight to be roasted by Jeremy Vine on the day of Shipman's sentencing.
        12. Six-year old Jack Adcock died in Leicester Royal Infirmary on 18th February 2011 partly as a result of failings in his treatment. A junior doctor, Hadiza Bawa-Garba, was subsequently found guilty of manslaughter on the grounds of gross negligence. She was swiftly struck off the GMC register, triggering howls of protest across the profession. Bawa-Garba's personal culpability was questioned in the context of systemic failures and under-staffing. The decision was overturned at appeal but not before much damage had been done to the reputation of the GMC.

more sessions and more women were part-timers.[99] While most GPs were partners in their practice, almost a third were salaried by 2015. Three quarters of partners worked full time (44 hours/week), less than half of the others did so and an increasing number of entrants wanted to work part time.

Governments are generally loth to alienate general practitioners. They fear the vitriol that might pour over 6 million patients per week. General practitioners have never been averse to tribal shroud-waving but their disgruntlement was pardonable. Longer days and mounting workloads had coincided with declining pay over several years.[100] The most dispiriting feature of the recruitment crisis was that it had long been predicted.[101]

A central issue was one of understanding. Demeaningly, ministers appeared to believe that general practice exists solely to provide a filter for minor illness and to manage chronic disease in a manner that reduces the demands on expensive hospitals. In reality, the distinction between acute and chronic, immediate and long-term care, is blurred. 'Trivial' encounters are the building blocks that make up longer term relationships. Much care is acute-on-chronic. Many patients seeking same-day appointments have complex needs. The longest term condition is life itself.

Doctors of a conspiratorial caste of mind suspected the government was bent on destruction of the current model in a rigged market. After all, successive regimes had overseen an increase in consultant numbers of more than two thirds while the GP workforce grew less than a fifth.[101] Ministers responded with a series of hollow recruitment targets and gimmicks but the problems were deep and systemic.

Finally, in 2016 the government published the *GP Forward View*, a plan for the future. Welcomed by the profession, it promised increased investment, a review of funding formulae and the recruitment of more general practitioners.[102] There was growing support for radical restructuring to manage increasing patient demand amid cuts in resources. A variety of models emerged, the common factor being the formation of larger practice groupings or federations to share existing services and develop new ones. Economies of scale were possible, for example by centralising support services and reducing back-office overheads. It takes ten years to train a GP. In the meantime, doctors are burning out and leaving early.[103] There has been little sign of reduced workloads or increased numbers thus far.

Crisis, what crisis?
For much of my career, the BMA and RCGP have regarded one another with mutual suspicion: town v. gown, rapacious trades unionists versus pointy-headed, other-worldly academics. The BMA had to get used to another power base setting training standards and finally accrediting newly minted GPs. Trainees were inevitably socialised in the image of the College. On the other hand, stock-jobbing

GP trainers were ever reliant on the negotiating wiles of the GPC. Over time, these enmities have diminished. An alliance was easier to sustain against austere, Tory administrations which might harbour plans to privatize the system or sell it off to American multinationals.

It is hard to deny the vulnerable state of general practice today. The roots of the current workforce crisis are complex but reflect poverty of central planning, political ignorance and neglect. The combination of competitive markets in primary care, designed to break GPs' monopoly of provision, and crude managerialism have changed practice irrevocably. The personal, implicit contract with the patient has loosened just as the public, explicit contract between doctor and state has tightened.[104] Public satisfaction with general practice dropped by 7 percentage points in 2018 to 65 per cent, the lowest level since the survey began in 1983.[105]

Political neglect has been manifest in years of underfunding. The expansion and technical complexity of modern hospital specialties mean that, although 90% of patient contacts in the UK occur in general practice, the latter receives less than 9% of NHS funding. Good general practice saves the NHS money by doing things hospitals cannot do: caring for them in their own homes, managing uncertainty, gauging when and when not to push for a diagnosis. More hospital spending has furthered sub-specialisation and worsened the problem.

The benefits of high technology seldom outweigh the disadvantages of ill-coordinated or fragmented care. General practice used to be regarded as one of the main reasons for the relative efficiency of the NHS but the creation of numerous access points has further complicated the patient experience.

At the same time, primary care workloads have increased for a familiar triad of reasons: rising numbers of multi-morbid older people, technological advances that have shifted care of common chronic diseases into the community, and rising consumer demand. Bureaucratic micromanagement and increasing regulation have aggravated professional unhappiness. The falling popularity of general practice reflects an increasing gap between health workers' expectations and the job's realities.

There is an analogous mismatch between public expectations and what is (or can affordably be) provided. Modern day 'healthism'- characterized by high health awareness, information-seeking, a partiality towards alternative models of illness and anxiety - often leads to mutually distrustful patient-professional relationships.[106] The fear of litigation has in turn fostered defensive medicine and the overuse of diagnostics.

Meeting health care users' stated concerns involves inevitable trade-offs and policy responses have frequently been incoherent. For example, users place a high priority on continuity of personal care while at the same time wanting immediate access. Initiatives to increase available contacts, e.g. through extending opening hours or increasing access routes, have come at the expense of continuity of individual care.[107]

The self-interested mind-set of the independent contractor has not helped. General practitioners' representatives are notoriously prone to shroud-waving and bouts of professional militancy. Perennial 'crises' have been a feature of life on the front line since the eighteenth century but there are good reasons for taking today's concerns seriously. Many doctors fear for the very future of general practice.

Reversing the global decline
Primary health care (PHC) has often been defined in terms of '4Cs': it is continuous, comprehensive, the point of first contact and co-ordinates other care. This co-ordinating function underlies its efficiency and cost effectiveness.[108] The work of Barbara Starfield and colleagues explored international health systems in terms of the extent to which they were primary care oriented.[109] They found that those countries with more family doctors with registered lists acting as gatekeepers were more likely to deliver better health outcomes, lower costs and greater patient satisfaction.[110] Screening, monitoring and follow-up is most effectively conducted through the co-ordinated efforts of various health workers on the basis of the populations they serve.

Ironically, UK general practice is beleaguered at a time when the global health community has woken up once more to the pivotal importance of PHC. In 1978 at Alma Ata, the World Health Organisation (WHO) declared PHC to be the key to delivering health for all by the year 2000.[111] For WHO, primary health care was *'based on practical, scientifically sound and socially acceptable methods and technology made universally accessible through people's full participation and at a cost that the community and country can afford.'* Primary health care in this context included both primary medical care and activities tackling determinants of ill health. Efforts at expanding primary health care in the late 1980s and 90s were overtaken in many parts of the developing world by economic crisis, sharp reductions in public spending, political instability, and emerging disease. The social and political goals of Alma Ata provoked early ideological opposition and were never fully embraced in market-oriented, capitalist countries.

As in the UK, hospitals retained their disproportionate share of local health economies. A medical model of primary care dominated by professional vested interests resisted the expansion of community health workers with less training. Such programmes anyway proved difficult to sustain, and little empirical research existed to justify them. Geographic and financial inaccessibility, limited resources, erratic drug supply, and shortages of equipment and staff left many low-income countries' primary care services disappointingly restricted in their coverage and impact.[112] The failure in most countries to provide even limited packages, coupled with the proliferation of vertical initiatives to tackle specific global health problems, hastened its eclipse.

All countries face an increasing prevalence of non-communicable disease and this epidemiological transition poses considerable challenges to existing health systems. In all settings, affordability and workforce shortages remain the over-riding challenges. What services can realistically be provided free at the first point of contact and who can provide them? Effective primary health care is more than a simple summation of individual technological interventions. Its power resides in linking different sectors and disciplines, integrating different elements of disease management, prevention, and health maintenance. Systems must be appropriately adapted to local epidemiological, economic, historic and sociocultural contexts. No single model of primary health care can therefore be universally applicable.[113]

Forty years on in 2018, WHO produced an updated declaration from Astana reaffirming its commitment to universal healthcare coverage.[114] This anniversary provided another opportunity to establish a shared view of what PHC is for and the values which underpin it. Whether it will have more impact than the previous manifesto remains to be seen.

Conclusion
In the United Kingdom, the rhetoric of Alma Ata was of largely symbolic importance.[115] The manifesto was leftward leaning and framed PHC delivery in purely technocratic terms, one-sided and top-down. Pivotal turning points in the post-war development of general practice - notably the Family Doctor Charter of 1966 - had left this country boasting some of the best primary medical care in the developed world. The same cannot be claimed with confidence today. The UK is one of many industrialized countries with well-developed state-funded health systems where primary health care has been in comparative decline for many years.

Sanctimonious commentators (like myself) decried many of the market-oriented reforms listed above. Simultaneously, enterprising GPs exploited these opportunities to expand their services and increase their incomes (footnote 13). True to their shop-keeping roots, GPs displayed their customary agility and resourcefulness. They were the fifth columnists that helped to entrench these reforms. The costs and benefits - for patients, managers and doctors themselves - are hard to compute. Arguably, these changes have diverted GPs' energies from their core purpose.

Footnote 13. The average income of GP 'principals' - partners who share full responsibility for running a practice - is approximately £110,000. Many earn considerably more from other private sources, such as dispensing. Salaried partners earn rather less (£60,000 to £90,000).

When patients consult their doctors, they are seeking their attention. Being 'attentively present' generally requires emotional engagement. Only in this manner can caregivers look beyond their frame of reference and empathize with the patient. This in turn demands flexibility and reflection.[116] (Martha Nussbaum places equality and respectful recognition of the other as central to meaningful interaction.[117]) A successful consultation explores patients own ideas and capabilities for improving their health. For the GP, thinking and acting on these priorities requires time. Time that under today's pressures, in ten minute consultations, they do not have.

It is chastening for the practitioner to acknowledge the relative nature of scientific truths. I have doubtless taken a partial view of the policy developments described above. Supposed gains in effectiveness are not always evident to those at ground level. Mostly, I come to the end of my working life full of gratitude for having fallen into a trade that was and remains richly rewarding.

General practices today are organisms of amazing complexity accomplishing much that could not have been dreamt of when I undertook my first surgery in 1982. Exposure to all the travails of humankind in a single morning is still weirdly stimulating. I imagine that any one of the seven generations of my predecessors might have said the same.

'The study of the past with one eye on the present is the source of all sins and sophistries in history. It is the essence of what we mean by the word 'unhistorical.''[118] Mindful of Butterfield's dictum, I shall nevertheless conclude with reflections on what the past may suggest of the future.

Conclusion – After The Fall

'Don't it always seem to go that you don't know what you've got till it's gone.
They paved paradise and put up a parking lot.'
(Joni Mitchell)

Neurobiologists have demonstrated that many of the supposedly free choices we make are predetermined by our genes (footnote 1). In other words, unexpected inclinations can be passed down generations.[1] Perhaps my forebears were hard-wired to be doctors. Certainly, epigeneticists should have no difficulty 'explaining' eight generations of doctors. You are imbued at a young age with the merits of public service and thrill at the supposed rewards of 'doing good'. You observe more of the rewards at first hand. As perceptions are moulded early, you are mostly unaware of the personal costs. The choice of a medical career generally earns the family's approbation. Whatever the residual limitations to your natural fitness for the role, environmental influences finally trump them.

This book is partly about personal and professional identities. A certain dull worthiness is common to these pen portraits. The doctors were sometimes debonair, even dashing, but mostly they displayed the discreet virtues of the trustworthy. They were seldom ostentatious or flashy - but they were 'fortunate' in Berger's sense. They are united by a certain quality of steadfastness. From the early nineteenth century, their stories reflected the fortunes of the 'middling sort'.

Their liberal values were part of a Victorian value system that promoted individual hard work and self-reliance as essential to economic growth and moral rectitude. The social and family ties of these middle-class families were means through which they sustained the professional opportunities and privileges of their class.[2] They were infected at public schools (like Gresham's) with that anti-industrial ethos to which has been attributed Britain's long-term economic decline.[3] In any event, gentlemen entered the new professions and played at country sports rather than pursuing messy money as entrepreneurial business folk.

The essence of general practice lies in the overlap between healing and medicating but it is hard to assess our contribution to society. After all, a society that does not know how to value the lives of its people (beyond their economic contribution) cannot adequately value an easing of their suffering. *'What is the social value of a pain eased? What is the value of a life saved? How does the cure of a serious*

Footnote 1. *'...vast swathes of our complex behaviours are ingrained. Handed down the generations by mind-blowing mechanisms, written into our DNA code and through the volume dial for our genes, to direct the construction of the circuitry that makes up our minds.'*[1] What inherited traits have helped to perpetuate this dynasty? Height and physical resilience, stamina and a capacity for hard work, intelligence, a need to be liked, a judicious blend of compliance and rebelliousness, occasional ruthlessness...all these traits serve Darwinist ends. All are useful in doctoring.

illness compare in value with one of the better poems of a minor poet? (As Fenwick might have asked.) *How does making a correct but difficult diagnosis compare with painting a great canvas?'[4]* The questions are intrinsically absurd but they have, in effect, already been framed - to the detriment of general practice today. The patients encountered by all those Drs Skrimshire and Gillam suffered from the same problems as those visiting my surgery this morning - depression, cardiac problems, minor injuries - but the landscape of health care is very different. Try to imagine practising without agreed qualifications and training standards, extended teams and purpose-built premises, managers and regulation, let alone guaranteed pay and effective remedies.

The song remains the same

So what would George Burrows, a founding father (see chapter 2), make of UK general practice today? He always rued the loss of independence that would have been enshrined in a new College for GPs and would be gratified by its Royal appellation. He would approve developments in training but be surprised by the disappearance of most surgery from practice. He might be permitted some *schadenfreude* in respect of the other Colleges and their desire to keep upstart GPs at bay. In that early disunity, he would discern the roots of the 'independent contractor' status that divides the NHS to this day.[5] He might note wryly how little has changed in the volumes of physic that GPs prescribe and their dependence on dispensing. On the other hand, he would be astounded by the complexity of a modern practice. He would observe how their origins as tradesmen have equipped them as entrepreneurs and commissioners. Finally, he would note that doctors have always grumbled about their lot.

Constant advance characterizes biomedicine and the range of treatments available today would bemuse Burrows. Yet while many aspects of practice have greatly changed, it is more striking how little this is reflected in the day-to-day dynamics of general practice. The main business of front-line work is, as it always was, managing mental health and acute as well as chronic illness. My forbears understood the effectiveness of the 'drug doctor' and placebos. (My grandfather prescribed 'Tempest mixture' to his patients in Suffolk. *"Worthless"*, he said, *"but they wouldn't go without some coloured concoction."*) What their patients prized was continuity of care, a relationship of trust and dependability.

True, GPs now have many more complex decisions to make - which diagnostic tests to request, which medicines to prescribe, which fellow professionals to involve or refer to. The job is supposedly more stressful and demanding. Against that, fewer house calls or protracted bedside vigils are required and good pay is guaranteed. Though the cliché is well worn, clinical decision-making - the whether and how to intervene - remains art as well as science. Many of the rhythms and rituals of today's consultations would therefore be recognizable to my great-great-great-great-great grandfather working over 200 years ago.

The perils of progressivism

Some of the 'problems' described in the previous chapter can be viewed as the perverse consequences of the very successes of medical science and the NHS. Medicine has over-reached itself to the detriment of both patients and doctors. Longevity owes more to the social environment than to new treatments and technologies. Professional practice is ever more inefficient while increasingly in demand. This unwarranted rise of medical prestige is an extension of the shamanic function: a magical ritual for the achievement of goals which are beyond technical and political reach.

Illich suggested that this can be countered only through actions which amount to the 'deprofessionalisation' of health care.[6] This does not mean negating the competence of specialised healers or the denial of public funds for curative purposes. It does imply a bias against mystification, the dominance of rigid orthodoxy, and the control of health systems by guild-members, rather than users.

History suggests that unbridled optimism in medical science is unwarranted. Proponents of the new genetics and Artificial Intelligence (AI) peddle reductionist fantasies. The notion that we will ever explain and control all disease is illusory. Genuine progress is always welcome but an ideological obsession with the 'new' has undermined doctors' most valuable asset: knowledge based on practical experience. Medicine has never been synonymous with scientific progress. Its knowledge base has increased spectacularly over the last century but much of what doctors do remains much the same as in Ancient Greece. William Osler extolled the virtues of careful observation and of cultivating *the reasoning faculty so as to be able to know the true from the false.'* Blowing away the millenarian promises of technophiles would liberate medicine to concentrate on the task, in William Blake's words, of 'doing good in minute particulars.'[7]

Over the last thirty years, the individualistic culture of general practice has been eroded and replaced by a management culture that threatens its traditional role.[8] Rule following (guidelines and algorithms) have replaced action based on understanding. Externally imposed targets have replaced internal, personal motivations. Measurable parts (bodily systems) have distracted from indefinable wholes (people). Training has replaced education. More mandatory education (footnote 2) leaves less room for self-directed learning. The common thread is a preoccupation with process (the 'how') rather than purpose (the 'why'). Little room nowadays for the minute particulars.

Footnote 2. James Willis once argued for the establishment of a Ministry of Leaving Well Alone (MOLWA). He felt that bureaucratic interference was stifling the NHS with politicians seeking to leave their mark through needless organisational change. The MOLWA would reward those with the wisdom to maintain satisfactory institutions unchanged (for example, giving knighthoods for services to stability). Another function of the MOLWA would be to dismantle regulations as fast as new ones were created, reducing central control to a minimum.[8] Things have only worsened since.

The endpoint is a culture that is risk averse and unable to tolerate living with uncertainty, that attends to surface appearances rather than deeper content, to mechanism not meaning. And as Peter Drucker put it: 'culture eats strategy for breakfast.'[9]

Other paradoxes have attended medical 'progress'. We have already considered the doctrine of perverse consequences in relation to health policy. More rigidly evidence-based care is ultimately less flexible and less user-friendly. Care is made more accessible (shorter waiting times) at the cost of continuity (the doctor of choice). More bureaucratic regulation distracting attention from clinical priorities may yield less safety. Think, for example, of the scandal at Mid Staffs (footnote 3). The louder politicians proclaim that NHS staff are their greatest asset, the surer you can be sure that workers' needs are being neglected. The most pervasive irony echoes Eliot's dictum: ever more information (patient data, drug alerts, treatment guidelines, referral algorithms, etc) crowds out the personal knowledge that properly underpins clinical wisdom.[10]

A system under pressure

We are rightly proud of our health service but the care it provides nowadays is often mediocre by international standards.[11] The Commonwealth Fund publishes annual rankings of OECD health services. The NHS is consistently ranked highly as efficient and equitable providing a (restricted) range of care for all comers but is judged poorly for health outcomes.[12] Monolithic and monopolistic, it is relatively unresponsive to the needs of its users. Certainly, we are no longer proud enough to fund it properly.

Rudolf Klein once characterised the NHS as garage and church: the first as repair shop, the second as object of worship and repository of societal mores.[13] The 70th birthday celebrations had an ecclesiastical tenor but faith in the established church is weakening. Despite its egalitarian foundations, the NHS has never adequately addressed the inverse care law. How many users actively endorse the founders' communitarian values today and are they aware of how little the medical mechanics' tinkering and testing actually yields?

Footnote 3. The scandal at the Mid Staffordshire Hospital Trust rocked the nation. In his eponymous report, Robert Francis QC identified as critical conflicting central objectives and local managers' preoccupation with targets, against a backdrop of financial constraints and staffing shortages. Notoriously, the CQC had identified no causes for concern in a recent visit. Unfortunately, much of the subsequent coverage placed 'blame' at the door of uncaring managers and health professionals. It is axiomatic that the root causes of such disasters generally point to flaws in systems not individuals.[14]

If general practice is no longer safe alongside the NHS, it is reasonable to pose counterfactual questions. What could replace the current system? More doctors might today accept salaried service. Would the public be more inclined to take responsibility for their own health with appropriate incentives under a social insurance scheme? Might such a scheme unlock solutions to the continuing crisis in social care?

The problems are part of a deeper malaise. Welfarism tends to create dependency. A grotesque caricature of Beveridge's original vision, the welfare state has corrupted the charitable ideals that originally underpinned it.[15] Better living standards over time have arguably been associated with increased entitlement, reduced sense of duty to work and lowered resilience. In other words, rising levels of sickness are a social phenomenon. To what extent should the right to health care be detached from responsibilities for one's own well-being and appropriate use of the health system?

David Runciman has written cogently on the decline of democracy.[16] Like democracy, the NHS is looking tired these days. Like democracy, its flaws and inflexibility are a source of its resilience. Like democracy, evidence still suggests it is the worst system except for all the others. So all being well, the NHS will lurch on for a while yet, scaled back and periodically topped up with ever more inadequate sums. That does not preclude our continuing to explore alternative models. Its performance may come to be judged less generously post-Covid. The NHS may one day come to symbolize conservatism, entitlement and monopolistic, professional self-interest. The spaces needed to deliver decent primary care are under threat. To paraphrase Runciman, the NHS may not be dead but the recent trajectory of general practice suggests how it could die. And, if this history tells us anything, it is that general practice was not a product of the NHS. It can survive and thrive under another system of health care.

Unchain my heart
What of its users? Most people still believe that health care spending (on hospitals) is bound to improve health. Consider the initial preoccupation with the NHS in preference to public health infrastructure during the Covid-19 pandemic.[17] Media coverage of medical developments accentuates the wondrous potential of new drugs. Newspaper reports distort public perceptions.[18] Soaps heroize doctors and portray their work in melodramatic terms. The realities are more prosaic. The latest magic bullet for, say, dementia does little more than enrich pharmaceutical shareholders. Drug companies have obvious commercial incentives for inflating the worth of new products that are in the pipeline. In truth, the pharmaceutical industry is in trouble in the face of rising regulation and the dearth of new drugs.

How can the public's emotional investment in medicine be reversed? Doctors have too readily assumed credit for the ascendency of modern medicine. They need more readily to acknowledge the provisional nature of much technological and therapeutic innovation. The end of an 'Age of Optimism' was heralded long ago.[19] Doctors can help journalists ratchet down public expectations.

Politicians have an important role too. No greater charge haunts ministers more than that the NHS may not be 'safe in their hands'. The NHS was thus protected from the worst ravages of recent austerity. Health care investment yields diminishing returns; spending on the NHS should not be sacrosanct. Budgets might better be spent on housing, measures that increase employment and reduce environmental degradation. Climate change is by far the most pressing threat to population health. That no lasting solution has been found to the funding of social care - despite numerous commissions offering practicable proposals - is a measure of political ineptitude and electoral myopia. In their defence, it is not possible for politicians alone to 'fix' the NHS. Addressing its deficiencies is everyone's business.

Policy makers, like practitioners, are easily seduced by interventions that appear to provide short term relief. The first descriptive reports from 'early adopters' of any new drug or service tend to be enthusiastic. For example, extended access and telephone triage form part of the solution to rising demand for same day appointments but may increase the burden on hospitals, especially if access to routine surgeries is compromised for work out-of-hours. This is a perfect example of what Ben Ramalingam calls 'best-practicitis': the short-term, localised modelling of technical fixes that don't work.[20] First wave pilot projects also tend to be more generously funded. More rigorous economic evaluation is important - if only to detect the unforeseen.

There remain huge deficits in public understanding about disease and its origins.

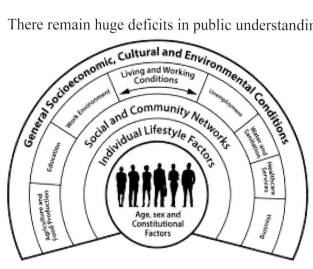

Most illnesses are preventable, if not self-inflicted. Health, in the jargon, is co-created. Few chronic diseases can be managed successfully without the active engagement and commitment of the sufferer. For example, diabetes costs the NHS £15 billion a year; its drug treatments have minimal impact on life expectancy. Type 2 diabetes can be reversed by the simpler expedients of losing weight and exercising more. Rapacity on an

Figure C.1 Determinants of health

even larger scale is perpetrated in the name of interventional cardiology. However, the societal changes required to prevent obesity and chronic diseases like ischaemic heart disease and diabetes are notoriously complex. Responsibility ranges across multiple sectors (figure C.1).

There is much, in other words, that can be done to reduce society's dependence on health services but, given the forces arraigned in opposition, there is little prospect of early change. Staff heroics notwithstanding, the recent, relentless emphasis on 'protecting the NHS' has reinforced the people's faith in technical wizardry. Less glamorous public health interventions are always more important in reducing pandemic mortality.

'Good' general practice
Today's 'crisis' in general practice is also the result of a more fundamental, quasi-philosophical questions - as yet unresolved. What is good general practice and what is it really for?

In a seminal monograph published a quarter of a century ago, Peter Toon elegantly delineated three principal models of general practice: a preventive, public health approach with Hippocratic roots; a biomedical model with its basis in scientific medicine and the Enlightenment; and a humanist model (of which the Balint movement is an example) which is expressive of an older philosophical tradition.[21] All three models have distinctive strengths, weaknesses and sometimes conflicting ethical foundations. For example, the utilitarian values underpinning population-oriented care are often at odds with the individualistic nature of the doctor-patient relationship.

As we have seen, from the early 1800s, general practitioners served public health functions as local medical officers superintending sanitary projects and vaccination programmes at a time when they had but a few symptomatic remedies in their armamentarium. What Armstrong calls 'surveillance medicine' emerged early in the twentieth century.[22] Disease was henceforth mapped not onto bodily components but onto societies and populations. 'Problematisation of the normal' began most obviously in the development of child health surveillance. Epidemiological enquiry has continued to break down the binary distinction of health from illness, transforming symptoms and signs into 'risk factors'. Despite undoubted benefits, screening and other forms of health promotion have come at a cost: the medicalization of normal life. The effectiveness of preventive medicine is contested. Charged with changing behaviours they cannot control, many GPs resent responsibility for essentially political objectives.[23]

From the biomedical perspective, the main focus of general practice today is chronic disease management. Scientific progress has extended impressively the technological range of general practice. Information and communication technologies are continuing to transform medical knowledge and practice. However, most day-to-day practice remains, as it always has been, acute-on-chronic.

Evidence-based medicine requires clinical decisions to be rooted in 'health intelligence' rather than the practitioner's wisdom. The Quality and Outcomes Framework (QOF), a large pay-for-performance programme, represented a zenith in this regard (see chapter 8). Worthily based on the latest evidence, it successfully reduced variations between practices against a basket of process indicators but, overall, over £1 billion of annual expenditure yielded little evidence of improved outcomes in population health.[24]

Such over-enthusiastic application of 'scientific management' methods has weakened swathes of the public sector. In the meantime, health care has been depersonalised. The medical gaze is nowadays refracted through computerised protocols and algorithms; first we check the template, then we listen to the patient. The screen has replaced the body as the emblem of contemporary medicine. Actual practice is no longer tactile. We scan before we undertake physical examinations. If we lay on hands at all, we do so for symbolic reasons.[25] The subjective sense of illness and bodily unease arising from disease, tiredness and unhappiness has been invalidated by scientific medicine with its emphasis on disease.[26]

For all biomedicine's triumphs, central questions concerning the causes of common chronic disease and how best to manage them remain unanswered. The portentous claims made down the decades on behalf of the new genetics ('genohype') have yet to materialize. Comparable disappointment will attend the seductive declarations now being made for 'Big Data'. Biomedicine is in many respects a confidence trick, prone to 'techno-solutionism' and the neglect of holistic care.

Toon's third domain sees medicine as quintessentially concerned with human relationships. Rejecting a dualist model of personhood, the role of the doctor is (sometimes) to enhance the patient's coping abilities and promote acceptance of illness as meaningful. For much of what presents in general practice cannot simply be suppressed or removed. The goal of care then is psychological adjustment and understanding.

Foremost among contemporary commentators, Iona Heath writes eloquently of the need to recalibrate consultations with more emphasis on those aspects for which evidence-based medicine (EBM) has no answers. Scientific reductionism devalues individual experience. While EBM describes people in terms of biomedical data, clinicians must interpret more complex information to help individuals make sense of their illness - and do so under conditions of uncertainty. *'A profound problem is that the map of biomedical science only roughly matches the territory of human suffering.'* She uses literary examples beautifully to bridge the gulf between medical science and human experience.[27]

For many practitioners, the language of this humanist domain is arcane and abstruse. The work of Michael Balint (see chapter 6) on the psychodynamics of the doctor-patient relationship is no longer central to the training of general practitioners. Too much emphasis on such soft skills can cloak technical failings. Anyway, the argument goes, continuity of care is less important for younger users meeting all their informational needs from their smartphones. In theory, the internet has empowered patients by extended the distribution of medical knowledge. Such knowledge is no longer so esoteric and expert patients can manage their own conditions or share decision-making.[28] But for those less scientifically literate, e-medicine can be a source of confusion and vulnerability. Their priorities may be subservient to those of medical-industrial interests.

Ironically, it is this third domain that underpins general practitioners' ability to deliver both effective prevention and efficient technical care. It is facilitated by - and sometimes conflated with - continuity of personal care. Despite evidence that such continuity may be associated with reduced mortality[29], policy makers continue to prioritize access. Practitioners recognize this domain as it comprises much of their everyday. Biomedicine is positively unhelpful in promoting the delusion that 'something (technical) can be done' for many conditions. AI is not going to displace the doctor as drug any time soon. Rather, personal contact with a known and trusted source of support will become ever more precious.

Health systems are part of the fabric of social and civic life. They both signal and enforce societal norms through the personal experiences of providers and users.[30] These norms may indirectly be as salutogenic as the technologies provided. Practices of themselves generate social capital within their communities. Direct experience is what will shape future support for general practice too. However, workforce trajectories suggest that 'relationship-based care' may soon be nurse-led or the preserve of the affluent.[31]

Toon's typology (here simplified) helps to map our professional territory. Having analysed the philosophical concepts underlying his paper's title, Toon's conclusions were deceptively simple. He noted two fundamentally different aims of general practice: hedonic (helping patients avoid suffering) and hermeneutic (concerned with patients' search for meaning). He regretted the absence of a theory of justice properly able to reconcile these different aims.

The shifting gaze
Written at a time when general practice was also 'afflicted by serious anxiety and uncertainty', Toon's magisterial monograph is relevant today. However, there is an artificial sense of permanence about his categories. Michel Foucault long ago described how, over time, new scientific discourses shaped the way doctors viewed disease, stressing the links between medical knowledge and the increasing subservience of patients.[32] Foucault reminded us that how disease is understood and what doctors 'see' changes over time.

Movements in epidemiology, social and behavioural sciences, management theory, political and moral philosophy have changed doctors' perception of 'what is wrong' and 'how we know it'. These terms avoid the rational, biotechnical meanings associated with 'diagnosis' and 'clinical method'.[33] These disciplines have left their own distinct sedimentary stains of language, values and practice. Some of these stains have been washed away; others are fading as I write; others will disappear in future. These influences continue to ebb and flow.

GPs' notion of what is wrong has always been linked to the zeitgeist of the age. The first William Skrimshire would have studied texts still imbued with Paracelsian astrology. Miasmas caused infection but he was ahead of the curve, by today's standards, in recognizing environmental contributions to his patients' agues. The emphasis on prevention and behavioural change was stronger then and doubtless delivered in a more paternalistic manner. His dietary prohibitions may not always have accorded with our own but many of his recommendations regarding the 'non-naturals' resonate today. Doctors today are disinclined to nannying.

Over the next generations, medical discourse became recognizably biomedical. As doctors are still wont to do, Truscott and his sons discussed their 'cases'. As a boy, I watched my father and grandfather, with clinking whiskies to hand, standing either side of the sitting room fire and doing the same. Nowadays, it is regarded as a lapse of taste to refer to patients as 'cases' as though they were the receptacle inside which the doctor's true object (the name of the disease) is concealed. For generations now, GPs have recognised the named patient as the true object of the consultation.

Up until the mid-nineteenth century, most illnesses described were acute and surgical rather than medical, reflecting the profession's historical roots. To this day in the UK, GPs and patients refer to the practice premises and doctor's consulting hours, as 'surgeries'. Till half a century ago, the psychological was regarded as the antithesis of the physical - a distraction that seduced the doctor from fidelity to the clinical task. *'I make it an absolute rule never, under any circumstances, to tell a patient what his blood pressure is. Instead I say 'not bad for our age', or 'quite reasonably satisfactory'. Once a patient knows he or she has hypertension, symptoms multiply enormously, and misery grows...* '[34] Paternalism ruled. GPs frequently disdained 'psychologising'. For GPs such as Stephen Taylor, the diagnostic prizes were the diseases he first encountered at medical school.

Psychodynamic approaches to consulting gathered momentum in the 1960s and 70s, in tune with the individualistic spirit of the period. They readjusted the GP's clinical focus: first from disease diagnosis to the meaning of the illness, secondly from the illness to the patient, thirdly from the patient to the doctor patient relationship. There was little overtly Freudian terminology in Balint's written work but it bore the master's stamp. The influence of Balint declined with the rejection of psychoanalysis for lack of evidence for its effectiveness.

Syncretic biopsychosocial approaches to teaching moved centre-stage in 1970s and 1980s.[35] They framed diagnosis in physical, psychological and social terms. This represented a major break from the established instrumental, hospital-centred orientation. Adherence to the biopsychosocial model was always more rhetorical than real. GPs' preferred default is biomedical for that is the basis on which they are schooled, selected and trained.

The 1980s also saw a steady resurgence of the preventive agenda of public health. *'Illness became a prediction, a variable probability, a genetic weakness or a human frailty in behaviour, in which treatment must be invested now, in the expectation of benefit later.'*[33]

Tudor Hart, most notably, sought the fusion of epidemiology with primary care. Illness was once more re-located from 'in here' (the body-mind) to 'out there' in the socio-economic characteristics of the community. Illness became a measure of the patient's social and economic deficit. Tudor Hart's openly Marxist view of the doctor's place in society was starkly contrasted with Balint's Freudian analysis. He criticized the Balint model on three counts: as doctor-centred, for downplaying the organic despite its holistic philosophy, and for ignoring social context. (In fairness, Balint himself warned against brushing aside the somatic and making a bee-line to the psychological.)

GPs' public health role was further extended from the 1990s onwards. Engagement in commissioning on behalf of practice populations inevitably shifted their ethical compass away from one-person clinical medicine. Ironically, there were intriguing similarities in the language of Tudor Hart and proponents of the health care markets he so abhorred. The authors of *Working for Patients* talked of producers and consumers. For Tudor Hart, the consultation was the point of 'co-production' of important health-related consumptions.[36]

Proponents of markets require that goods/risks or states of ill-health be described, quantified and costed. The bright light of accountability presented GPs with obvious difficulties. The relationship between the state and GP came to be substantially determined by economic factors, state-defined targets and 'performance indicators'. A necessary part of the practitioner's armamentarium has always been the ability to subvert official controls.

The evangelists of Evidence Based Medicine were unwitting foot soldiers in the brave new world of a pseudo-market. Quantification as an aid to decision-making fostered a growth industry in the production of guidelines, protocols and algorithms. Criteria for diagnosis, investigation and treatment were henceforth determined by combing the world literature and adducing best evidence. The randomised controlled trial (RCT) came to exercise a tyrannical domination over other forms of evidence (footnote 4). The easily measurable outcome is not always the most important. Mental health interventions, for example, are often inherently more difficult to evaluate. Economists refined a calculus of cost and benefit in the search for a morally neutral basis for rationing decisions. The QUALY is now institutionally enshrined in NICE (footnote 5).

The intentions were worthy; the results were often baleful. They reached their apogee in the QOF with its single unitary measure of quality (chapter 8). The early decades of the twenty-first century have certainly seen reductions in the wide variations in clinical practice. These are, in part, due to the idiosyncracies of doctors. Whether doctors have increased, or indeed sacrificed, their responsiveness to the needs of their patients is moot.

For the internet age, the language of personal care is taking a paradoxical turn. 'Personalized medicine' is being redefined by its very antithesis: a late product of the human genome project. Individuals' polygenic risk scores are being linked to their 'datome', that mass of real time information collected by tech companies.[37] AI and cloud computing will supposedly revolutionize prevention. I do not doubt the potential value of pharmacogenetics in tailoring treatment more specifically. I do doubt the marginal benefits of personalised prevention for the foreseeable future. We already know what we need to do to stay healthy but millions of dollars will be made from the gullible.

In general practice nowadays, we have apps and online services that meet the needs of the tech savvy and worried well. They 'creamskim' younger people, leaving more dependent, less profitable patients alone.[38] In our present state of knowledge, clinical algorithms are rarely superior to clinical judgement.[39] This brand of general practice is marketed in terms of convenience and responsiveness. This may be an artificial form of personal care but it is the future.

Footnotes 4. The randomised controlled trial as described by Austin Hill rightly remains a methodological gold standard. Unfortunately, not all questions are susceptible to controlled trials. (For example, interviews or questionnaires would best answer the question: what qualities in your doctor are most important to you?) Reassuringly, Gill et al found that over 80% of interventions in general practice were based on evidence from clinical trials.[40]

5. The main purpose of the National Institute of Health and Care Excellence (NICE) is the assessment of new health technologies including drugs. Central to their evaluations is the Quality Adjusted Life Year. The QUALY is a generic measure that allows for the comparison of different interventions in terms of their health outcomes. One QUALY equates to one year in perfect health. It is and has always been controversial. As a general rule, NICE accepts interventions with an incremental cost effectiveness ratio of less than £20,000/QUALY.

The politics of practice

The quest for early intervention has strong historical and philosophical links with another precept of public health medicine - the pursuit of social justice. Despite the march of technology and the advent of the NHS with its founding principle of social equity, general improvements in health have had little effect on relative class and geographical differences (figure C.2). These have persisted in a series of studies, notably the Black report of 1980. Michael Marmot's review of 2010 again affirmed the importance of social determinants of health, particularly in early childhood.[41] Since then health inequalities have, if anything, widened with a stalling in life expectancy Marmot attributes to the effects of economic austerity.[42]

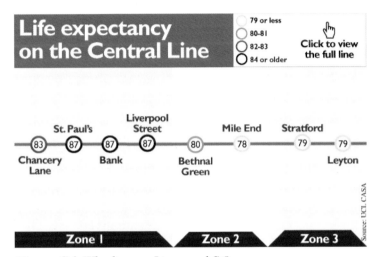

The evidence regarding the relationship between poverty and premature death points inexorably to one remedy: the redistribution of wealth. This is a nakedly political aim in a tradition going back to Rudolf Virchow (footnote 6) and exposes obvious divisions. On the one hand, sympathetic to Tudor Hart's objectives,

Figure C.2 Why live on Liverpool St?

are those who extoll GPs' role in creating healthy communities by changing society.[43] Social determinants, after all, account for up to 90% of health outcomes while less than 5% of the health budget is spent on prevention. They argue that practices should work alongside public health teams proactively to engage with local communities in furtherance of health promotion.

There are several reasons why their call is likely to go unheeded (footnote 7). Few GPs have ever embraced the role of Tudor Hart's 'community physician'.[35] In part, this is because the vision is essentially ideological. Public health inclines to centralisation and is largely 'left wing.' General practitioners, on the other hand, have always been politically heterogeneous. They come in all shapes and sizes - free traders, suffragettes, bravura biomedics, corporatist commissioners, public health zealots and anarcho-syndicalists work alongside one another.

Footnote 6. Rudolf Virchow (1821-1902) was a German pathologist, nowadays regarded as the founder of social medicine. More than a laboratory physician, Virchow was an impassioned advocate for social and political reform. He recognised social inequality as the cause of diseases which required political actions. He famously stated that: *'Medicine is a social science, and politics is nothing else but medicine on a large scale.'*

Closet 'Corbynistas', often working in inner cities, rub shoulders with more reactionary colleagues from the shires. Vulgar caricatures, of course, but general practitioners are understandably suspicious of grand plans. The utilitarian values underpinning population-oriented care and budget-holding are often at odds with the individualistic nature of the doctor-patient relationship.[44] Then there is the ever-present problem of time. Beyond the day job, can GPs really engage with Health and Wellbeing Boards, Joint Strategic Needs Assessments and Better Care Fund activity[41] (footnote 8)?

While the justification for such role diversification may seem compelling, the evidence to justify it is often rather less so. Do we really know how much impact such activities will have? The vogue for 'social prescribing' is instructive here. Few of the activities GPs are currently being encouraged to promote are yet grounded in decent evidence[45] (footnote 9). GPs are ill-trained to act as effective advocates for the population's health. Changes to their training might help. While no-one doubts the scope for improving how public health is taught in medical schools, history suggests it will always be a minority interest.[46]

Thus, on the other hand, sit a sceptical majority who question our legitimacy in attempting to effect social change. The durability of the inverse care law reflects GPs' lack of enthusiasm for redistribution of even medical resources ('rewarding the losers'). They would rather follow Archie Cochrane in 'finding out which treatments are effective, and then ensuring that these treatments are given efficiently to all who need them.'[47] These treatments are not necessarily complex or high tech. Smoking is an important driver of health inequality. 25% of routine and manual workers smoke, compared with 10% in the professional and managerial group.[48] The simple expedient of helping people to stop smoking would go a long way to abolish class differentials in health.

Footnotes 7. The Deep End Project supporting practices in the most deprived areas of Glasgow, and now being emulated in other cities, provides a laudable exception.[49] These networks are trying in various ways, under challenging conditions, to address health inequalities at practice level.

8. These are examples of the many recent initiatives which in different ways addressed determinants of demand for health care. They usually involved sprawling committees, paralysed by representation from every conceivable 'stakeholder'. In the author's experience, extended participation was not compatible with the will to live.

9.'Social prescribing' connects people via linkworkers to community groups and statutory services for practical and emotional support. Activities typically provided include arts, gardening, befriending, cookery and a range of sports. GPs are interested in anything that may reduce their workload. For this, sadly, there is as yet little evidence but a whole new cadre of staff is being created. Enthusiasm for such initiatives generally wanes when later research shows that they cater mostly for the better off and 'worried well'.

The causes of these differentials anyway go beyond material deprivation and may reflect other threats to stress, self-esteem and social relations. More unequal societies may be inherently less healthy (footnote 10). Climate change is now the biggest threat to planetary health and implies a rather different set of practice imperatives (footnote 11).[50]

Covid-19 and the death of the family doctor

As discussed in chapter 4, the notion of the family doctor emerged over the second half of the nineteenth century. The NHI Act of 1911 further reinforced it; 'panels' became the forerunners of patient 'lists' in the NHS. In 1948, the National Health Service extended health care to families. The terms 'family doctor' and 'general practitioner' continued to be conflated.

In the mid-1960s, the Family Doctor Charter stemmed the post-war decline in general practice. Ironically, the decline of the family doctor might be seen as dating back to that same settlement. As practice teams and the range of services they provided thereafter expanded, the legitimacy of family practice began to be questioned.

The main problem with the concept lies in establishing what it means. Does it embrace nuclear families, more extended families or simply those living at the same address? Recent decades have seen a decline in marriage rates and of the two-parent family as a societal norm. The Royal College of General Practitioners included caring for families in its definition of the GP's job but who exactly is the patient?[35]

Countries such as Australia and Holland with models of primary care similar to Britain's have general practitioners. The USA and Canada boast 'family physicians.' Yet even the most probing north American analyses have struggled to define the meaning of 'family medicine'.[51] Was it nothing more than a marketing exercise designed to appeal to the conservative intuitions of middle America where 'family values' are axiomatically good?[21]

At its simplest, the concept is based on a theoretical model that understands the patient's health in the context of their family relationships. In the UK, this accords

Footnotes 10. Richard Wilkinson and Kate Pickett have purported to show that material inequalities directly affect health by eroding trust, increasing anxiety and encouraging excessive consumption.[52] They claim that health and social problems (such as drug abuse, poor educational attainment, violence and teenage pregnancies) are significantly worse in more unequal countries, whether rich or poor. Suffice to say that, while their thesis is compelling, their evidence is contested.

       11. The NHS is responsible for a third of public sector carbon emissions. Practices can do much to reduce their own carbon footprints. Beyond understanding how climate change impacts on health and health inequalities, staff need advocacy skills. At an individual level, the health co-benefits of relevant behaviour change, adaptation and mitigation strategies are substantial.

closely with the psychoanalytic teaching of Michael Balint. One reason for the declining interest in family medicine in this country may be that Balint filled that ecological niche.

Critics drew attention to the inherent conflicts of interest and confidentiality between different members of the family and household. Marinker regarded the concept as 'inimical' to personal care.[53] Surveys suggested that enthusiasm for family care was inversely related to the number of partners in the practice and single-handed practice was in decline.[54]

Yet the idea of family doctoring persisted despite such ambiguities and potential moral hazards. There has always been emotional and epidemiological support for the sobriquet 'family doctor'. Three quarters of the population, after all, live with relatives who share the same doctor. They may confuse the concept with a 'personal doctor' but it has retained significance for many patients too.

Doctors are largely unmoved by theoretical models of the family as patient. Rather they remain attached to the idea of a family doctor for the connotations of intimacy and extended biography it suggests. It is hard to ignore the influence of family on presentation, diagnosis and management.

In classical descriptive studies, Huygen meticulously documented the sickness behaviour of families over generations.[55] He demonstrated how life events are played out in fluctuating consultation rates and, in particular, that new generations learn how to be ill from their parents. Frequent consulters breed frequent consulters. Such insights can be invaluable in practice.

Other changes have continued to erode family practice: the end of round the clock responsibility; the growth of part-time salaried practice; declining rates of home visiting, the source of so much intimate knowledge. The associated administrative demands of pay-for-performance, commissioning and regulation have crowded out the space for the style of practice upon which the popularity of the discipline was founded.

The principal change to practice being driven by the Covid epidemic is a shift to remote consulting. The limited evidence base suggests that the acceptability and effectiveness of video-consultations compares with that of traditional clinic-based care[56] but few studies have been carried out in general practice. How well does virtual health care serve the needs of those whose physical symptoms mask underlying anxiety and depression? To what extent does its safety depend on antecedent face-to-face encounters? What physical signs are missed? In such encounters, can doctors be as fully 'present'?

General practice will continue to mutate and Covid-19 may yield unexpected benefits. It has become a cliché to describe the virus as an accelerant of pre-existing trends. We are fast-forwarding our use of new communication technologies, for example. The role of primary care in communicable disease control may also be reinvigorated. The public may emerge with a greater understanding of health care's limitations. They may have a greater sense of responsibility for their own health. They may appreciate the value of exercise and community. They may not.

Those heralding the transformation of general practice should beware of what they wish for. Admittedly, the family doctor was in poor health. The concept has helped to create a false dichotomy: between medical science and technology on one hand and caring and compassion on the other. Nevertheless, patients will mourn their passing. Less personal care will be the consequence.

Reasons for optimism
I am not by nature inclined to Jeremiads. It is easy to form sewage-tinted impressions of the present day. There are many ways in which general practice today has steadily improved. Today's practices deliver care that is incomparably more sophisticated through large, well-trained teams. No-one involved in teaching medical students can fail to be moved by their zeal and intelligence. They bring largely the same values and expectations to their interviews for admission. No-one involved in the training of GP registrars can be but similarly impressed. The quality of trainers and training has continued to evolve over the last 50 years. The quality of new recruits is my greatest reassurance.

Standards of teaching and examination may be high but a common refrain of established doctors is that their trainees are 'undercooked'. They are factually knowledgeable but have been less brutally immersed in day-to-day clinical realities. Consequently, newly qualified doctors' ability to apply knowledge and expertise to a clinical situation is often lacking. Clinical reasoning, alongside resilience and how to cope with the 'hidden curriculum', is a staple of today's undergraduate curricula (footnote 12).

In 2012, then health secretary Jeremy Hunt promised to increase GP numbers by 5000 in five years. Such pledges from health ministers are regarded with understandable suspicion. They betray little understanding of the lead times involved for it takes 10 years to train a GP from scratch. Predictably, GP numbers have continued to decline leading to practice closures in urban areas and increasing

Footnote 12. The psychology of reasoning distinguishes between two different 'systems' in reasoning. System 1 is intuitive and unconscious whereas System 2 is deductive and evaluative. Students take time to develop their System 1 thinking. The 'hidden curriculum' refers to the pressures and constraints that operate outside the formal curriculum and that are often unarticulated. Medical students' survival has always required an appreciation of these institutional customs and rituals.

difficulty gaining access to a family doctor. The *GP Forward View* pledged extra funding for general practice.[57] Another new contract has since scaled down the QOF and sought to address other grievances. All this came way too late to avert a workforce crisis but does suggest that politicians have belatedly recognized the importance of general practice.

When I started in practice forty years ago, the majority of GPs were white, middle-aged and male. Today, the largest group is young, female and from different ethnic backgrounds. In every respect, this transformation has been beneficial. Without descending to the patronizing stereotypes that have gendered career paths in the past, women excel in this branch of medicine by dint of their aptitudes and life experiences. Increasingly, they dominate general practice politically. (At the time of writing, three of the last five Presidents of the RCGP have been women, though this is not to deny many obstacles to career progression still faced by women in medicine.)

The future of general practice is female for other reasons. Practice nurses have assumed steadily more responsibility for chronic disease management as nurse practitioners have taken on the management of acute illness and prescribing. GPs are becoming de-skilled. Other new cadres - healthcare assistants, practice-based pharmacists, paramedics, physician assistants, counsellors and linkworkers - are emerging to take on those functions previously exclusive to the doctor. Members of these tribes see the world in ways that reflect their own training. They have different strengths and blind spots. The front line is diversifying and the tasks of the intimate consultation - screening, diagnosis and treatment - are being shared. This may relieve workloads in the community but only if these newcomers can work holistically, picking up the time-consuming burden of the psychosocial. Coping with 'heartsinks' is far harder than coping with heart disease.

Finally, there will be space on the parking lot for wondrous new machines. Biomedicine will continue to add true quality and quantity to many people's lives.

Wounded healers
I entered practice during a supposedly 'golden age' when general practice was the most popular career choice. That said, I might rather like to have practiced in the 1820s or indeed the 1920s, both periods of repressed optimism within the profession. Yet seemingly in every generation, GPs writing about their lot have never had it so bad. They have always felt over-worked and under-paid.

Doctors' lives are rich and rewarding but they come at a price. At least two of my forebears died young from diseases contracted from patients. One committed suicide. Many were what might delicately be described as sometimes intemperate. These men were first and foremost doctors. Contemporary concerns for 'work-life' balance would have sounded quaint to them. Life was work. *"Today's doctors are first and foremost people"* (Raj Khanchandani, personal observation).

Care has become 'transactional' rather than 'relational'.[58] This has consequences for both doctors and patients. We too struggle with the consequences of a move from person-centred to object-oriented health systems. With less in the way of technological armour, GPs are only too well aware that they sometimes wear no clothes. Burn out is common. They are retiring earlier than ever, at a pace that will defy even the most grandiose recruitment pledges. Fifty years ago provided, Berger captured the unique value of British general practice.[4] Today's GPs are in certain respects, well, less fortunate.

It is a truism of consulting practice that our patients often evince in us the feelings - of anger, frustration, confusion - that they too are experiencing. (It is another source of that burn out.) At a systemic level, the NHS mirrors wider society. It is clear that the organisational context of care has changed greatly and that the quality of care we provide reflects wider social changes. We may no longer have Dr Finlay but we have the care we demand, can afford or wish to pay for (footnote 13). We have the care we deserve.

This has also been a book about 'place' - a specific house and town. The landscapes we grow up in inform who we are. Of all medical disciplines, general practice is the most physically embedded in particular locations. These GPs knew the fields, hills, homesteads, roads, estates, factories, shops and pubs that framed their patients' daily lives (footnote 14). Much intimate knowledge was imparted in a single home visit. They were rooted in a community and therefore sustained by it. That too has changed, leaving GPs more vulnerable.

'This is the end'
In this book I have betrayed my biases. After all those years steeped in the isolating routines of the one-to-one consultation, it is hardly surprising that I privilege individuality. I am wary of the commercial drivers to conformity in medical practice. I am suspicious of the industrial imperatives to wasteful and ineffective health care consumption. Many readers will justifiably have a more appreciative view of the many wonders of modern biomedicine but its soaring costs have become a major threat to the long-term solvency of most advanced nations.[59]

Footnotes 13. *Dr. Finlay's Casebook* was a television drama series, produced and broadcast by the BBC from 1962 until 1971. Based on A J Cronin's novella entitled *Country Doctor*, the storylines centred on a general practice in the fictional Scottish town of Tannochbrae during the late 1920s. Bill Simpson, the lead, became something of a national treasure.

14. For many years, one of our middle-aged female patients operated *Shirley's Temple* (a 'massage parlour') a few hundred yards from my practice. I regret I never summoned up the courage to go in.

Without rebalancing service priorities - away from technical hospital-based care towards spending on community-based and social care - general practice will continue to wither.

This project began as a paean to a passing style of practice but the future looks more nuanced. The public will continue to rank general practitioners as trusted advisors. Despite negative press coverage, most people appreciate the weight of GPs' responsibilities and fear for the loss of local doctors. They value the NHS and the 'expert generalists' needed to help them navigate their way around it.

Covid-19 for a while bathed the NHS in the glow of quasi-religious adoration, still symbolizing our best communitarian endeavours, still central to the welfare state. However, the power of this 'national religion' is waning. Today's adherents are anyway ever more secular. They want somewhere to go for swift, efficient repairs when the bodywork is broken. Virtual care suits their requirements for instant, technical fixes. Nurses nowadays provide much of the care while GPs are becoming distanced from the front line. There will always be a need for generalists but the future priesthood may no longer be medical.

At the heart of many health policy debates over these past 250 years has been the reconciliation of alternative libertarian and collectivist views of the task of medicine. These can be traced back to the eighteenth century and development of the medical profession from physic, pharmacy, surgery and man-midwifery. The first doctors Skrimshire were shopkeepers but we have all benefited in changing ways from our communities' individual and collective resources. What has bound us together down these eight generations are shared values - not policy or politics, not praxis or prescription, not evidence or estimation, but common humanity.

Always at the last, the job's greatest rewards stem from the exercise of compassion and a sense of shared understanding. These will endure so that future histories of my trade will cover much the same ground as I have done and echo many of the same dilemmas.

In case you are wondering, one of my three daughters is studying to be a 'proper doctor' (with a PhD in psychology) but otherwise my line, after 250 years, stops… here.

References

Preface

1. Rimmer A. "My mum made me do it"—doctors and their medical dynasties. BMJ, 15 Dec 2014.
2. National Institute for Career Education and Counselling. Medical Career Advice and Guidance Survey 2014: Initial findings.
3. Loudon I. Medical Care and the General Practitioner, 1750-1850. Oxford: Clarendon Press, 1986.
4. Gillam SJ. The traditional healer as village health worker. J Inst Med Nep 1989; 11: 67-76.

Introduction

1. Soanes C, Stevenson, A. Concise Oxford English Dictionary. Oxford: Oxford University Press, 2011.
2. Carr EH. What is History? London: Pelican, 1985.
3. Butterfield H. The Whig Interpretation of History. London: WW Norton & Co, 1965.
4. Thompson EP. The Making of the English Working Class. London: Penguin, 1963.
5. Digby A. The Evolution of British General Practice, 1850-1948. Oxford: Oxford University Press, 1999.
6. Hippocrates. Air, Waters, Places. Transl by W Jones. Cambridge, MA: Harvard University Press, 1923.
7. Galen, The Art of Medicine. In Galen, Selected Works. Singer PN ed. Oxford: Oxford University Press, 1997, pp345-8.
8. Porter R. The Greatest Benefit to Mankind: A Medical History Humanity from Antiquity to the Present. London: Fontana, 1999.
9. Whitehead AN. Process and Reality (1929). New York: The Free Press, 1978.
10. Feder G. Paradigm lost: a celebration of Paracelsus on his quincentenary. Lancet 1993; 341: 1396-8. https://doi.org/10.1016/0140-6736(93)90954-F
11. Cunningham A. Thomas Sydenham: epidemics, experiment and the 'good old cause'. In French R, Wear A eds. The Medical Revolution of the Seventeenth Century. Cambridge: Cambridge University Press, 1989, pp164-90.
12. De Renzi S. Old and new models of the body. Chapter 7 in Elmer P ed. The Healing Arts. Health, Disease and Society in Europe. Manchester: Manchester University Press, 2004, pp166-195.
13. Grell OP. Medicine and Religion in Sixteenth-Century Europe. Chapter 4 in Elmer P ed. The Healing Arts. Health, Disease and Society in Europe. Manchester: Manchester University Press, 2004, pp84-107.

14. Skrimshire F. The Village Pastor's Surgical and Medical Guide; in letters from an old physician to a young clergyman, his son, on his entering upon the duties of a parish priest. London: John Churchill, 1838.
15. Waddington K. An Introduction to the Social History of Medicine. Europe Since 1500. London: Palgrave Macmillan, 2011.
16. Siraisi N. Medicine and the Italian Universities 1250-1600. Boston: Brill, 2001, pp187-200.
17. Foucault M. The Birth of the Clinic: An Archaeology of Medical Perception. New York: Random House, 1963.
18. Le Fanu J. The Rise & Fall of Modern Medicine. London: Abacus, 2011.
19. Jewson N. The disappearance of the sick-man from medical cosmology, 1770-1870. Sociology 1976; 10: 225-44.
20. Jewson N. Medical knowledge and the patronage system in eighteenth-century England. Sociology 1974; 8: 369-85.
21. Ackerknecht E. Medicine at the Paris Hospital. Baltimore: Johns Hopkins University Press, 1967.
22. Jacyna L. The Localisation of Disease. Chapter 1 in Brunton D. ed. Medicine Transformed. Health, Disease and Society in Europe, 1800-1930. Manchester: Manchester University Press, 2004, pp1-30.
23. Nicholson M. Commentary: Nicholas Jewson and the disappearance of the sick man from medical cosmology, 1770–1870. Int J Epidemiol 2008; 38: 639-42.
24. Fissell ME. Patients, Power, and the Poor in Eighteenth-Century Bristol. Cambridge, London and New York: Cambridge University Press; 1991.

Chapter 1

1. De Renzi S. The Sick and their Healers. Chapter 2 in Elmer P ed. The Healing Arts. Health, Disease and Society in Europe. Manchester: Manchester University Press, 2004, pp136-165.
2. Clark G. A History of the Royal College of Physicians of London. London: RCP, 1966, pp476-9.
3. Wall C, Cameron H, Underwood E. A History of the Worshipful Society of Apothecaries. London: WSA, 1963, pp 389-402.
4. Schlich T. The Emergence of Modern Surgery. Chapter 3 in Brunton D ed. Medicine Transformed. Health, Disease and Society in Europe, 1800-1930. Manchester: Manchester University Press, 2004, pp61-91.
5. Kocher E. Concerning Pathological Manifestations in Low-Grade Thyroid Diseases. Nobel Lecture, 11 December 1909.
6. Temkin O. The role of surgery in the rise of modern medical thought. Bulletin for the History of Medicine 1951; 25: 248-59.
7. De Renzi S. Women and medicine. Chapter 8 in Elmer P ed. The Healing Arts. Health, Disease and Society in Europe. Manchester: Manchester University Press, 2004, pp 196-227.

8. Evenden D. Mothers and their midwives in seventeenth-century London. In Marland H (ed) The Art of Midwifery: Early Modern Midwives in Europe. London: Routledge, 1993, pp 9-19.

9. Grundy I. Sarah Stone: Enlightenment midwife. In Nutton V, Porter R. (eds). The History of Medical Education in Britain. Amsterdam: Rodopi, 1995, pp 128-44.

10. Shorter E. The management of normal deliveries and the generation of William Hunter. In Bynum WF, Porter R (eds). William Hunter and the Eighteenth Century Medical World. Cambridge: Cambridge University Press, 1985, pp 371-83.

11. Wilson A. The Making of Man-Midwifery: Childbirth in England, 1660-1770. London: University College Press, 1995.

12. Mann JL. Recollections of my Early and Professional Life. London: Welcome Institute Library, 1887.

13. Chamberlaine W. Tirocinium Medicum: Or a Dissertation on the Duties of Youth apprenticed to the Medical Profession. London: Welcome Institute Library, 1813.

14. Lucas J. A Candid Inquiry into the Education, Qualification and Offices of a Surgeon-Apothecary. Bath: Hazard, 1800.

15. Makittrick JK. Commentaries. London: Welcome Institute Library, 1772 (MS 4958).

16. Van Zwanenberg D. The training and careers of those apprenticed to apothecaries in Suffolk, 1815-1858. Medical History 1983; 27: 139-50.

17. Bristol Infirmary Biographical Memoirs. The papers of Richard Smith junior, surgeon of Bristol, 1772-1843. Bristol, 14 volumes.

18. Plassart A. The rise of the working class? Unit 3 in Lawrence P., ed. Ambition and Anxiety, 1789-1940. Milton Keynes: Open University Press, 2017.

19. Jordanova L. The Social Construction of Medical Knowledge. Social History of Medicine 1995; 8: 361-81.

20. Doe V. The Diary of James Clegg of Chapel-en-Frith, 1708-1755. Derbyshire Record Society, 3 vols, (1978, 1979, 1981).

21. Medico-Chirurgicus. A Letter addressed to the Medical Profession on the Encroachments on the Practice of the Surgeon-Apothecary by a New Set of Physicians. London, 1826.

22. Reid J. Report of the diseases admitted to the Finsbury Dispensary. Monthly Magazine, 1 April 1800, 287.

23. Morris R, Kendrick J. Edinburgh Medical and Physical Dictionary, 2 vols. Edinburgh, 1807.

24. Marryat T. Therapeutics: Or the Art of Healing. Birmingham: Pearson and Rollason, 1785, 7th edition.

25. Eyre-Brooke AL. Richard Smith junior and his Life and Times. Bristol Medical Chirurgical Journal 1969; 84, 1.

26. Blane G. Selected Dissertations on Medical Science. London: Underwood, 1822.
27. Loudon I. The nature of provincial medical practice in eighteenth-century England. Medical History 1985; 29: 1-32.
28. du Laurens A. (1599) A Discourse of the Preservation of the Sight. Translated out of French into English by Richard Surphlet. London: Felix Kingston, 1599, pp58-60.
29. Bradwell S. Physick for the Sicknesse, Commonly Called the Plague. London, Benjamin Fisher, 1636, pp5-11.
30. Slack P. The Invention of Improvement: Information and Material Progress in Seventeenth-Century England. Oxford: Oxford University Press, 2015.
31. Waddington I. The Medical Profession in the Industrial Revolution. Dublin: Gill and Macmillan, 1984, p181.
32. Loudon I. Medical Care and the General Practitioner, 1750-1850. Oxford: Oxford University Press, 1986.
33. Smith A. An Inquiry into the Nature and Causes of the Wealth of Nations. London: J M Dent, 1901 (1776).
34. Brown J. Rab and his Friends and Other Essays. London: Everyman, 1858.
35. Trudeau EL. To Comfort Always: An Autobiography. New York: Doubleday, 1915.

Chapter Two

1. Crompton G, Nelson E. The herbarium of William Skrimshire (1766-1829) of Wisbech. Watsonia 2000; 23: 23-38.
2. Skrimshire W. On the absorption of electric light by different bodies, and some of their habitudes with respect to electricity. Nicholson's J Natural Philosophy 1807; 16: 101-107.
3. Skrimshire W. Account of a British vegetable product [Iris pseudacorus], that may be substituted for coffee. Nicholson's J Natural Philosophy 1809; 22: 70-73.
4. Bird M. Mary Hardy and her World. Vol I, A working family. Burnham: Burnham Press, 2020.
5. Lawson J, Silver H. A Social History of Education in England. London: Methuen & Co Ltd, 1973.
6. Skrimshire F. A Series of Popular Chymical Essays, 1802.
7. Skrimshire F. A Series of Essays as an Introduction to Natural History. The Animal Kingdom. 1805, pp 64–65.
8. Colley L. Britons: forging the nation 1707-1837. Yale: Yale University Press, 1992.
9. Skrimshire F. Information to Parents Respecting the Vaccine Inoculation; or, the Inoculation for Cow-Pox. Wisbech: John White, 1800.
10. Bate J. John Clare: A Biography. Farrar, Strauss and Giroux, 2003.
11. Grainger M (ed). The natural history prose writings of John Clare. Oxford: Oxford University Press, p34.

12. Skrimshire F. The Village Pastor's Surgical and Medical Guide; in letters from an old physician to a young clergyman, his son, on his entering upon the duties of a parish priest. London: John Churchill, 1838.

13. Thompson J, Goldin G. The Hospital: A Social and Architectural History. New Haven: Yale University Press, 1975.

14. Marland H. The changing role of the hospital, 1800-1900. Chapter 2 in Brunton D ed. Medicine Transformed. Health, Disease and Society in Europe, 1800-1930. Manchester: Manchester University Press, 2004, pp 31-60.

15. McKeown T, Brown R. Medical evidence related to English Population Changes in the Eighteenth Century. Population Studies 1955; 9: 119-141.

16. Webb KA. One of the most useful charities in the city': York Dispensary 1788-1988, York: University of York, 1988.

17. Barlow E. An Attempt to develop the Fundamental Principles which should guide the Legislature in Regulating the Profession of Physic. EMSJ 1818; 14: 1-26.

18. Baine B. Bill from Mr Bernard Baine, surgeon apothecary to Thomas Carew. Somerset CRO, Taunton, DD/TB box 14/20, 1755.

19. Good JM. The History of Medicine so far as it relates to the Profession of Apothecary. London: Underwood, 1795.

20. Harrison E. Remarks on the Ineffective State of the Practice of Physic in Great Britain with Proposals for its Future Regulation and Improvement. 1813.

21. Barlow E. A Disinterested Physician. MPJ 1813, 30, 265-296.

22. Burrows GM. A Statement of Circumstances Connected with The Apothecaries' Act, and Its Administration. London: J Callow, 1817.

23. Bettany GT. Burrows, George Man. In Stephen, Leslie. Dictionary of National Biography. London: Smith, Elder & Co, 1886.

24. Loudon I. Two Thousand Medical Men in 1847. Bulletin of the Society for the Social History of Medicine 1983: 33: 4-8.

25. Burrows GM. An Inquiry into certain Errors relative to Insanity and their Consequences, Physical, Moral, and Civil. London: Underwood, 1820.

26. Bloor DU. The Rise of the General Practitioner in the Nineteenth Century. J Roy Coll Gen Pract 1978; 28: 288-91.

27. Dickens C. Martin Chuzzlewit. London: Chapman and Hall, 1844.

28. Wakley T. Editorial. The Lancet 1843; 39: 719-22 (Saturday, Feb 11th).

29. Loudon IS. Medical Care and the General Practitioner, 1750-1850. Oxford: Oxford University Press, 1986, pp 171-6.

Chapter Three

1. Burn WL. The Age of Equipoise: A Study of the Mid-Victorian Generation. London: George Allen & Unwin, 1964.

2. Anderson B. Imagined Communities: Reflections on the Origin and Spread of Nationalism. London: Verso, 2006.

3. Bird M. Mary Hardy and her World. Vol I, A working family. Burnham: Burnham Press, 2020.
4. Mee A. The King's England. Norfolk. London: Hodder & Stoughton, 1940..
5. Radford L. History of Holt. A Brief Study of Parish, Church and School. Norwich: Goose & Son, 1908.
6. Williamson T. The Origins of Norfolk. Manchester: Manchester University Press, 1994.
7. Hales J. Norfolk Places. Wymondham: Boydell, 1987, pp55-58.
8. Hales J, Bennett W. Looking at Norfolk. Wisbech: Veal & Co, 1988.
9. Benson S. The Holt Workhouse. The Holt Society, 2005.
10. Morris B, Loftus D. The making of the British middle class. Unit 12 in Confidence and crisis, 1840-1880, Loftus D ed. Milton Keynes: Open University Press, 2017, pp225-277.
11. Davidoff L, Hall C. Family Fortunes: Men and Women of the English Middle Class, 1780-1850. London: Routledge, 2002.
12. Owens A. Property, gender and the life course: inheritance and family welfare provision in early nineteenth-century England. Social History 2001; 26: 297-315.
13. Friedson E. Profession of Medicine: A Study of the Applied Sociology of Knowledge. University of Chicago Press: Chicago, 1988.
14. Perkin H. The Origins of Modern English Society, 1780-1880. London: Routledge, Kegan and Paul, 1969.
15. Brunton D. The Emergence of a Modern Profession. Chapter 5 in Brunton D ed. Medicine Transformed. Health, Disease and Society in Europe, 1800-1930. Manchester: Manchester University Press, 2004, pp119-150.
16. Lawrence S. Charitable Knowledge: Hospital Pupils and Practitioners in Eighteenth Century London. Cambridge: Cambridge University Press, 1996.
17. Porter R. The Greatest Benefit to Mankind: A Medical History Humanity from Antiquity to the Present. London: Fontana, 1999.
18. Bradley J, Dupree M. Opportunity on the edge of orthodoxy: medically qualified hydropathists in the era of reform, 1840-60. Social History of Medicine 2001; 14: 417-37.
19. Ramsey M. Medical power and popular medicine: illegal healers in nineteenth century France. Journal of Social History 1977; 10: 560-587.
20. Schepers R. Towards unity and autonomy: the Belgian medical profession in the nineteenth century. Medical History 1994; 38: 237-54.
21. Waddington K. An Introduction to the Social History of Medicine. Europe Since 1500. London: Palgrave Macmillan, 2011.
22. Dickens C. The Posthumous Papers of the Pickwick Club. London: Chapman & Hall, 1836.
23. Peterson M. Gentlemen and Medical Men: the Problem of Professional Recruitment. Bulletin of the History of Medicine 1984: 58; 457-73.
24. 'Medicus'. On Practitioners. Gazette of Health 1817; 2: 603-5.
25. Reader W. Professional Men. London: 1966, p68.

26. Loudon I. Medical Care and the General Practitioner, 1750-1850. Oxford: Oxford University Press, 1986, pp 282-296.
27. Medical Education and Rank. London Medical Repository 1820; 14: 123-9.
28. On the Medical Reform Bill. EMSJ 1845; 64: 255-6.
29. Wakley T. Lancet, 1842-3; ii: 719-22.
30. 1841 census: tables of occupation, Parliamentary Papers (1844), XXVII.
31. Robertson I. Doctors in Opera. An Irreverent Look at Operatic Medicine. Glasgow: Scottish Opera, 2012.
32. Loudon I. Historical Importance of Out-Patients. BMJ 1978; 1: 974-7.
33. Loudon I. A Doctor's Cashbook. Medical History 1983; 27: 249-68.
34. Lindert PH, Williamson JG. English workers' living standards during the Industrial Revolution. Economic History Review 1983; 36: 1.
35. Hudson JC. The Parent's Handbook. London, 1842.
36. Griffin R. Grievances of the Poor Law Medical Officers. London, 1859.
37. Crowther MA. Paupers or Patients? J History of Medicine and Allied Sciences 1984; 60: 33-54.
38. Rumsey HW. Essays in State Medicine. Cheltenham, 1857.
39. Wakley T. Lancet, 1829-30; i: 807.
40. Waddington I. The Medical Profession in the Industrial Revolution. Dublin: Gill and Macmillan Press, 1984, pp 136-43.
41. Stevens R. Medical Practice in Modern England. New Haven: Yale University Press, 1966.
42. Brunton D. The Rise of Laboratory Medicine. Chapter 4 in Brunton D ed. Medicine Transformed. Health, Disease and Society in Europe, 1800-1930. Manchester: Manchester University Press, 2004, pp 92-118.
43. Id. An introductory discourse on the Duties and Conduct of Medical Students and Practitioners. 1843, 15-17.
44. The Times, quoted in Loudon IS. Medical Care and the General Practitioner, 1750-1850. Oxford: Oxford University Press, 1986.

Chapter Four

1. Wright D. The certification of insanity in nineteenth-century England and Wales. History of Psychiatry 1998; 9: 267-90.
2. Inkster I. Marginal Men. Aspects of the Social Role of the Medical Community in Sheffield, 1790-1850. In Woodward, J, Richards D (eds). Health Care and Popular Medicine in Nineteenth Century England. London: 1977, 128-63.
3. Cherry S. Medical Services and the Hospitals in Britain. Cambridge: Cambridge University Press, 1996.
4. Cherry S. General practitioners, hospitals and medical services in rural East Anglia c.1800-1948, in Barona L and Cherry S (eds), Health and Medicine in Rural Europe. Valencia: University of Valencia, 2005, pp 171-192.
5. Armstrong A. The Population of Victorian and Edwardian Norfolk. Norwich: Centre of East Anglian Studies, 2000, pp 9-53.

6. Cherry S. Medicine and rural health care in eighteenth and early twentieth century Europe. Int J Regional and Local Studies 2006; 2: 7-30.

7. Elmer P. The care and cure of mental illness. Chapter 9 in Elmer P ed. The Healing Arts. Health, Disease and Society in Europe. Manchester: Manchester University Press, 2004, pp344-381.

8. MacDonald M. Mystical Bedlam: Madness, Anxiety, and Healing in Seventeenth- Century England. Cambridge: Cambridge University Press, 1981.

9. Barker-Benfield GJ. The Culture of Sensibility: Sex and Society in Eighteenth Century Britain. Chicago and London: University of Chicago Press, 1992, pp15-36.

10. Andrews J. The Rise of the Asylum in Britain. Chapter 11 in Brunton D ed. Medicine Transformed. Health, Disease and Society in Europe, 1800-1930. Manchester: Manchester University Press, 2004, pp298-330.

11. Foucault M. Madness and Civilisation: A History of Insanity in the Age of Reason. New York: Random House, 1965.

12. Scull AT. The Most Solitary of Afflictions: Madness and Society in Britain, 1700-1900. New Haven and London: Yale University Press, 2005.

13. Wright D. Getting out of the asylum: understanding the confinement of the insane in the nineteenth century. Soc Hist Med, 1997; 10: 137-55.

14. Brunton D. Cities, disease and health. Unit 13 in Confidence and crisis, 1840-1880, Loftus D ed. Milton Keynes: Open University Press, 2017, pp279-332.

15. Flinn MW. (ed) Report on the Sanitary Condition of the Labouring Population of Great Britain. Edinburgh: Edinburgh University Press, 1965.

16. Hamlin C. Nuisances and community in mid-Victorian England: the attractions of inspection. Social History 2013; 38: 346-79.

17. Mooney G. Intrusive Interventions: Public Health, Domestic Space, and Infectious Disease Surveillance in England, 1840-1914. Rochester, NY: University of Rochester Press, 2015.

18. McKeown T. The Modern Rise of Population. London: Edward Arnold, 1976.

19. Szereter S. The importance of social intervention in Britain's mortality decline, c.1850-1914: a reinterpretation of the role of public health. Social History of Medicine 1988; 1: 1-38.

20. Kitson Clark G. Churchmen and the Condition of England, 1832-1885. London: Methuen, 1973, p182.

21. Glyn A. Elinor Glyn: A Biography. London: Hutchinson, 1955.

22. Perkin H. The Pattern of Social Transformation in England. In Jarausch KH (ed), The Rise of Professional Society. England Since 1889. Chicago: University of Chicago Press, 1983.

23. Peterson MJ. The Medical Profession in Mid-Victorian London. Berkeley: University of California Press, 1978.

24. Allsopp G, Burns J, Page R. The GP consultant. British Journal of General Practice 2018; 68 (668): 119. DOI: https://doi.org/10.3399/bjgp18X694949
25. Michael Beverley, MD. BMJ 1930; ii: 500.
26. CMAC, GP 29/2/59, Samuel Isaacs.
27. Loudon I. The Concept of the Family Doctor. Bulletin of the History of Medicine. 1984; 58, No. 3: 347-362.
28. Hints on Choosing a Doctor. A Penny Magazine 1832; 1: 309-10.
29. Lemon M. Loved at Last, 3 vols. London: Bradbury & Evans, 1864, i, 8.
30. Byron HJ. Paid in Full. Temple Bar Magazine 1864-5; 13: 246-7.
31. Cooke W. Separation without dissension: Observations respectfully addressed to general practitioners on the best means of maintaining their privileges and respectability. London: Longman Rees and Co, 1831, p66.
32. Thomson A. Lecture at London University. Lancet 1836-7; i: 77.
33. Escott TH. Social Transformation of the Victorian Age: a survey of court and country. London, 1897, pp388-97.
34. Kunitz SJ. The Personal Physician and the Decline of Mortality. In Scofield R, Reher D, Bideau A (eds), The Decline of Mortality in Europe. Oxford: Oxford University Press, 1991, pp249-50.
35. Clarke JF. Autobiographical Reflections. London: Seeley, 1874.
36. Batten L. The Medical Adviser, James McKenzie Lecture of the RCGP, 1960. Practitioner 1961; 180: 102-12.
37. Schernhammer E. Taking Their Own Lives - The High Rate of Physician Suicide. NEJM 2005; 352: 2473-6.

Chapter Five

1. Gillam JB. Case of Ovarian Cyst, Repeated tapping. BMJ 1901.
2. Gillam JB. Cases of Diphtheria treated with anti-toxin. BMJ 1905.
3. Entwhistle K. Holt, An Illustrated History. Vol 1: 1900-1920s. Aylsham: Brick Kiln Books, 2004.
4. Gilbert B. The Evolution of National Insurance in Great Britain: The Origins of the Welfare State. London: Michael Joseph, 1966.
5. Fitzroy A (chair). Report of the Interdepartmental Committee on Physical Deterioration. London: HMSO, 1904.
6. Alderson H. The Wants of the General Practitioner of the Present Day. Inaugural address to the West London Medico-Chirurgical Society. London: 1886, 6, 10.
7. Dawson. Ministry of Health. Interim report on the future provision of medical and allied services. (Chairman: Dawson of Penn) Consultative Council on medical and allied services, Cmd 693. London: HMSO, 1920.
8. Loudon I. Death in Childbirth. An International Study of Maternal Care and Maternal Mortality, 1800-1950. Oxford: Oxford University Press, 1992.
9. Halsey AH. (ed). British Social Trends since 1900. London: HMSO, 1951, p406.

10. Gillam S, Yates J, Badrinath P eds. Essential Public Health – theory and practice. 2nd Edition. Cambridge University Press, Cambridge, 2012. ISBN 978-107-60176-5.
11. CMAC, GP 24/2/48, Bertie Dover.
12. Stewart RE. Out of Practice. Memories of General Practice during the 1950s. Southport, 1996, p43.
13. Pooler H. My Life in General Practice. London: Christopher Johnson Publishers, 1948.
14. Digby A. Making a Medical Living. Doctors and Patients in the English Market for Medicine, 1720-1911. Cambridge, Cambridge University Press, 1994.
15. Hansard 1951, vol 470, col 2244.
16. Lodge FE. Reminiscences from a Fenland Practice. BMJ 1984; 289: 1760-2.
17. Digby A, Bosanquet N. Doctors and Patients in an Era of National Health Insurance and Private Practice. Economic History Review 1988; 2nd Series, xli.
18. Morris-Jones H. The Country Doctor of Fifty Years Ago. Country Quest, Autumn 1961, p22.
19. BMJ 1890: i; 272.
20. Digby A. The Evolution of British General Practice, 1850-1948. Oxford: Oxford University Press, 1999.
21. Peterson JM. The Medical Profession in Mid-Victorian London. Berkeley: University of California Press, 1978, pp 200-205.
22. Briggs IG. How to Start in General Practice. London: John Murray, 1928, p17.
23. Woods R. Physician Heal Thyself; the Health and Mortality of Victorian Doctors. SHM 1996; 9: 24-30.
24. Cronin AJ. The Citadel. London: Gollancz, 1937.
25. BMJ Supplement, 26th Sept 1953, 151, 703.
26. Archer F. The Village Doctor. Gloucester, 1986, p55.
27. BMJ 1905; 25th Sept.
28. Hansard, 1950, 472, col 962.
29. Bradford Hill A. The Doctor's Pay and Day, JRSS civ, 1951, 23.
30. Taylor S. Good General Practice. A Report of a Survey. Oxford: Nuffield Provincial Hospitals Trust, 1954.
31. PRO, MH 62/130, Interdepartmental Committee, Jan 1920.
32. CMAC, GP 29/2/63, Robert (Tony) Leake.
33. Hansard 1951, vol 470, col 2242.
34. Smith FB. The People's Health, 1830-1910. Canberra: Australian National University Press, 1979, p417.
35. MoH. Eighteenth Annual Report of Ministry of Health. London: MoH 1936-7, 48, 223.
36. Garcia J, Kilpatrick R, Richards M (eds). The Politics of Maternal Care. Oxford: Oxford University Press, 1990.

37. Hansard 1917, vol 322, col 1084.
38. Ryle JA. Active service medical societies. BMJ 1939; 2, 1202.
39. Bayly HW. Triple Challenge: A Doctor's Memoirs of the Years 1914 to 1929. London: Hutchinson, 1934.
40. Montgomery SL. Codes and combat in biomedical discourse. Science as Culture 1991; 12: 341-90.
41. Cooter R. Medicine in War. Chapter 12 in Brunton D ed. Medicine Transformed. Health, Disease and Society in Europe, 1800-1930. Manchester: Manchester University Press, 2004, pp331-363.
42. Crowther MA, Dupree MW. Medical Lives in the Age of Surgical Revolution. Cambridge: Cambridge University Press, 2010.
43. Pereira Gray D, ed. Forty Years On. The Story of the First Forty Years of the Royal College of General Practitioners. London: RCGP, Atalink, 1992.
44. Flexner A. Medical Education In Europe. New York: Carnegie Foundation, 1912.
45. Haldane R (chair) The Haldane Commission. London: HMSO, 1918.
46. Goodenough Committee. Report of the Inter-Departmental Committee on Medical Schools, (Chairman: Sir William Goodenough). London: Ministry of Health and Department of Health for Scotland, HMSO, 1944.
47. Medical World, 28 April, 1944.
48. Moberley Bell E. Storming the Citadel: The Rise of the Woman Doctor. London: Constable, 1953.
49. Ivens F. Some of the Essential Attributes of an Ideal Practitioner, Inaugural Address. London: Magazine of London, Oct 1914, ix.
50. Honigsbaum F. The Division in British Medicine: A History of the Separation of General Practice from Hospital Care, 1911-1968. New York: St Martin's Press, 1979, pp 304-7.
51. Hamilton L. The distribution of capital among the medical profession in England and Wales, 1940-1. Bull Oxf Institute Statistics 1950; 12: 1-6.
52. James A. Divagations of a Doctor. Edinburgh: Oliver & Boyd, 1924.
53. Levy H. National Health Insurance. A Critical Study. Cambridge: Cambridge University Press, 1944.
54. Porter R. Doing medical history from below. Theory and Society 1987; 14: 167-174.
55. Shaw GB. The Doctor's Dilemma. London: Methuen, 1906.
56. BMJ 1950; ii: 420.
57. Stone D. Physicians as Gatekeepers: Illness certification as a rationing device. Public Policy 1979; xxvii: 227.
58. Oxfordshire Archives, PLU2/6/1A16, Bicester Union District Medical Officers' Official Returns of Sick Paupers Attended, 1836, 1846, 1892.
59. Digby A. Pauper Palaces. London: Routledge and Kegan Paul, 1978.
60. PRO, 62/200, Report of Special Committee into Medical Certification in South Wales.
61. Loudon I. Historical importance of outpatients. BMJ 1978; 3: 7-9.

62. Stevens R. Medical Practice in Modern England. New Haven: Yale University Press, 1966, p33.
63. BMJ 1929; i: 130.
64. CMAC, SA/RNI/H8/1. Report from West Penrith Medical Society to the Penzance and Madron Nursing Association, May 1908.
65. Lancet 1926; ii: 863.
66. Harris J. Private Lives, Public Spirit. A Social History of Britain, 1870-1914. Oxford: Oxford University Press, 1993.
67. Lloyd George D. Speech at the 25th anniversary dinner of the NHI. BMJ 2nd July, 1933.
68. Lawrence C. Incommunicable Knowledge. Science, Technology and the Clinical Art in Britain, 1850-1914. J Contemporary History 1985; 20: 517.

Chapter Six

1. PWHR. Obituary: JFE Gillam. BMJ 1987; 294: 1425.
2. CLP. Obituary: JFE Gillam. BMJ 1987; 294: 1425.
3. Gordon R. Triple Knock-Out: Disastrous Surgical Enthusiasm. Great Medical Disasters. London: Hutchinson & Co, 1983, pp13–15.
4. Nussey AM. Munk's Roll. London, Royal College of Physicians, 1970. https://history.rcplondon.ac.uk/inspiring-physicians/geoffrey-gerrard-gillam
5. Freeden M. The Stranger at the Feast: Ideology and Public Policy in Twentieth Century Britain. Twentieth Century British History 1990; I: 29.
6. Dawson. Ministry of Health. Interim report on the future provision of medical and allied services. (Chairman: Dawson of Penn) Consultative Council on medical and allied services, Cmd 693. London, HMSO, 1920.
7. Beveridge W. Report on social and insurance and allied services. (Chairman: Sir William Beveridge.) Cmd 6040. London: HMSO, 1942.
8. Klein R. The New Politics of the NHS. 6th ed. Oxford: Radcliffe Publishing, 2016.
9. Honigsbaum F. Health, Happiness and Security. The Creation of the National Health Service. 1989, 213-218.
10. Eckstein H. Pressure group politics. The case of the British Medical Association. San Francisco: Stanford University Press, 1960.
11. Spens W. Report of the inter-departmental committee on remuneration of general practitioners. (Chairman: Sir William Spens.) Cmd 6810. London: HMSO, 1946.
12. Rivett G. From Cradle to Grave. Fifty years of the NHS. London: King's Fund, 1998.
13. Lancet. The first month (leading article). Lancet 1948; 2: 223-5.
14. Digby A. The Evolution of British General Practice, 1850-1948. Oxford: Oxford University Press, 1999, pp325-6.
15. Webster C. The Health Services since the War, I Problems of Health Care: The National Health Service before 1957. London: HMSO, 1988.

16. Central Health Services Council. Report on the committee on general practice within the NHS. (Chairman: Sir Henry Cohen) London: HMSO, 1954.
17. Collings JS. General practice in England today. A reconnaissance. Lancet 1950; 1: 555-79 + appendices.
18. Jefferys M, Sachs H. Rethinking General Practice: Dilemmas in Primary Medical Care. London: Tavistock Publications, 1983, pp3-4.
19. Ministry of Health. Report for the year 1953. Cmd 9321, London: HMSO, 1954.
20. Ball J. Review of the work of the Medical Practices Committee (internal papers). London: British Medical Association, 1989.
21. Lancet. The Act in action. The general practitioner. Lancet 1948; 2: 823.
22. Dickinson, KG. Changing face of general practice. BMJ 1981; 283: 958-9.
23. Fry J. A year of general practice: a study in morbidity. BMJ 1952; 2: 249-52.
24. Hopkins P. Referrals in general practice. BMJ 1956; 2: 873.
25. Sweeney B. The referral system. BMJ 1994; 309: 1180-1.
26. Godber G. The British National Health Service. Conversations with Sir George Godber. Washington DC: US Department of Health, Education and Welfare, 1976, 10.
27. BMJ. Demand for early settlement (leading article). BMJ 1950; 2: 93.
28. Anthony E. The GP at the crossroads. BMJ 1950; 1: 1077-9.
29. BMJ editorial, 26th Sept, 1953.
30. Fox T. Mechanism and purpose (leading article). Lancet 1950: 1: 27.
31. McLachlan G. A history of the Nuffield Provincial Hospitals Trust. 1940-1990. London: NPHT, 1992.
32. Collings JS. Group practice: existing patterns and future policies. Lancet 1953; 2: 31-3.
33. Collings JS. Group practice: what needs to be done. Lancet 1953; 2: 611-15.
34. Collings JS. Basic group practice: how it can be done. Lancet 1953; 2: 875-7.
35. Hadfield SJ. A field survey of general practice 1951-2. BMJ 1953; 2: 683.
36. Dopson L. The changing scene in general practice. London: Johnson, 1957.
37. General practice today and tomorrow (leading article). BMJ 1953; 2: 717-18.
38. Ministry of Health. Report for the year 1952. Part I, 37-9. Cmd 8933. London: HMSO, 1953.
39. Ministry of Health. The NHS (General Medical and Pharmaceutical) amendment (No 2) Regulations 1953. SI 1953, No. 505. London: HMSO, 1953.
40. Ministry of Health. Report for the year ended 31 December 1954. Cmd 9566. London: HMSO, 1955.
41. Powell JE. Medicine and politics. London: Pitman Medical, 1966.

42. Fry J, Hunt J, Pinsent RJFH, editors. A history of the Royal College of General Practitioners: the first 25 years. Lancaster: MTP Press, 1983.
43. Pereira Gray D, ed. Forty Years On. The Story of the First Forty Years of the Royal College of General Practitioners. London: RCGP, Atalink, 1992.
44. BMJ. Doctors' surgeries (leading article). BMJ 1954; 2: 799-800.
45. Balint M. Training general practitioners in psychotherapy. BMJ 1954; 1: 115-20.
46. Balint M. The doctor, his patient and the illness. London: Pitman, 1957.
47. RCGP. The teaching of general practice by general practitioners. BMJ 1953; 1: 36.
48. Logan WPD, Cushion AA. Morbidity statistics from general practice, vol. 1. Studies on medical and population subjects, no. 14. London: HMSO, 1958.
49. Moran C. Evidence to the Royal Commission on Doctors' and Dentists' Remuneration. BMJ 1958; 1, suppl: 27-30.
50. Moran C. The 'Ladder'. Lancet 1959; 1: 216.
51. Grant ID. Status of the general practitioner, past, present and future. BMJ 1961; 2: 1279-82.
52. MacFeat G. The family doctor in the NHS. BMJ 1950; 1: 663-4.

Chapter Seven

1. Gillam P, Prichard B. Use of Propranolol in Angina Pectoris. BMJ 1965; 2: 337–339.
2. Prichard B, Gillam P. Treatment of Hypertension with Propranolol. Br Med J 1969; 1: 7. doi: https://doi.org/10.1136/bmj.1.5635.7
3. General Medical Council. Duties of a doctor. London: GMC, 1995.
4. Whitty C, MacEwen C, Goddard A et al. Rising to the challenge of multimorbidity. BMJ 2020; 368 doi: https://doi.org/10.1136/bmj.l6964
5. Berger J. A Fortunate Man. London: Pantheon, 1967.
6. Collings J. General practice in England today: a reconnaissance. *Lancet* 1950; 1: 555-85
7. Cartwright A, Scott R. The work of a nurse employed in general practice. BMJ 1961; 1: 807-13.
8. Royal College of General Practitioners. The Future General Practitioner: learning and teaching. London: RCGP, 1972.
9. Irvine D. Quality in general practice. In McLachlan G, editor. A question of quality? London: Nuffield Provincial Hospitals Trust, 1976.
10. Central Health Services Council, Standing Medical Advisory Committee. The Field of Work of the Family Doctor: Report of the Sub-Committee. The Gillie Report; London: HMSO, 1963.
11. The Family Doctor Charter. London: HMSO, 1966.
12. BMJ. Discussions must continue (leading article). BMJ 1965; 2: 181.
13. BMJ. Towards a new contract (leading article). BMJ 1965; 2: 889.

14. Royal College of General Practitioners. Trends in General Practice. London: RCGP, 1977.

15. Reedy BI. Changing face of general practice. BMJ 1967; 1: 54.

16. Bosanquet N, Salisbury C. In Loudon I, Horder J, Webster C eds. General Practice under the National Health Service, 1948-1997. Chapter 2. The Practice. Clarendon Press, London, 1998, pp50-7.

17. Marsh GN. Group practice nurse: an analysis and comment on six months' work. BMJ 1967; 1: 489-91.

18. Dopson L. The changing scene in general practice. London: Johnson, 1971.

19. Todd. Royal Commission on medical education 1965-68. (Chairman: Lord Todd.) Cmnd 3569. London: HMSO, 1968.

20. Tudor Hart J. A New Kind Of Doctor. London: Merlin Press, 1985.

21. Medical Practitioners' Union. Health centre report. London: MPU, 1960.

22. Fry J. General practice tomorrow. BMJ 1964; 2: 1064-7.

23. Department of Health and Social Security. On the state of the public health. Report of the CMO for 1974. London: HMSO, 1975.

24. BMJ. Conference on vocational training for GPs. BMJ 1968; 2: 758-60.

25. Reedy BLEC, Philips PR, Newell DJ. Nurses and nursing in primary medical care in England. BMJ 1976; 2: 1304-6.

26. Stilwell B. Nurse in a doctor's world. Nursing Times 1982; Apr 21, 651.

27. Tudor Hart J, Thomas C, Gibbons B et al. Twenty five years of case finding and audit in a socially deprived community. BMJ 1991; 302: 1509-13.

28. Rose G. The Strategies of Preventive Medicine. Oxford: Oxford University Press, 1993.

29. Holdstock G, Wiseman M, Loehry CA et al. Open access endoscopy service for general practitioners. BMJ 1979; 1: 457-9.

30. Irvine D, Jeffreys M. BMA planning unit survey of general practice 1969. BMJ 1971; 4: 535-43.

31. Whewell J, Marsh GN, Angus McNay R. Changing patterns of home visiting in the north of England. BMJ 1983; 286: 1259-61.

32. Gillam S. The Family Doctor Charter – fifty years on. BJGP 2017; 67: 229-30. https://doi.org/10.3399/bjgp17X690809

33. Morrell, D. In Loudon I, Horder J, Webster C eds. General Practice under the National Health Service, 1948-1997. Introduction and Overview. London: Clarendon Press, 1998, p8.

34. Cartwright A, Anderson R. General Practice Revisited: A Second Study of Patients and their Doctors. London: HMSO, 1981.

35. Esmail A. Asian doctors in the NHS: service and betrayal. B J Gen Pract 2007; 57(543): 827–834.

36. Jeffery R. Recognizing India's doctors: the institutionalization of medical dependency, 1918–1939. Mod Asian Stud 1979; **13**(2): 301–326.

37. Esmail A, Everington S. Racial discrimination against doctors from ethnic minorities. BMJ 1993; 306 (6879): 691–692.

38. Spens W. Report of the inter-departmental committee on remuneration of general practitioners. (Chairman: Sir William Spens.) Cmd 6810. London: HMSO, 1946.

39. Horder JP, Swift G. The history of vocational training for general practice. Journal Royal Coll Gen Practitioners 1979; 29: 24-32.

40. Cohen H. General practice and the training of the General Practitioner (chairman Sir Henry Cohen) The report of a committee of the BMA. London: BMA, 1950.

41. Marinker M. Changing patterns in general practice education. In: Teeling Smith G, editor. Health, education and general practice. London: Office of Health Economics, 1965.

42. Balint M. The other part of medicine. Lancet 1961; 1: 41-3.

43. Horder JP. Training for general practice. Journal Coll Gen Practitioners 1964; 7: 303-4.

44. Whitfield MJ. Training for general practice: result of a survey. BMJ 1966; 1: 663-7.

45. College of General Practitioners. Reports from general practice, no. 5. Evidence to the Royal Commission on medical education. London: CGP, 1966.

46. BMJ. Good general practice (leading article). BMJ 1967; 3: 754.

47. Marinker M. Should general practice be represented in the university medical school? BMJ 1983; 286: 855-9.

48. Crowther MA, Dupree MW. Medical Lives in the Age of Surgical Revolution. Cambridge: Cambridge University Press, 2010.

49. Mackenzie J. The Opportunities of the General Practitioner are Essential for the Investigation of Disease and the Progress of Medicine. BMJ 1921; i: 797-804.

50. Mackenzie J. Principles of the Diagnosis and Treatment of Heart Affections. 1916.

51. Pickles W. Epidemiology in Country Practice. NEJM 1948; 239: 419.

52. Hodgkin P. Towards Earlier Diagnosis. London: Livingstone, 1963.

53. Fry J. Why patients go to hospital. BMJ 1959; 2: 1323-7.

54. Shepherd M. General Practice, Mental Illness, and the British National Health Service, Am J Public Hlth 1974; 64: 230-32.

55. Culyer AJ. Supporting Research and Development in the NHS. London: HMSO, 1994.

56. Balint M. The Doctor, his Patient and the Illness. London: Pitman Medical, 1957.

57. Byrne P, Long B. Doctors Talking To Patients. London: HMSO, 1976.

58. Neighbour R. The Inner Consultation. London: MTP, 1987.

59. Elwyn G, Laitner S, Coulter A et al. Implementing shared decision making in the NHS. BMJ 2010; 341 doi: https://doi.org/10.1136/bmj.c5146

60. Parsons T. The Social System. Glencoe: The Free Press, 1951.

61. Jefferys M, Brotherston J, Cartwright A. Consumption of Medicine on a Working-Class Housing Estate. Brit J Preventive and Social Med 1960; 14: 64-76.

62. Dunnell K, Cartwright A. Medicine-takers, Prescribers and Hoarders. London: Routledge & Kegan Paul, 1972.

63. Zola IK. Pathways to the Doctor: From Person to Patient. Soc Sci Med 1973; 7: 677-89.

64. Goffman E. Asylums. Harmondsworth: Penguin, 1961.

65. Brown G. Social Causes of Disease. Chapter 9 in Tuckett D, ed. An Introduction to Medical Sociology. London: Tavistock Publications, 1976, pp 291-333.

66. Helman C. Culture, Health and Illness. Bristol: John Wright & Sons, 1984.

67. Kleinman A. Patients and Healers in the Context of Culture. Berkeley: University of California Press, 1980.

68. Littlewood R, Lipsedge M. Aliens and Alienists. Harmondsworth: Penguin, 1982.

69. Strong P. Sociological imperialism and the profession of medicine: a critical examination of the thesis of medical imperialism. Soc Sci Med 1979; 13A: 199-215.

70. Dubos R. The Mirage of Health. London: Allen and Unwin, 1960.

71. Tait I. Dubos' Mirage of Health. JRCGP Apr 82, 248.

72. McKeown T. The Role of Medicine, Oxford: Nuffield, 1976.

73. Szereter S. The importance of social intervention in Britain's mortality decline, c.1850-1914: a reinterpretation of the role of public health. Social History of Medicine 1988; 1: 1-38.

74. Illich I. Limits to Medicine. Medical nemesis: the expropriation of health. London: Marion Boyars, 1974.

75. Smith R. Limits to Medicine. Medical nemesis: the expropriation of health. BMJ 2002; 324; 923. http://dx.doi.org/10.1136/jech.57.12.928

76. Foucault M. The Birth of the Clinic: An Archaeology of Medical Perception. New York: Random House, 1963.

77. Waddington K. An Introduction to the Social History of Medicine. Europe Since 1500. London: Palgrave Macmillan, 2011.

78. Curwen M. Lord Moran's Ladder: a study of motivation in the choice of general practice as a career. J Coll Gen Pract 1964; **7**: 38-64.

79. Le Fanu J. The Rise and Fall of Modern Medicine. London: Abacus, 2011.

Chapter Eight
1. Tudor Hart J. The inverse care law. Lancet 1971; 297: 405-12. https://doi.org/10.1016/S0140-6736(71)92410-X

2. Le Fanu J. The Rise and Fall of Modern Medicine. London: Abacus, 2011.

3. Gillam SJ. The traditional healer as village health worker. J Inst Med Nep 1989; 11: 67-76.

4. O'Dwyer M, Gillam S. Children discharged from a nutritional rehabilitation centre: a follow-up study. Tropical Doctor 1995; 25: 173-177.

5. Gillam SJ, Jarman B, White P, Law R. Ethnic differences in consultation rates in urban general practice. BMJ 1989; 299: 953-958.

6. Gillam SJ. Provision of health promotion clinics in relation to population need: another example of the inverse care law? Br J Gen Pract 1992; 42: 54-6.

7. Sladden J. Medical marriages. BMJ 2004; 329 doi: https://doi.org/10.1136/bmj.329.7478.s227-a

8. Beiser C, Roberts J. Medical marriage. BMJ 1994; 309 doi: https://doi.org/10.1136/bmj.309.6970.1673

9. Gillam S, Schamroth A. Community-oriented primary care experience in the United Kingdom. American J Public Hlth 2002; 92: 1721-25.

10. Black N. Evidence-based policy: proceed with care. BMJ 2001; 323: 275–279.

11. Department of Health. Public Health in England. Report of the Committee of Inquiry into the Future Development of the Public Health Function. London: HMSO, 1988.

12. Gillam S, Maudsley G. Public health education for medical students: rising to the professional challenge. J Public Hlth 2010; 32: 125-31.

13. Gillam SJ. Sociocultural differences in patients' expectations at consultations for upper respiratory tract infection. J R Coll Gen Pract 1987; 37: 205-206.

14. Gillam S. Confessions of a CQC inspector. BJGP 2020; 692 128-9. doi: https://doi.org/10.3399/bjgp20X708605

15. Klein R. The New Politics of the NHS. 6th ed. Oxford: Radcliffe Publishing, 2016.

16. Warden J. Make or break year for NHS? BMJ 1988; 296: 302.

17. Thatcher M. The Downing Street years. London: HarperCollins, 1993, 606-16.

18. Warden J. Clarke's ringing testimony to the health service. BMJ 1989; 297: 1006.

19. Secretaries of State for Health. Working for Patients. Cm 555. London: HMSO, 1989.

20. Glennerster H, Matsaganis M, Owens R, Hancock S. GP fundholding: wild card or winning hand? In Robinson R, Le Grand J, editors. Evaluating the NHS reforms. London: King's Fund Institute/Hermitage, 1994, 74-107.

21. Appleby J. Fundholding. Health Service Journal 1994; Aug 11: 32-3.

22. Ham C. A primary care market. BMJ 1996; 313: 127-8.

23. Stewart-Brown S, Gillam S, Jewell T. The problems of fundholding. BMJ 1996; 312: 1311-12.

24. Bailey J. The Special Branch. Health Service Journal 1994; Jul 28: 30-1.

25. Gillam SJ. Outreach clinics in the new NHS: not yet the end of outpatients. Br J Gen Pract 2001; 465: 261-2.

26. Dixon J, Glennerster H. What do we know about fundholding in general practice? BMJ 1995; 311: 727-30.

27. Mays N, Mulligan J-A, Goodwin N. The British quasi market in health care: a balance sheet of the evidence. J Health Services Research and Policy 2000; 5: 49-58.

28. Goodwin N. 'GP Fundholding' in Le Grand J, Mays N and Mulligan J (eds) Learning from the NHS Internal Market, London: King's Fund, 1998.

29. NHS Executive. Developing NHS purchasing and GP fundholding. Towards a primary care-led NHS. EL(94)79. Leeds: NHSE, 1994.

30. The Times, ed. New Year, New Labours. The Times 1996; Dec 31.

31. Smith JA, Mays N, Dixon J, Goodwin N, Lewis R, McClelland S, McLeod H, Wyke S. A review of the effectiveness of primary care-led commissioning and its place in the UK NHS. London: The Health Foundation, 2004.

32. Department of Health. Health and Social Care Act. London: Department of Health, 2012.

33. Smith J, Mays N. GP led commissioning: time for a cool appraisal. BMJ 2012; 344: e980.

34. Walshe K. The consequences of abandoning the Health and Social Care Bill. BMJ 2012; 344 doi: https://doi.org/10.1136/bmj.e748

35. Wilson T, Lewis R. Primary care networks: well intentioned but overambitious. BMJ 2019; 366 doi: https://doi.org/10.1136/bmj.l5311

36. Morrell D. London general practice is there a solution? BMJ 1981; 282: 161-3.

37. Acheson D. London Health Planning Consortium. Primary health care in inner London. (Chairman: Donald Acheson.) London: DHSS, 1981.

38. Jarman B. Underprivileged areas: validation and distribution of scores. BMJ 1984; 289: 1587-92.

39. Pringle M, Dennis J, Hutton A. Computerisation, the choice. BMJ 1982; 284: 165-8.

40. Smith R. Computers in medicine: searching for the rainbow and the crock of gold. BMJ 1982; 284: 1859-6.

41. Donabedian A. Evaluating the quality of medical care. Millbank Mem Fund Q 1966; 44: 166-206.

42. Lindblad U, Ek J, Eckner J et al. Prevalence, awareness, treatment, and control of hypertension: Rule of thirds in the Skaraborg project. Scand J Prim Health Care 2012 Jun; 30(2): 88–94.

43. Ministry of Health. Final report of the committee on cost of prescribing. (Chairman: Sir Henry Hinchcliffe.) London: HMSO, 1959.

44. Hoffenberg R. Clinical freedom. Rock Carling Fellowship, 1986. London: Nuffield Provincial Hospitals Trust, 1987.

45. BMJ. Mr Fowler's statement on the limited list (from the GMSC). BMJ 1984; 290: 724.

46. Audit Commission. Fundholding: what the doctor ordered. London: Audit Commission, 1996.

47. Jagger R, Richards K. Mother's little helper. London: Decca, 1965.

48. Charlesworth J, Petkovic G, Kelley J et al. Effects of placebos without deception compared with no treatment: A systematic review with meta-analysis. J Evidence-Based Medicine 2017; 10: 97-107.

49. Ebrahim S. Changing patterns of consultation in general practice: fourth national morbidity study, 1991-1992. Brit J Gen Practice 1995; 45: 283-4.

50. Livingstone A, Widgery D. The new general practice: changing philosophies of primary care. BMJ 1990; 301: 708-10.

51. RCGP. Health and prevention in primary care. Report from general practice no. 18. (Chairman: J Horder.) London: Royal College of General Practitioners, 1981.

52. Fowler G. What is preventable? BMJ 1982; 284: 1017-18.

53. Fullard E, Fowler G, Gray M. Facilitating prevention in primary care. BMJ 1984; 284: 1585-7.

54. MrFit Study Group. Multiple Risk Factor Intervention Trial. JAMA 1982; 248: 165-77.

55. DHSS. Promoting better health: the government's programme for improving primary health care. Cm 249. London: HMSO, 1987.

56. BMJ. Government's formidable firepower on GPs' contract. BMJ 1989; 299: 1068.

57. Department of Health. On the state of the public health. Report of the CMO for 1991. London: HMSO, 1992.

58. Baker R, Thompson J. Innovation in general practice: is the gap between training and non-training practices getting wider? Brit J Gen Practice 1995; 45: 297-300.

59. Doctor. Nursing the hope of lighter GP workload. Doctor 1994; Dec 15th.

60. Hasler J. The primary health care team. BMJ 1992; 305: 232-4.

61. Lenehan C, Watts A. Are nurse-practitioners here to stay? Brit J Gen Practice 1994; 44: 291-2.

62. Stilwell B, Greenfield S, Drury M, Hull FM. A nurse practitioner in general practice. Journal Royal Coll Gen Practitioners 1987; 37: 154-7.

63. Coulter A. Shifting the balance from secondary to primary care. BMJ 1995; 311: 1447-8.

64. Leese B, Bosanquet N. Family doctors and change in practice strategy since 1986. BMJ 1995; 310: 705-8.

65. Marsh GN. Efficient care in general practice. Oxford: Oxford University Press, 1991.

66. Marsh GN, Daces ML. Establishing a minor illness nurse in a busy general practice. BMJ 1995; 310: 778-80.

67. Gillam SJ. Funding for social care – the continuing conundrum. BJGP 2011; 591: 600-601.

68. Heath I. Long term care for older people. BMJ 2002; 324: 1534-5.

69. Dilnot A (chair). Commission on Funding of Care and Support. Fairer care funding. London: Dept of Health, 2011. https://www.wp.dh.gov.uk/carecommission/files/2011/07/Fairer-Care-Funding-Report.pdf.

70. Barker K (chair). Commission on the Future of Health and Social Care in England. A new settlement for health and social care. Final report. London: King's Fund, September 2014.

71. Gillam S. The future funding of health and social care in England. BJGP 2014; 64: 499-500.

72. NHS Executive. Primary care: the future. London: NHS Executive, 1996.

73. Department of Health. Choice and opportunity. Primary care: the future. Cm 3390. London: Stationery Office, 1996.

74. Pringle M, Heath I. Distributing primary care fairly. BMJ 1997; 314: 95-9.

75. Lewis R, Gillam S, Jenkins C (eds). Personal Medical Services Pilots. Modernising primary care? London: King's Fund, 2001.

76. Lewis R, Gillam S. Personal medical services. Have made steady, if unspectacular, progress. BMJ 2002; 325: 1126-27.

77. Pollock A. NHS plc. The Privatisation of Our Health Care. London: Verso, 2004.

78. NHS Employers and the General Practitioners Committee. Quality and Outcomes Framework for 2012/13. Guidance for PCOs and practices. London: NHS Employers, 2012. (http://www.nhsemployers.org/Aboutus/Publications/Documents/QOF_2012-13.pdf)

79. MacBride-Stewart SP, Elton R, Walley T. Do quality incentives change prescribing patterns in primary care? An observational study in Scotland. Fam Pract 2008; 25: 27-32.

80. Ariely D, Gneezy U, Loewenstein G et al. Large stakes and big mistakes. Rev Econ Stud 2009: 76 (2): 451–469.

81. Heath I. Divided we fail. The Harveian Oration. London: Royal College of Physicians, 2011. http://www.rcplondon.ac.uk/sites/default/files/harveian-oration-2011-web-navigable.pdf

82. Maisey S, Steel N, Marsh R, Gillam S, Fleetcroft R, Howe A. Effects of payment for performance in primary care: qualitative interview study. J Health Serv Res Policy 2008; 13: 133-139.

83. Campbell SM, McDonald R, Lester H. The experience of pay for performance in English family practice: a qualitative study. Ann Fam Med 2008; 6: 228-234.

84. Bunker J. The role of medical care in contributing to health improvement within society. Int J Epid 2001; 30(6): 1260-3.

85. Gillam S, Siriwardena N, Steel N. Pay for performance in the UK: the impact of the Quality and Outcomes framework. Ann Fam Med 2012; 10: 461-468. http://annfammed.org/content/10/5/461.full

86. Scott A, Sivey P, Ait Ouakrim D, Willenberg L. Naccarella L, Furler J, Young D. The effect of financial incentives on the quality of health care provided by primary care physicians. Cochrane Database Systematic Reviews 2011; 9: CD008451, doi:10.1002/14651858.CD008451.pub2

87. Rivett G. From Cradle to Grave. Fifty years of the NHS. London: King's Fund, 1998.

88. Munro J, Nicholl J, O'Cathain A et al. Evaluation of NHS Direct first wave sites. Second interim report to the Department of Health. Sheffield: Medical Care Research Unit, University of Sheffield, 2000.

89. Salisbury C, Pope C, Banks J et al. An evaluation of approaches to improving access to general practitioner appointments. National Institute for Health Research, London, 2008. http://www.nets.nihr.ac.uk/__data/assets/pdf_file/0017/81341/RS-08-1310-070.pdf

90. Bunn F, Byrne G, Kendall S. Telephone consultation and triage: effects on health care use and patient satisfaction. Cochrane Database Systematic Reviews 2004; (4). https://doi.org/10.1002/14651858.CD004180.pub2

91. Huibers L, Smits M, Renaud V et al. Safety of telephone triage in out-of-hours care: a systematic review. Scand J Prim Health Care 2011; 29(4): 198-209.

92. Campbell J, Fletcher E, Britten N, Green C et al. Telephone triage for management of same-day consultation requests in general practice (the ESTEEM trial): a cluster randomised controlled trial and cost consequence analysis. Lancet 2014; 384; 1859-1868. http://dx.doi.org/10.1016/S0140-6736(14)61058-8

93. Gillam S. Telephone triage – does it work? BJGP 2014; 64: 327-8.

94. Freeman G, Hjortdahl P. What future for continuity of care in general practice. BMJ 1997; 314: 1870. https://doi.org/10.1136/bmj.314.7098.1870

95. Pereira-Gray D, Sidaway-Lee K, White E, Thorne A, Evans PH. Continuity of care with doctors - a matter of life and death? A systematic review of continuity of care and mortality. BMJ Open 2018; 8: 6. http://dx.doi.org/10.1136/bmjopen-2017-021161

96. Baker R, Freeman G, Haggerty J et al. Primary medical care continuity and patient mortality: a systematic review. Br J Gen Pract 2020; 698: 438.

97. Daily Telegraph. Dangerous GP surgeries are named and shamed. Daily Telegraph, 11 December 2013.

98. Care Quality Commission. Annual report and accounts, 2018/19. Newcastle: CQC https://www.cqc.org.uk/publications/major-report/annual-report-accounts-201819

99. Nuffield Trust. General Practice - a crisis? London: Nuffield Trust.

100. BMA News. GP pay continues to fall, finds report. London: British Medical Association, Sept 2014. http://bma.org.uk/news-views-analysis/news/2014/september/gp-income-continues-to-fall-finds-report

101. Irish B. Not another primary care workforce crisis… Br J Gen Pract 2012; 62: 178-9.
102. NHS England. GP Forward View. London: NHSE, April 2016.
103. Gerada C. Understanding burnout. BMJ 2020; 369m: 1595.
104. Marinker M. In Loudon I, Horder J, Webster C eds. General Practice under the National Health Service, 1948-1997. Chapter 3. 'What is wrong' and 'How we know it': Changing Concepts of Illness in General Practice. London: Clarendon Press, 1998, pp88-9.
105. National Centre for Social Research. British Social Attitudes Survey. London, NCSR, 2018.
106. Gray JAM. Postmodern medicine. Lancet 1999; 354: 1553.
107. Gillam S. The future shape of general practice in England. BMJ 2014; 349: 7.
108. Doherty J, Govender R. The cost-effectiveness of primary care services in developing countries: a review of the international literature. Washington, DC: World Bank, 2004.
109. Starfield B. Is primary care essential? Lancet 1994; 344, 1129–33.
110. Macinko J, Starfield B, Shi L. The contribution of primary care systems to health outcomes within organization for economic cooperation and development (OECD) countries, 1970-1998. Health Serv Res 2003; 38: 831-65.
111. World Health Organisation. Declaration of Alma Ata. International conference on primary health care, Alma-Ata, USSR, 6-12 September 1978. Geneva: WHO, 1978. www.who.int/hpr/NPH/docs/declaration_almaata.pdf.
112. Tejada de Rivero D. Alma-Ata revisited. Persp Health 2003; 8: 1-6.
113. Meads G. Primary care in the twenty-first century. An international perspective. Oxford: Radcliffe, 2006.
114. Walraven G. The Astana Declaration on Primary Health Care – is it useful? J Glob Health 2019 Jun; 9(1): 010313. doi: 10.7189/jogh.09.010313
115. Gillam SJ. Is the declaration of Alma Ata still relevant to primary health care? BMJ 2008; 336: 536-8.
116. Klaver K, Baart A. How can attending physicians be more attentive? On being attentive versus producing attentiveness. Med Health Care Philos 2016; 19(3): 351-359.
117. Nussbaum MC. (ed) Creating capabilities. Cambridge, MA: Harvard University Press, 2013.
118. Butterfield H. The Whig Interpretation of History. London: WW Norton & Co, 1965.

Conclusion
1. Critchlow H. The Science of Fate. London: Hodder & Stoughton, 2019.
2. Morris B, Loftus D. The making of the British middle class. Unit 12 in Confidence and crisis, 1840-1880, ed Loftus D. Milton Keynes: Open University Press, 2017, pp 225-277.

3. Mackie R. Industry and finance. Unit 17 in Decline and renewal, 1880-1914, ed Mackie R. Milton Keynes: Open University Press, 2017, pp 57-113.
4. Berger J. A Fortunate Man. London: Pantheon, 1967.
5. Majeed A. Should all GPs become NHS employees? BMJ 2016; 355: i5064.
6. Illich I. Limits to Medicine. Medical nemesis: the expropriation of health. London: Marion Boyars, 1974.
7. Le Fanu J. The Rise and Fall of Modern Medicine. London: Abacus, 2011.
8. Willis J. The Paradox of Progress. Oxford: Radcliffe Medical Press, 1995.
9. Drucker P. Peter Drucker on the Profession of Management. Boston: Harvard Business School Publishing, 1998.
10. Eliot TS. The Rock. London: Faber & Faber, 1934.
11. Mossialos E, McGuire A, Anderson M, Pitchforth E, James A, Horton R. The future of the NHS: no longer the envy of the world? Lancet 2018; 391: 1001-1003. https://doi.org/10.1016/S0140-6736(18)30574-9e
12. Schneider E et al. Mirror, Mirror 2017: International Comparison Reflects Flaws and Opportunities for Better U.S. Health Care. New York: Commonwealth Fund, 2017.
13. Klein R. The New Politics of the NHS. 6th ed. Oxford: Radcliffe Publishing, 2016.
14. Gillam S. The Francis inquiry: a lost opportunity? Quality in Primary Care 2013; 21: 205-6.
15. Massey A. Sick-Note Britain: How Social Problems Became Medical Issues. London: Hurst, 2019.
16. Runciman D. How Democracy Ends. London: Profile Books, 2018.
17. Gillam S. An awkward truth. Economist, 25th April, 2020, p 12. https://www.economist.com/letters/2020/04/23/letters-to-the-editor
18. Harrabin R, Coote A, Allen J. Health in the News: Risk, Reporting and Media Influence. London: King's Fund, 2003.
19. Dollery C. The End of an Age of Optimism. London: Nuffield Provincial Hospitals Trust, Rock Carling Lecture, 1978.
20. Ramalingam B. Aid on the Edge of Chaos: Rethinking International Co-operation in a Complex World. Oxford: Oxford University Press, 2014.
21. Toon P. What is Good General Practice. Occasional Paper 65. London: Royal College of General Practitioners, 1994.
22. Armstrong D. Space and time in British general practice. Soc Sci Med 1985; 20/7: 659-66.
23. Fitzpatrick M. The Tyranny of Health. London: Routledge, 2001.
24. Ryan AM, Krinsky S, Kontopantelis E, Doran T. Long-term evidence for the effect of pay-for-performance in primary care on mortality in the UK: a population study. Lancet 2016; 388: 268-74. http://doi:10.1016/S0140-6736(16)00276-2
25. Spence D. Bad medicine: chest examination. BMJ 2012; 345 doi: https://doi.org/10.1136/bmj.e4569

26. Heath I. The Mystery of General Practice. London: Nuffield Provincial Hospitals Trust, 1995.

27. Heath I. Medicine needs an injection of humanity. BMJ 2016; 355: i5705. http://dx.doi.org/10.1136/bmj.i5705

28. Stiggelbout A, De Wit M, Legare F et al. Shared decision-making: really putting patients at the heart of healthcare. BMJ 2012; 344 doi: https://doi.org/10.1136/bmj.e256

29. Pereira-Gray D, Sidaway-Lee K, White E, Thorne A, Evans PH. Continuity of care with doctors-a matter of life and death? A systematic review of continuity of care and mortality. BMJ Open 2018, 8, 6. http://dx.doi.org/10.1136/bmjopen-2017-021161

30. Freedman L. Achieving the MDGs: health systems as core social institutions. Development 2005; 48: 19-24.

31. Gillam S. What is good general practice? Recollected. BJGP 2019; 686: 392-3. https://doi.org/10.3399/bjgp19X704801

32. Foucault M. The Birth of the Clinic: An Archaeology of Medical Perception. New York: Random House, 1963.

33. Marinker M. In Loudon I, Horder J, Webster C eds. General Practice under the National Health Service, 1948-1997. Chapter 3. 'What is wrong' and 'How we know it': Changing Concepts of Illness in General Practice. London: Clarendon Press, 1998, pp88-9.

34. Taylor S. Good General Practice. A Report of a Survey. Oxford: Nuffield Provincial Hospitals Trust, 1954.

35. Royal College of General Practitioners. The Future General Practitioner: Learning and Teaching. London: RCGP, 1972.

36. Tudor Hart J. A New Kind of Doctor. London: Merlin Press, 1985.

37. The Economist. Technology Quarterly. Personalised medicine. The coming of the datome. March 14th, 2020, pp 11-12. https://www.economist.com/technology-quarterly/2020/03/12/medicine-is-getting-to-grips-with-individuality

38. Oliver D. Lessons from the Babylon Health saga. BMJ 2019; 365: l2387 doi: https://doi.org/10.1136/bmj.l2387

39. Dambha-Miller H, Everitt H, Little P. Clinical scores in primary care. British Journal of General Practice 2020; 70 (693): 163. doi: https://doi.org/10.3399/bjgp20X708941.

40. Gill P, Dowell AC, Neal RD et al. Evidence based general practice: a retrospective study of interventions in one training practice. BMJ 1996; 312: 819-21.

41. Marmot M, Patel C, North F et al. The Marmot Review: Fair Society, Healthy Lives: Strategic review of health inequalities in England post-2010. London: University College, 2010.

42. Marmot M. Health equity in England: the Marmot review 10 years on. BMJ 2020; 368 doi: https://doi.org/10.1136/bmj.m693

43. Allen L, Barry E, Gilbert C et al. How to move from managing sick individuals to creating healthy communities. Brit J Gen Practice 2019; 69 (678): 8-9. http://doi.org/10.3399/bjgp19X700337

44. Pratt J. Practitioners and practices. A conflict of values? Oxford: Radcliffe Medical Press, 1995.

45. Bickerdike I, Booth A, Wilson PM, Farley K, Wright K. Social prescribing: less rhetoric and more reality. A systematic review of the evidence. BMJ 2017; 7, 4. http://dx.doi.org/10.1136/bmjopen-2016-013384

46. Lyons A, Hothersall E, Gillam S. Teaching public health in UK medical schools: 'Things have improved. Teaching no longer feels like an expensive hobby.' Journal of Public Health 2015 doi:10.1093/pubmed/fdv127

47. Cochrane A. Effectiveness and Efficiency. London: Nuffield Provincial Hospitals Trust, 1971.

48. Hopkinson, N. The path to a smoke-free England by 2030. BMJ 2020; 368: m518. https://dx.doi.org/10.1136/bmj.m518

49. Watt G. Reflections at the Deep End. Brit J Gen Pract 2012; 62: 6-7.

50. Gillam S, Barna S. Sustainability in general practice. Education for Primary Care 2011; 22: 36-37.

51. Christie RJ, Hoffmaster CB. The Ethical Issues in Family Medicine. New York: Oxford University Press, 1986.

52. Wilkinson R, Pickett K. The Spirit Level: Why More Equal Societies Almost Always Do Better. London: Allen Lane, 2009.

53. Marinker M. The Family in Medicine. Proc Royal Soc Med 1976; 69: 115-24.

54. Cartwright A, Anderson R. General Practice Re-visited: A Second Study of Patients and their Doctors. London: Pitman, 1981.

55. Huygen F. Family Medicine: The Medical Life History of Families. Nijmegen: Dekker & Van De Vegt, 1978.

56. Greenhalgh T, Wherton J, Shaw S et al. Video consultations for covid-19 BMJ 2020; 368 doi: https://doi.org/10.1136/bmj.m998

57. NHS England. GP Forward View. London: NHSE, 2016.

58. Salisbury H. Is transactional care enough? BMJ 2020; 368 doi: https://doi.org/10.1136/bmj.m226

59. Gawande A. Being Mortal. London: Profile Books, 2014.

Bibliography

Balint M. The doctor, his patient and the illness. London: Pitman, 1957.

Berger J. A Fortunate Man. London, Pantheon, 1967.

Berridge V, Gorsky M, Mold A. Public Health in History. Milton Keynes: Open University Press: 2011.

Butterfield H. The Whig Interpretation of History. London: WW Norton & Co, 1965.

Brunton D ed. Medicine Transformed. Health, Disease and Society in Europe, 1800-1930. Manchester: Manchester University Press, 2004.

Bynum W, Porter R (eds). Companion Encyclopedia of the History of Medicine, vols 1 and 2. London: Routledge, 1993.

Carr EH. What is History? London: Pelican, 1985.

Crowther MA, Dupree MW. Medical Lives in the Age of Surgical Revolution. Cambridge: Cambridge University Press, 2010.

Digby A. Making a Medical Living. Doctors and Patients in the English Market for Medicine, 1720-1911. Cambridge, Cambridge University Press, 1994.

Digby A. The Evolution of British General Practice, 1850-1948. Oxford: Oxford University Press, 1999, pp 325-6.

Dubos R. The Mirage of Health. London: Allen and Unwin, 1960.

Elmer P ed. The Healing Arts. Health, Disease and Society in Europe. Manchester: Manchester University Press, 2004.

Fissell M. Patients, Power and the Poor in Eighteenth Century Bristol. Cambridge: Cambridge University Press, 1991.

Foucault M. Madness and Civilisation: A History of Insanity in the Age of Reason. New York: Random House, 1965.

Foucault M. The Birth of the Clinic: An Archaeology of Medical Perception. New York: Random House, 1963.

Gilbert B. The Evolution of National Insurance in Great Britain: The Origins of the Welfare State. London: Michael Joseph, 1966.

Goffman E. Asylums. Harmondsworth, Penguin, 1961.

Granshaw L, Porter R (eds). The Hospital in History. London: Routledge, 1989.

Hamlin C. Public Health and Social Justice in the Age of Chadwick: Britain 1850-54. Cambridge: Cambridge University Press, 2009.

Harris J. Private Lives, Public Spirit. A Social History of Britain, 1870-1914. Oxford: Oxford University Press, 1993.

Helman C. Culture, Health and Illness. Bristol: John Wright & Sons, 1984.

Honigsbaum F. The Division in British Medicine: A History of the Separation of General Practice from Hospital Care, 1911-1968. New York: St Martin's Press, 1979.

Honigsbaum F. Health, Happiness & Security: the Creation of the NHS. London: Routledge, 1989.

Huygen F. Family Medicine: The Medical Life History of Families. Nijmegen: Dekker & Van De Vegt, 1978.

Illich Limits to Medicine. Medical nemesis: the expropriation of health. London: Marion Boyars, 1974.

Klein R. The New Politics of the NHS. 6th ed. Radcliffe Publishing, Oxford, 2016.

Le Fanu J. The Rise and Fall of Modern Medicine. London: Abacus, 2011.

Littlewood R, Lipsedge M. Aliens and Alienists. Harmondsworth: Penguin, 1982.

Loudon I. Medical Care and the General Practitioner, 1750-1850. Oxford: Oxford University Press, 1986.

Loudon I, Horder J, Webster C. (eds) General Practice under the National Health Service, 1948-1997. Oxford: Oxford University Press, 1998.

Mazower M. Dark Continent. Europe's Twentieth Century. London: Penguin, 1999.

McCartney M. The State of Medicine: Keeping the Promise of the NHS. London: Pinter & Martin Ltd, 2016.

McKeown T. The Modern Rise of Population. London: Edward Arnold, 1976.

Perkin H. The Origins of Modern English Society, 1780-1880. London: Routledge, Kegan and Paul, 1969.

Pooler H. My Life in General Practice. London: Christopher Johnson Publishers, 1948.

Porter R. Health for Sale: Quackery in England, 1650-1850. Manchester: Manchester University Press, 1989.

Porter R. The Greatest Benefit to Mankind: A Medical History Humanity from Antiquity to the Present. London: Fontana, 1999.

Rivett G. From Cradle to Grave. Fifty years of the NHS. London: King's Fund, 1998.

Scull AT. The Most Solitary of Afflictions: Madness and Society in Britain, 1700-1900. New Haven and London: Yale University Press, 2005.

Sontag S. Illness as Metaphor. London: Penguin, 1978.

Stevens R. Medical Practice in Modern England. New Haven: Yale University Press, 1966.

Szasz T. The Myth of Mental Illness. London: Penguin, 1972.

Thompson EP. The Making of the English Working Class. London: Penguin, 1963.

Timmins N. The Five Giants. A Biography of the Welfare State. London: Harper Collins, 1995.

Tudor Hart J. A New Kind Of Doctor. London: Merlin Press, 1985.

Waddington K. An Introduction to the Social History of Medicine. Europe Since 1500. London: Palgrave Macmillan, 2011.

Webster C. The National Health Service: A Political History. Oxford: Oxford University Press, 2002.

Willis J. The Paradox of Progress. Oxford: Radcliffe Medical Press, 1995.

Wilkinson R, Pickett K. The Spirit Level: Why More Equal Societies Almost Always Do Better. London: Allen Lane, 2009.

Index

Acknowledgements

Firstly, to John Gillam for all his support and genealogical studies, and to Edward Cooper for painstaking corrections. To Lucille Abrahams, Jenny Amery, William Barr, Anne Digby, Anthony Gillam, Iona Heath, Irvine Loudon, Roger Jones, Humphrcy Keenlyside, Raj Khanchandani, Euan Lawson, Marshall Marinker, John O'Brien Bell, Denis Pereira Gray, Diane Plamping, Jayshree Ramsurun, Martin Roland, John Salinsky, Niro Siriwardena, Sue Smart, Julian Tudor Hart, Martin Woolaway and Anne Yardumian. To Valery Bowers for her patient support and, finally, to Doris.

(For the reproduction of various illustrations - to St John's College, Cambridge; Oxford University Press; Punch magazine.)

Appendix

My maternal grandfather, Louis O'Brien, lies outside this genealogy but merits more than a passing reference. He was born on the 18th January, 1898 in Downpatrick, County Down. He met my grandmother, Greta, at St Vincents where she was training to be a paediatric nurse. Opportunities in Dublin during the Depression were limited. They came to England and he spent his short career in the slums of Birmingham.

Louis was an extrovert who loved to sing and dance. His voice 'rivalled that of John McCormack and Josef Locke' according to my mother, Anne. He taught her to dance and sing. She would entertain his friends with music hall favourites. The family lived above the surgery in Springhill. The house was on a corner. Green glass darkened the windows of the waiting room. Sixteen year old Nora, from Shanagarry, was their maid. She kept house and washed medicine bottles. An early 'health care assistant', she was also trained up to do first aid. Louis compounded his own medicines. There were no reception staff or appointment systems. Rudimentary records were green, orange or white according to the category of panel patient.

Louis went out early on rounds and returned for soup as they were eating breakfast before morning surgery. In the afternoon, he took a rest before starting evening surgery. Most of his catchment population were working class. The men had gone to war or worked in local munitions factories like Bulpits. His patients lived in 'back-to-back' red brick terraces with outside toilets and water supplies. Houses in the slum areas had boarded up windows, barefoot children played in the streets.

Anne would accompany her daddy on home visits. She was sometimes allowed to stand at the door and wave, otherwise she would sit in the car. She recalls the fear of sick children and remembers a young girl with suspected diphtheria being rushed to the 'fever hospital'. Louis kept a separate 'midder' bag for obstetric cases, under no circumstances was it to be touched for fear of transmitting the dreaded puerperal fever.

Life was a struggle, even for one as hard working as Louis. Household finances were finely balanced. My mother recalls arguments between her parents over unpaid bills: *'I've bills to pay and a house to run!'* Patients would pay in kind, for example with bags of coal. One patient appeared one day with a grandfather clock on a wheelbarrow. (My mother still possesses it.) Her father nevertheless *'employed locums in the busier winter months, usually from across the water. Irish doctors looked after one another.'* He was sometimes consulted for a second opinion by one or two contemporaries who had also come over from Ireland.

A Jewish doctor and his family lived opposite. They supported one another. Indeed, Louis and Greta had many Jewish friends. *'They were very kind and had an affinity with the Irish fellow immigrants, also discriminated against.'*

Many doctors sent their families back to Ireland when the bombing raids commenced. Anne had been evacuated to Shropshire where she attended her convent school (transplanted to a local church hall).

Early in 1939, Louis developed uncharacteristic fatigue and a hacking cough. He was diagnosed with TB and briefly admitted to a nursing home, before returning to work. As his health failed over the following couple of years, Greta went back to work as a matron in a residential nursery. Louis had returned to Dublin for one last consultation with his favoured chest specialist at his alma mater. He suffered a massive haemoptysis while climbing the hospital stairs and died on 21st August 1943. He was 44 years old.

Anne recalls the morning when the mother superior told her she was to return to Birmingham. She learnt of her father's death on Macclesfield railway station. She was ten years old. The following summer, Anne joined as the youngest member a dancing troupe that entertained troops on leave. She later trained as an actress.

Her brother John entered general practice but became increasingly disillusioned with NHS working conditions in the early 60s. He finally emigrated to British Columbia and became embroiled in medical politics there. He later served as President of the Canadian Medical Association. He practised into his mid 80s. My godfather John's infectious energy and enthusiasm has left a lasting imprint upon me.

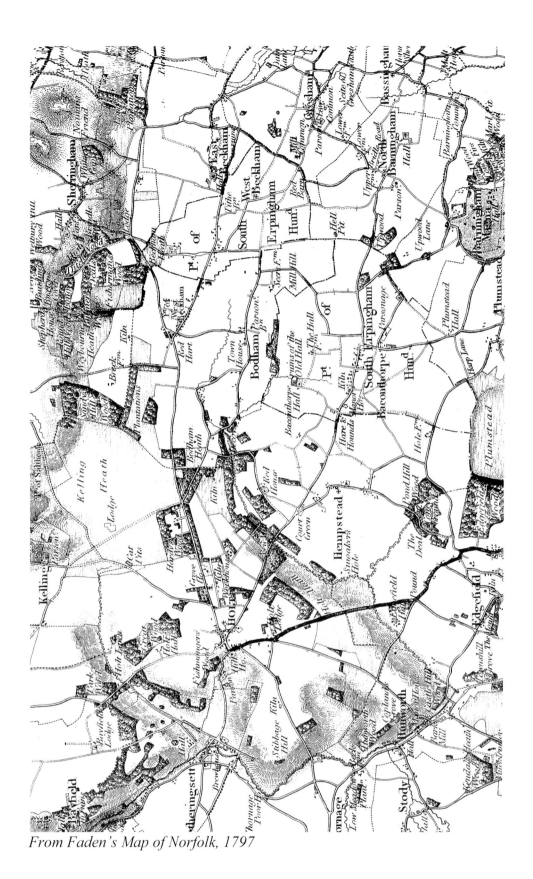

From Faden's Map of Norfolk, 1797